PEARSON CUSTOM
Education

Teaching Math in Early Childhood Education
62.340
Bloomsburg University

Pearson Learning Solutions

New York   Boston   San Francisco
London   Toronto   Sydney   Tokyo   Singapore   Madrid
Mexico City   Munich   Paris   Cape Town   Hong Kong   Montreal

Senior Vice President, Editorial and Marketing: Patrick F. Boles
Senior Sponsoring Editor: Natalie Danner
Development Editor: Abbey Briggs
Assistant Editor: Jill Johnson
Operations Manager: Eric M. Kenney
Production Manager: Jennifer Berry
Art Director: Renée Sartell
Cover Designer: Kristen Kiley

Cover Art: "Textbooks and apple" used by permission of iStock; "Teacher and students" used by permission of iStock; "Classroom, globe on desk, US flag hanging from blackboard" Copyright © 1999–2008 Getty Images, Inc. All rights reserved. "Mulitcolored crayons"— Courtesy of iStockphoto. "Colorful crayons"— Courtesy of iStockphoto. "Toddler boy playing with alphabet puzzle"— Courtesy of Mimi Haddon/Getty Images. "School Hallway" courtesy of Matt symons/iStockphoto Lp. "Locker" courtesy of Jose Gil/iStockphoto Lp.

Printed in the United States of America.
V092

Please visit our website at *www.pearsoncustom.com.*

Attention bookstores: For permission to return any unsold stock, contact us at *pe-uscustomreturns@pearson.com.*

Pearson Learning Solutions, 501 Boylston Street, Suite 900, Boston, MA 02116
A Pearson Education Company
www.pearsoned.com

ISBN 10: 1-256-02903-3
ISBN 13: 978-1-256-02903-8

Contents

Algebraic Thinking: Generalizations, Patterns, and Functions

From Chapter 14 of *Elementary and Middle School Mathematics: Teaching Developmentally*, 7/e. John A. Van de Walle.
Karen S. Karp. Jennifer M. Bay-Williams. Copyright © 2010 by Pearson Allyn and Bacon. All rights reserved.

Algebraic Thinking: Generalizations, Patterns, and Functions

Algebra is an established content strand in most, if not all, state standards for grades K to 12 and is one of the five content standards in NCTM's *Principles and Standards*. Although there is much variability in the algebra requirements at the elementary and middle school levels, one thing is clear: The algebra envisioned for these grades—and for high school as well—is not the algebra that you most likely experienced in high school. That typical algebra course of the eighth or ninth grade previously consisted primarily of symbol manipulation procedures and artificial applications with little connection to the real world. The focus now is on the type of thinking and reasoning that prepares students to think mathematically across all areas of mathematics.

Algebraic thinking or algebraic reasoning involves forming generalizations from experiences with number and computation, formalizing these ideas with the use of a meaningful symbol system, and exploring the concepts of pattern and functions. Far from a topic with little real-world use, algebraic thinking pervades all of mathematics and is essential for making mathematics useful in daily life.

Big Ideas

1. Algebra is a useful tool for generalizing arithmetic and representing patterns in our world.

2. Symbolism, especially involving equality and variables, must be well understood conceptually for students to be successful in mathematics, particularly algebra.

3. Methods we use to compute and the structures in our number system can and should be generalized. For example, the generalization that $a + b = b + a$ tells us that $83 + 27 = 27 + 83$ without computing the sums on each side of the equal sign.

4. Patterns, both repeating and growing, can be recognized, extended, and generalized.

5. Functions in K–8 mathematics describe in concrete ways the notion that for every input there is a unique output.

6. Understanding is strengthened with functions that are explored across representations, as each one provides a different view of the same relationship.

Mathematics Content Connections

As Kaput (1998) notes, it is difficult to find an area of mathematics that does not involve generalizing and formalizing in some central way. In fact, this type of reasoning is at the heart of mathematics as a science of pattern and order.

- **Number, Place Value, Basic Facts, and Computation:** The most important generalizations at the core of algebraic thinking are those made about number and computation—arithmetic. Not only does algebraic thinking generalize from number and computation, but also the generalizations themselves add to understanding and facility with computation. We can use our understanding of 10 to add $5 + 8$ ($5 + 8 = 3 + 2 + 8 = 3 + 10$) or $5 + 38$ ($5 + 38 = 3 + 2 + 38 = 3 + 40$). The generalized idea is that 2 can be taken from one addend and moved to the other: $a + b = (a - 2) + (b + 2)$. Although students may not symbolize this general idea, seeing that this works is algebraic thinking.

- **Operation Concepts:** As children learn about the operations, they also learn that there are regularities in the way that the operations work. Examples include the commutative properties ($a + b = b + a$ and $a \times b = b \times a$) as well as the way that operations are related to one another.

- **Proportional Reasoning:** Every proportional situation gives rise to a linear (straight-line) function with a graph that goes through the origin. The constant ratio in the proportion is the slope of the graph.

- **Measurement:** Measures are a principal means of describing relationships in the physical world, and these relationships are often algebraic. Measurement formulas, such as circumference of a circle, are functions. You can say that the height of a building is a function of how many stories it has.

- **Geometry:** Geometric patterns are some of the first that children experience. Growing patterns give rise to functional relationships. Coordinates are used to generalize distance concepts and to control transformations. And, of course, functions are graphed on the coordinate plane to visually show algebraic relationships.

- **Data Analysis:** When data are gathered, the algebraic thinker is able to examine them for regularities and patterns. Functions are used to approximate trends or describe the relationships in mathematically useful ways.

Algebraic Thinking

Algebraic thinking begins in prekindergarten and continues through high school. According to *Curriculum Focal Points* (NCTM, 2006), in prekindergarten, "Children recognize and duplicate simple sequential patterns (e.g., square, circle, square, circle, square, circle, . . .)" (p. 11). Algebraic thinking continues to be included in every grade level, with the primary topics being (1) the use of patterns leading to generalizations (especially with the operations), the study of change, and the concept of function. Seeley & Schielack (2008) in their look at algebraic thinking in *Curriculum Focal Points* note:

> Underlying all these particular topics is the fundamental idea that, for students to be prepared to succeed in algebra, one of the best tools they can have is a deep understanding of the number system, its operations, and the properties related to those operations. (p. 266)

In fact, this chapter follows the chapters on these concepts so that you can see how closely related number concepts, operations, and algebraic thinking are.

Kaput (1999), a leader in crafting appropriate algebra curriculum across the grades, talks about algebra that "involves generalizing and expressing that generality using increasingly formal languages, where the generalizing begins in arithmetic, in modeling situations, in geometry, and in virtually all the mathematics that can or should appear in the elementary grades" (pp. 134–135). Although many authors and researchers have written about algebraic thinking, Kaput's description is the most complete, encompassing the ideas of many other contributors. He describes five different forms of algebraic reasoning:

1. Generalization from arithmetic and from patterns in all of mathematics
2. Meaningful use of symbols
3. Study of structure in the number system
4. Study of patterns and functions
5. Process of mathematical modeling, integrating the first four list items

Thus, algebraic thinking is not a singular idea but is composed of different forms of thought and an understanding of symbols. It is a separate strand of the curriculum but should also be embedded in all areas of mathematics. There is general agreement that we must begin the development of these forms of thinking from the very beginning of school so that students will learn to think productively with the powerful ideas of mathematics—basically so that they can think mathematically.

In this chapter, these five themes are used to discuss algebraic thinking. The categories themselves are not developmental, but within each category there are important developmental considerations. Therefore, in reading this chapter, you will find that each category offers considerations and effective instructional activities across the pre-K–8 curriculum.

Generalization from Arithmetic and from Patterns

The process of creating generalizations from number and arithmetic begins as early as kindergarten and continues as students learn about all aspects of number and computation, including basic facts and meanings of the operations.

Generalization with Addition

Young children explore addition families and in the process learn how to decompose and recompose numbers. The monkeys and trees problem illustrated in Figure 14.1 provides students a chance to not only consider ways to decompose 7, but also to see generalizable characteristics, such as that increasing the number in the small tree by one means reducing the number in the large tree by one.

Students may be asked to find all the ways the monkeys can be in the two trees. The significant question is how to decide when all of the solutions have been found. At one level, students will just not be able to think of any more and many will forget about using 0. Other children may try to use each number from 0 to 7 for one tree. The student who explains that for each number 0 to 7 there is one

Figure 14.1 Seven monkeys want to play in two trees, one big and one small. Show all the different ways that the seven monkeys could play in the two trees.
Source: Adapted from Yackel, E. (1997). "A Foundation for Algebraic Reasoning in the Early Grades." *Teaching Children Mathematics, 3*(6), 276–280. A similar task was explored in Carpenter, T. P., Franke, M. L., and Levi, L. (2003). *Thinking Mathematically: Integrating Arithmetic and Algebra in Elementary School.* Portsmouth, NH: Heinemann.

solution is no longer partitioning 7 into parts but is making a generalization that yields the number of solutions without even listing them (Yackel, 1997). That reasoning can be generalized to the number of ways 376 monkeys occupy the two trees. Second graders have articulated that there is always one more solution than the number of monkeys (Carpenter et al., 2003). Notice how this is a generalization that no longer depends on the numbers involved.

Generalizing does not need to involve symbols, but it is an important inclusion for older students (see the next major section). Seventh graders, for example, doing a problem like the monkeys but with 8 mice in a green or a blue cage, discovered three equations to describe the situation: $b + g = 8$, $8 - g = b$, and $8 - b = g$ (Stephens, 2005).

This is just one example of how algebraic thinking can and should be infused into work with number. To do so requires planning in advance—thinking of what questions you can ask to help students think about generalized characteristics within the problem they are working (when the number of monkeys in one tree goes down, the number in the other goes up by one) and to other problems that have the same pattern (376 monkeys).

Generalization in the Hundreds Chart

The hundreds chart is a rich field for exploring number relationships and should not be thought of solely as

a device for teaching numeration. Here are some additional tasks you might explore.

- Which numbers make diagonal patterns? Which make column patterns? Can you make up a rule for explaining when a number will have a diagonal or column pattern? (See Figure 14.2, noting that the patterns depend on how many columns the charts contain.)
- If you move down two and over one on the hundreds chart what is the relationship between the original number and the new number?
- Can you find two skip-count patterns with one "on top of" the other? That is, all of the shaded values for one pattern are part of the shaded values for the other. How are these two skip-count numbers related? Is this true for any pair of numbers that have this relationship. Will this be true on hundreds charts with different widths? Why or why not?
- Find any value on the hundreds chart. Add it with the number to the left and the one to the right, then divide by 3. What did you get? Why?

These examples are just some of the many questions that extend number concepts to algebraic thinking concepts. "Can you find a rule?," "Why does this work?," and "When will this be true?" are questions that require justification and reasoning, which in turn strengthen students' understanding of number and of algebra.

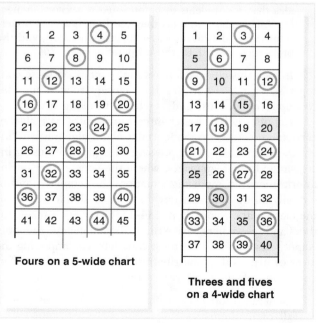

Figure 14.2 Patterns on hundreds charts of different widths.

Generalization Through Exploring a Pattern

One of the most interesting and perhaps most valuable methods of searching for generalization is to find it in the growing physical pattern. One method of doing this is to examine only one growth step of a physical pattern and ask students to find a method of counting the elements without simply counting each by one. The following problem is a classic example of such a task, described in many resources including Burns and McLaughlin (1990) and Boaler and Humphreys (2005).

Activity 14.1

The Border Problem

On centimeter grid paper, have students draw an 8 × 8 square representing a swimming pool. Next, have them shade in the surrounding squares, the tiles around the pool (see Figure 14.3). The task is to find a way to count the border tiles without counting them one by one. Students should use their drawings, words, and number sentences to show how they counted the squares.

There are at least five different methods of counting the border tiles around a square other than counting them one at a time.

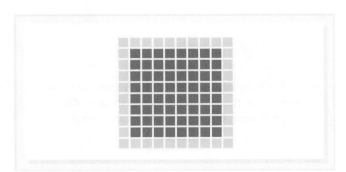

Figure 14.3 How many different ways can you find to count the border tiles of an 8 × 8 pool without counting them one at a time?

Pause and Reflect

Before reading further, see if you can find four or five different counting schemes for the border tiles problem. Apply your method to a square border of other dimensions.

A very common solution is to notice that there are ten squares across the top and also across the bottom, leaving eight squares on either side. This might be written as:

$$10 + 10 + 8 + 8 = 36 \text{ or } 2 \times 10 + 2 \times 8 = 36$$

Each of the following expressions can likewise be traced to looking at the squares in various groupings:

$$4 \times 9$$
$$4 \times 8 + 4$$
$$4 \times 10 - 4$$
$$100 - 64$$

More expressions are possible, since students may use addition instead of multiplication in the expressions. In any case, once the generalizations are created, students need to justify how the elements in the expression map to the physical representation.

Another approach to the Border Problem is to have students build a series of pools in steps, each with one more tile on the side (3 × 3, 4 × 4, 5 × 5, etc.) and then find a way to count the elements of each step using an algorithm that handles the step numbers in the same manner at each step. Students can find, for example, number sentences parallel to what they wrote for the 8 × 8 to find a 6 × 6 pool and a 7 × 7 pool. Eventually, this can result in a generalized statement, for example, taking $2 \times 10 + 2 \times 8$ and generalizing it to $2 \times (n + 2) + 2(n)$.

One important idea in generalization is recognizing a new situation where it can apply and adapting it appropriately. For example, students may explore other perimeter-related growing patterns, such as a triangle with 3, 4, and 5 dots on each side. Students should reason that this is the same type of pattern, except that it has three sides, and be able to use their previous generalization for this specific problem (Steele, 2005).

Meaningful Use of Symbols

Perhaps one reason that students are unsuccessful in algebra is that they do not have a strong understanding of the symbols they are using. For many adults, the word algebra elicits memories of simplifying long equations with the goal of finding x. These experiences of manipulating symbols were often devoid of meaning and resulted in such a strong dislike for mathematics that algebra has become a favorite target of cartoonists and Hollywood writers. In reality, symbols represent real events and should be seen as useful tools for solving important problems that aid in decision making (e.g., calculating how many we need to sell to make x dollars or at what rate do a given number of employees need to work to finish the project on time). Students cannot make sense of such questions without meaningful instruction on two very important (and poorly understood) topics: the equal sign and variables.

The Meaning of the Equal Sign

The equal sign is one of the most important symbols in elementary arithmetic, in algebra, and in all mathematics using numbers and operations. At the same time, research dating from 1975 to the present indicates clearly that "=" is a very poorly understood symbol (RAND Mathematics Study Panel, 2003).

⏸ ———————————— *Pause and Reflect*

In the following expression, what number do you think belongs in the box?

$$8 + 4 = \square + 5$$

How do you think students in the early grades or in middle school typically answer this question?

In one study, no more than 10 percent of students at any grade from 1 to 6 put the correct number (7) in the box. The common responses were 12 and 17. (How did students get these answers?) In grade 6, not one student out of 145 put a 7 in the box (Falkner, Levi, & Carpenter, 1999). Earlier studies found similar results (Behr, Erlwanger, & Nichols, 1975; Erlwanger & Berlanger, 1983).

Where do such misconceptions come from? Most, if not all, equations that students encounter in elementary school looks like this: 5 + 7 = ___ or 8 × 45 = ___ or 9(3 + 8) = ___. Naturally, students come to know = to signify "and the answer is" rather than a symbol to indicate equivalence (Carpenter, Franke, & Levi, 2003; McNeil & Alibali, 2005; Molina & Ambrose, 2006).

Why is it so important that students correctly understand the equal sign? First, it is important for students to see, understand, and symbolize the relationships in our number system. The equal sign is a principal method of representing these relationships. For example, 6 × 7 = 5 × 7 + 7. This is not only a fact strategy but also an application of the distributive property. The distributive property allows us to multiply each of the parts separately: (1 + 5) × 7 = (1 × 7) + (5 × 7). Other number properties are used to convert this last expression to 5 × 7 + 7. When these ideas, initially and informally developed through arithmetic, are generalized and expressed symbolically, powerful relationships are available for working with other numbers in a generalized manner.

A second reason is that when students fail to understand the equal sign, they typically have difficulty when it is encountered in algebraic expressions (Knuth et al., 2006). Even solving a simple equation such as $5x - 24 = 81$ requires students to see both sides of the equal sign as equivalent expressions. It is not possible to "do" the left-hand side. However, if both sides are the same, then they will remain the same when 24 is added to each side.

Conceptualizing the Equal Sign as a Balance.   Helping students understand the idea of equivalence can be developed concretely, beginning in the elementary grades. The next two activities illustrate how tactile objects and visualizations can reinforce the "balancing" notion of the equal sign (ideas adapted from Mann, 2004).

Activity **14.2**

Seesaw Students

Ask students to raise their arms to look like a seesaw. Explain that you have big juicy oranges, all weighing the same, and tiny little apples, all weighing the same. Ask students to imagine that you have placed an orange in each of their left hands (students should bend to lower left side). Ask students to imagine that you place another orange on the right side (students level off). Next, with oranges still there, ask students to imagine an apple added to the left. Finally, say you are adding another apple, but tell students it is going on the left (again). Then ask them to imagine it moving over to the right.

After acting out the seesaw several times, ask students to write Seesaw Findings (e.g., "If you have a balanced seesaw and add something to one side, it will tilt to that side," and "If you take away the same object from both sides of the seesaw, it will still be balanced").

Activity **14.3**

What Do You Know about the Shapes?

Present a scale with objects on both sides and ask students what they know about the shapes. You can create your own, but here is one as an example:

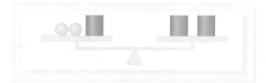

The red cylinders weigh the same. The yellow balls weigh the same. What do you know about the weights of the balls and the cylinders? Figure 14.4 illustrates how one third grader explained what she knew. (Notice that these tasks, appropriate for early grades, are good beginnings for the more advanced balancing tasks later in this chapter.)

After students have experiences with shapes, they can then explore numbers, eventually going on to variables.

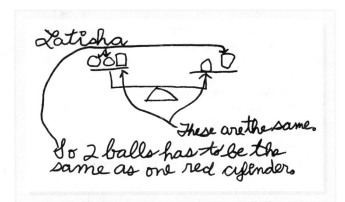

Figure 14.4 Latisha's work on the problem.
Source: Figure 4 from Mann, R. L. (2004). "Balancing Act: The Truth Behind the Equals Sign." *Teaching Children Mathematics, 11*(2), p. 68. Reprinted with permission. Copyright © 2004 by the National Council of Teachers of Mathematics, Inc. www.nctm.org. All rights reserved.

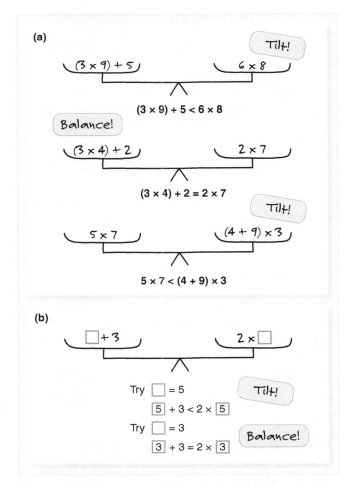

Figure 14.5 Using expressions and variables in equations and inequalities. The two-pan balance helps develop the meaning of =.

Figure 14.5 offers examples that connect the balance to the related equation. This two-pan-balance model also illustrates that the expressions on each side represent a number.

Activity 14.4

Tilt or Balance

On the board or overhead, draw a simple two-pan balance. In each pan, write a numeric expression and ask which pan will go down or whether the two will balance (see Figure 14.5(a)). Challenge students to write expressions for each side of the scale to make it balance. For each, write a corresponding equation to illustrate the meaning of =. Note that when the scale "tilts," either a "greater than" or "less than" symbol (> or <) is used.

After a short time, add variables to the expressions and allow students to solve them using whatever methods they wish (see Figure 14.5(b)). Do not make the task so easy that the solutions can be found by simple inspection.

The balance is a concrete tool that can help students understand that if you add or subtract a value from one side, you must add or subtract a like value from the other side to keep the equation balanced.

Figure 14.6 shows solutions for two equations, one in a balance and the other without. Even after you have stopped using the balance, it is a good idea to refer to the scale or balance-pan concept of equality and the idea of keeping the scales balanced.

As students begin to develop equations they wish to graph, the equations will often be in a form in which neither variable is isolated. For example, in the equation $3A - B = 2A$, they may want A in terms of B or B in terms of A. The same technique of solving for one variable can be used to solve for one variable in terms of the other by adjusting the expressions on both sides while keeping the equation in balance.

 An NCTM Illuminations applet titled *Pan Balance—Expressions* provides a virtual balance where students can enter what they believe to be equivalent expressions (with numbers or symbols) each in a separate pan to see if, in fact, the expressions balance. ◆

True/False and Open Sentences. Carpenter, Franke, and Levi (2003) suggest that a good starting point for helping students with the equal sign is to explore equations as either true or false. Clarifying the meaning of the equal sign is just one of the outcomes of this type of exploration, as seen in the following activity.

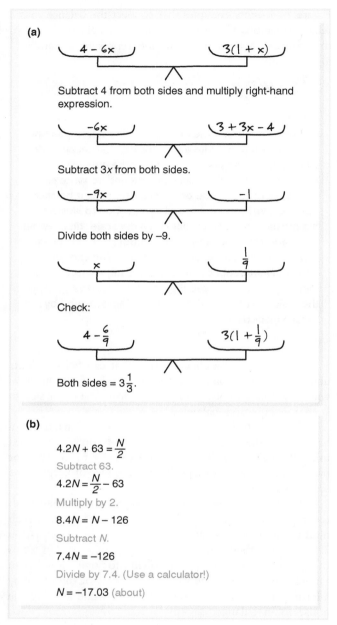

(a)

Subtract 4 from both sides and multiply right-hand expression.

Subtract 3x from both sides.

Divide both sides by –9.

Check:

Both sides = $3\frac{1}{3}$.

(b)

$4.2N + 63 = \dfrac{N}{2}$

Subtract 63.

$4.2N = \dfrac{N}{2} - 63$

Multiply by 2.

$8.4N = N - 126$

Subtract N.

$7.4N = -126$

Divide by 7.4. (Use a calculator!)

$N = -17.03$ (about)

Figure 14.6 Using a balance scale to think about solving equations.

Activity 14.5

True or False

Introduce true/false sentences or equations with simple examples to explain what is meant by a true equation and a false equation. Then put several simple equations on the board, some true and some false. The following are appropriate for primary grades:

$5 + 2 = 7$ $4 + 1 = 6$

$4 + 4 = 8$ $8 = 10 - 1$

Your collection might include other operations but keep the computations simple. The students' task is to decide which of the equations are true equations and which are not. For each response they are to explain their reasoning.

After this initial exploration of true/false sentences, have students explore equations that are in a less familiar form:

$4 + 5 = 8 + 1$ $3 + 7 = 7 + 3$ $6 - 3 = 7 - 4$ $8 = 8$
$4 + 5 = 4 + 5$ $9 + 5 = 14$ $9 + 5 = 14 + 0$

Do not try to explore all variations in a single lesson. Listen to the types of reasons that students are using to justify their answers and plan additional equations accordingly for subsequent days.

Students will generally agree on equations where there is an expression on one side and a single number on the other, although initially the less familiar form of $7 = 2 + 5$ may cause some discussion. For an equation with no operation ($8 = 8$), the discussion may be heated. Students often believe that there must be an operation on one side. Equations with an operation on both sides of the equal sign can elicit powerful discussions and help clear up misconceptions. Reinforce that the equal sign means "is the same as." Their internalization of this idea will come from the discussions and their own justifications. Inequalities should be explored in a similar manner.

After students have experienced true/false sentences, introduce an open sentence—one with a box to be filled in or letter to be replaced. To develop an understanding of open sentences, encourage students to look at the number sentence holistically and discuss in words what the equation represents.

Activity 14.6

Open Sentences

Write several open sentences on the board. To begin with, these can be similar to the true/false sentences that you have been exploring.

$5 + 2 = \square$ $4 + \square = 6$ $4 + 5 = \square - 1$

$3 + 7 = 7 + \square$ $\square + 4 = 8$ $\square = 10 - 1$

$6 - \square = 7 - 4$ $\square + 5 = 5 + 8$

The task is to decide what number can be put into the box to make the sentence true. Of course, an explanation is also required.

For grades 3 and above, include multiplication as well as addition and subtraction.

Initially, some students will revert to doing computations and putting the answer in the box. This is a result of too many exercises where an answer is to be written as a single number following an equal sign. In fact, the box is a forerunner of a variable, not an answer holder.

Relational Thinking. Once students understand that the equal sign means that the quantities on both sides are the same, they can use relational thinking in solving problems. Relational thinking takes place when a student observes and uses numeric relationships between the two sides of the equal sign rather than actually computing the amounts. Relational thinking of this sort is a first step toward generalizing relationships found in arithmetic so that these same relationships can be used when variables are involved rather than numbers.

Consider two distinctly different explanations for placing a 5 in the box for the open sentence $7 - \square = 6 - 4$.

a. Since $6 - 4$ is 2, you need to take away from 7 to get 2. $7 - 5$ is 2, so 5 goes in the box.
b. Seven is one more than the 6 on the other side. That means that you need to take one more away on the left side to get the same number. One more than 4 is 5 so 5 goes in the box.

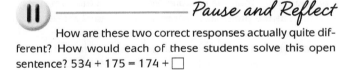

Pause and Reflect

How are these two correct responses actually quite different? How would each of these students solve this open sentence? $534 + 175 = 174 + \square$

The first student computes the result on one side and adjusts the result on the other to make the sentence true. The second student is using a relationship between the expressions on either side of the equal sign. This student does not need to compute the values on each side. When the numbers are large, the relationship approach is much more useful. Since 174 is one less than 175, the number in the box must be one more than 534 to make up the difference. The first student will need to do the computation and will perhaps have difficulty finding the correct addend.

In order to nurture relational thinking and the meaning of the equal sign, continue to explore an increasingly complex series of true/false and open sentences with your class. Select equations designed to elicit good thinking and challenges rather than computation. Use large numbers that make computation difficult (not impossible) to push them toward relational thinking.

True/False

$674 - 389 = 664 - 379$ $5 \times 84 = 10 \times 42$
$37 + 54 = 38 + 53$ $64 \div 14 = 32 \div 28$

Open Sentences

$73 + 56 = 71 + \square$ $126 - 37 = \square - 40$
$20 \times 48 = \square \times 24$ $68 + 58 = 57 + 69 + \square$

Pause and Reflect

One of the true/false statements is false. Can you explain why using relational thinking?

Marta Molina and Rebecca Ambrose (2006), researchers in mathematics education, used the true/false and open-ended prompts with third graders, none of whom understood the equal sign in a relational way at the start of their study. For example, all 13 students answered $8 + 4 = \_\_\_ + 5$ with 12. They found that asking students to write their own open sentences was particularly effective in helping students solidify their understanding of the equal sign. The following forms were provided as guidance (though students could use multiplication and division if they wanted):

$$\_\_\_ + \_\_\_ = \_\_\_ + \_\_\_$$

$$\_\_\_ - \_\_\_ = \_\_\_ - \_\_\_$$

$$\_\_\_ + \_\_\_ = \_\_\_ - \_\_\_.$$

Activity **14.7**

Writing True/False Sentences

After students have had ample time to discuss true/false and open sentences, ask them to make up their own true/false sentences that they can use to challenge their classmates. Each student should write a collection of three or four sentences with at least one true and at least one false sentence. Encourage them to include one "tricky" one. Their equations can either be traded with a partner or used in full-class discussions.

Repeat for open sentence problems.

When students write their own true/false sentences, they often are intrigued with the idea of using large numbers and lots of numbers in their sentences. This encourages them to create sentences involving relational thinking.

As students explore true/false and open sentence activities, look for two developments. First, are students acquiring an appropriate understanding of the equal sign? Look to see if they are comfortable using operations on both sides of the equal sign and can use the meaning of *equal* as "is the same as" to solve open sentences.

Second, look for an emergence of relational thinking. Students who rely on relationships found in the operations on each side of the equal sign rather than on direct computation have moved up a step in their algebraic thinking. ◆

The Meaning of Variables

Expressions or equations with variables allow for the expression of generalizations. When students can work with expressions involving variables without even thinking about the specific number or numbers that the letters may stand for, they have achieved what Kaput (1999) refers to as manipulation of opaque formalisms—they can look at and work with the symbols themselves. Variables can be used as unique unknown values or as quantities that vary. Unfortunately, students often think of the former and not the latter. Experiences in elementary and middle school should focus on building meaning for both, as delineated in the next two sections.

Variables Used as Unknown Values. Students' first experiences with variables tend to focus exclusively on variables as unknown values. In the open sentence explorations, the ☐ is a precursor of a variable used in this way. Early on, you can begin using various letters instead of a box in your open sentences. Rather than ask students what number goes in the box, ask what number the letter could stand for to make the sentence true. Initial work with finding the value of the variable that makes the sentence true—solving the equation—should initially rely on relational thinking. Later, students will develop specific techniques for solving equations when these relationships are insufficient.

The balancing ideas described in the previous section can also serve this purpose. NCTM Illuminations, for example, uses an applet titled "Pan Balance—Shapes," along with two excellent pre-K–2 lesson plans, for having students (virtually) weigh different shapes to figure out what number each shape represents.

Consider the following open sentence: ☐ + ☐ + 7 = ☐ + 17 (or, equivalently, $n + n + 7 = n + 17$). A convention for the use of multiple variables is that the same symbol or letter in an equation stands for the same number every place it occurs. Carpenter et al. (2003) refer to it as "the mathematician's rule." In the preceding example, the ☐ must stand for 10.

Many story problems involve a situation in which the variable is a specific unknown, as in the following basic example:

> **Gary ate five strawberries and Jeremy ate some, too. The container of 12 was gone! How many did Jeremy eat?**

Although students can solve this problem without using algebra, they can begin to learn about variables by expressing it in symbols: $5 + s = 12$. These problems can grow in difficulty over time.

With a context, students can even explore three variables, each one standing for an unknown value, as in the activity below.

Activity 14.8

Balls, Balls, Balls

How much does each ball weigh given the following three facts:

1. 🏈 + 🏉 = 1.25 pounds
2. 🏈 + ⚽ = 1.35 pounds
3. ⚽ + 🏉 = 1.9 pounds

Ask students to look at each fact and make observations that help them generate other facts. For example, they might notice that the soccer ball weighs 0.1 pounds more than the football. Write this in the same fashion as the other statements. Continue until these discoveries lead to finding the weight of each ball. Encourage students to use models to represent and explore the problem (activity adapted from Maida, 2004).

One possible approach: Add equations 1 and 2:

🏈 + 🏈 + 🏉 + ⚽ = 2.6 pounds

Then take away the football and soccer ball, reducing the weight by 1.9 pounds (based on the information in equation 3), and you have two baseballs that weigh 0.7 pounds. Divide by 2, so one baseball is 0.35 pounds.

You may have recognized this last example as a system of equations presented in a concrete manner. This type of work is accessible to upper elementary and middle school students when presented in this manner and helps build the foundation for working with systems of equations later.

Another concrete way to work on systems of equations is through balancing. Notice the work done in building the concept of the equal sign is now applied to understanding and solving for variables.

In Figure 14.7, a series of examples shows scale problems in which each shape on the scales represents a different value. Two or more scales for a single problem provide different information about the shapes or variables. Problems of this type can be adjusted in difficulty for children across the grades. Greenes and Findell (1999a,b) have developed a whole collection of these and similar activities in books for grades 1 to 7.

When no numbers are involved, as in the top two examples of Figure 14.7, students can find combinations of numbers for the shapes that make all of the balances balance. If an arbitrary value is given to one of the shapes, then values for the other shapes can be found accordingly.

In the second example, if the sphere equals 2, then the cylinder must be 4 and the cube equals 8. If a different value is given to the sphere, the other shapes will change accordingly.

❚❚ ──────── *Pause and Reflect*

How would you solve the last problem in Figure 14.7? Can you solve it in two ways?

You (and your students) can tell if you are correct by checking your solutions with the original scale positions. Believe it or not, you have just solved a series of simultaneous equations, a skill generally left to a formal algebra class.

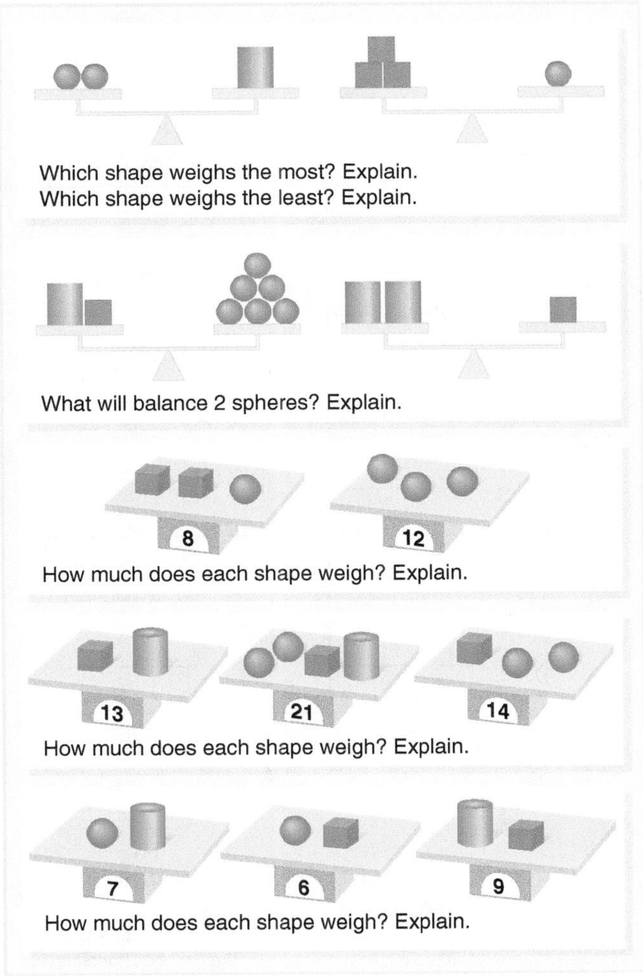

Simplifying Expressions and Equations. As noted earlier, simplifying equations and solving for x have often been meaningless tasks, and students are unsure of what steps to do when. Still, knowing how to simplify and recognizing equivalent expressions are essential skills to working algebraically. In *Curriculum Focal Points* (NCTM, 2006), one of the three focal points is about algebra: "Writing, interpreting, and using mathematical expressions and equations."

Students need an understanding of how to apply mathematical properties and how to preserve equivalence as they simplify. One way to do this is to have students look at simplifications that have errors and explain how to fix the errors (Hawes, 2007). Figure 14.8 shows how three students have justified the correct simplification of $(2x + 1) - (x + 6)$.

Figure 14.7 Examples of problems with multiple variables and multiple scales.

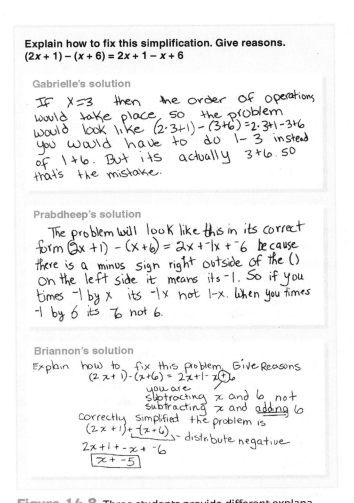

Figure 14.8 Three students provide different explanations for fixing the flawed simplification given.

Source: Figure 3 from Hawes, K. (2007). "Using Error Analysis to Teach Equation Solving." *Mathematics Teaching in the Middle School, 12*(5), p. 241. Reprinted with permission. Copyright © 2007 by the National Council of Teachers of Mathematics, Inc. www.nctm.org. All rights reserved.

Variables Used as Quantities That Vary. As noted earlier, the important concept that variables can represent more than one missing value is not well understood by students and is not as present in the elementary and middle school curriculum as it should be. When there are different variables in a single equation, each variable can represent many, even infinite, numbers. In the middle school grades, variables that are used to describe functions (e.g., $y = 3x - 5$) are variables that have many possible numeric solutions. This shift from the variable as an unknown to a variable representing a relationship can be difficult for students. This difficulty can be alleviated if students have experiences with variables that vary in the elementary curriculum.

Recall the monkeys in two trees problem in Figure 14.1 of this chapter. Even very young students can represent the possible solutions using symbols. For example, they might draw

to represent the number of monkeys in the small tree plus the number of monkeys in the big tree equals 7. Or you can use letters and help students make the connection from the context to the equation, for example writing: $b = 7 - s$ to communicate that the number of big tree monkeys is the number of total monkeys minus the number of small tree monkeys.

Context continues to be important in developing understanding of variables for students throughout middle school. Hyde et al. (2006) offer the following middle school context for exploring variables that vary:

> If you have $10 to spend on $2 Hershey bars and $1 Tootsie Rolls, how many ways can you spend all your money without receiving change? (p. 262)

This context is nice for students, as it is familiar and they can actually use minibars and rolls to physically model the problem, although using candy as a context is sometimes discouraged, as it can be interpreted as promoting unhealthy foods. You can pick any context that you think is engaging, culturally relevant, and appropriate for the mathematics being developed.

To begin exploring this problem, students record data in a table and look for patterns. They notice that when the number of Hershey bars changes by 1, the number of Tootsie Rolls changes by 2. Symbolically, this representation is $2H + T = \$10$, where H is the number of Hersheys and T is the number of Tootsie Rolls. It is also important to include decimal and fraction values in the exploration of variables. As any algebra teacher will confirm, students struggle most with these numbers—again resulting from

the lack of earlier, more concrete, and visual experiences mixing fractions and decimals with variables. For example, if you were buying $1.75 pencils and $1.25 erasers from the school store, and spending all of $35.00, how many combinations are possible? What equation represents this situation?

For students with special needs or students who might be unfamiliar with using a table, it is helpful to adapt the table to include both how many and how much, as shown in Figure 14.9 (Hyde et al., 2006). Reinforce the two elements with each entry (how many and how much). In addition, calculators can facilitate exploration of possible solutions. To increase the challenge for advanced or gifted students, ask students to graph the values or to consider more complex situations.

Once students have the expression in symbols (in this case, $1.75x + 1.25y = 35.00$), ask students to tie each number and variable back to the context. In this way, students can make sense of what is normally poorly understood and really develop a strong foundation for the algebra they will study in high school.

$1.75 item	$1.25 item	Total $35.00
$35.00	$0	
20	0	
$0	$35	
0	28	

Figure 14.9 A table adapted to include how many and how much for each row.
Source: Hyde, A., George, K., Mynard, S., Hull, C., Watson, S., & Watson, P. (2006). "Creating Multiple Representations in Algebra: All Chocolate, No Change," *Mathematics Teaching in the Middle School, 11*(6), 262–268. Reprinted with permission. Copyright © 2006 by the National Council of Teachers of Mathematics, Inc. www.nctm.org. All rights reserved.

Making Structure in the Number System Explicit

You learned in a previous chapter a few properties for each operation that are important for students as they learn basic facts and strategies for computation. For example, the commutative or order property for both addition and multiplication reduces substantially the number of facts necessary to learn. These and other properties are likely to be used informally as students develop relational thinking while working with true/false and open sentences as described in previous sections.

A next step is to have students examine these structures or properties explicitly and express them in general terms without reference to specific numbers. For example, a student solving $394 + 176 = N + 394$ may say that N must be 176 because $394 + 176$ is the same as $176 + 394$. This is a specific instance of the commutative property. To articulate this (and other structural properties of our number system) in a form such as $a + b = b + a$, noting that it is true for all numbers, is the goal of looking at structure. When made explicit and understood, these structures not only add to students' tools for computation but also enrich their understanding of the number system and provide a base for even higher levels of abstraction (Carpenter et al., 2003).

Making Conjectures about Properties

Properties of the number system can be built into students' explorations with true/false and open number sentences. For example, third-grade students will generally agree that the true/false sentence $41 \times 3 = 3 \times 41$ is true. The pivotal question, however, asks "Is this true for any numbers?" Some students will argue that although it seems to be true all of the time, there may be two numbers that haven't been tried yet for which it does not work.

The following classroom problem and discussion was focused on investigating the distributive and associative properties, not on whether the equation was true or false (from Baek, 2008):

Ms. J: [*Pointing at* $(2 \times 8) + (2 \times 8) = 16 + 16$ *on the board*] Is it true or false?

LeJuan: True, because two 8 is 16 and two 8 is 16.

Lizett: $(2 \times 8) + (2 \times 8)$ is 32 and $16 + 16$ is 32.

Carlos: 8 plus 8 is 16, so 2 times 8 is 16, and 8 plus 8 is 16, and 2 times 8 is 16.

Ms. J: [*Writing* $4 \times 8 = (2 \times 8) + (2 \times 8)$ *on the board*] True or false?

Students: True.

Ms. J: What does the 2 stand for?

Reggie: Two boxes of eight.

Ms. J: So how many boxes are there?

Students: Four.

Ms. J: [*Writing* $32 + 16 = (4 \times 8) + (a \times 8)$ *on the board*] What is a?

Michael: Two, because 4 times 8 is 32, and 2 times 8 is 16.

Ms. J: [*Writing* $(4 \times 8) + (2 \times 8) = (b \times 8)$ *on the board*] What is b?

Students: 6. (pp. 151–152)

Notice how the teacher is developing the aspects of these properties in a conceptual manner—focusing on exemplars to guide students to generalize, rather than presenting the properties as they appear in Table 14.1 as their first experience, which can be a meaningless, rote activity.

You can follow specific examples, such as those used in the dialogue, by asking students to try to state the idea in words without using a specific number. For example, when multiplying a number by a second number, you can split the first number and multiply each part by the second number, and you will get the same answer. If a generalization is not clear or entirely correct, have students discuss the wording until all agree that they understand what it means. Write this verbal statement of the property on the board. Call it a conjecture and explain that it is not necessarily a true statement just because we think that it is true. Until someone either proves it or finds a counterexample—an instance for which the conjecture is not true—it remains a conjecture.

Students can make conjectures about properties as early as first or second grade. By third or fourth grade, students should be challenged to translate verbal conjectures into open sentences. The preceding conjecture can be written using any two letters as follows: $a \times b = (c \times b) + (d \times b)$, where $c + d = a$. Ask students to state conjectures verbally before moving to the symbolic statement of the same idea. Then have them explain what each variable in the symbolic form means.

Activity 14.9

Conjecture Creation

Once students have seen a couple of conjectures developed out of your explorations of true/false sentences, challenge students to make up conjectures on their own—creating statements about numbers and computation that they believe are always true. It is best to have them state the conjectures in words. The full class should discuss the various conjectures, asking for clarity or challenging conjectures with counterexamples. Conjectures can be added to a class list written in words and in symbols.

Table 14.1 lists basic properties of the number system for which students may make conjectures.

> **Students are almost certainly not going to know or understand why division by zero is not possible. You will need to provide contexts for them to make sense of this property.**

Table 14.1

Properties of the Number System	
Number Sentence	**Student Statement of Conjecture**
Addition and Subtraction	
$a + 0 = a$	When you add zero to a number, you get the same number you started with.
$a - 0 = a$	When you subtract zero from a number, you get the number you started with.
$a - a = 0$	When you subtract a number from itself, you get zero.
$a + b = b + a$	You can add numbers in one order and then change the order and you will get the same number.
Multiplication and Division	
$a \times 1 = a$	When you multiply a number by 1, you get the number you started with.
$a \div 1 = a$	When you divide a number by 1, you get the number you started with.
$a \div a = 1, a \neq 0$	When you divide a number that is not zero by itself, you get 1.
$a \times 0 = 0$	When you multiply a number times zero, you get zero.
$0 \div a = 0, a \neq 0$	When you divide zero by any number except zero, you get zero.
$a \times b = b \times a$	When you multiply two numbers, you can do it in any order and you will get the same number.
Conjectures Derived from Basic Properties	
$a + b - b = a$	When you add a number to another number and then subtract the number that you added, you will get the number that you started with.
$a \times b \div b = a, b \neq 0$	When you multiply a number by another number that is not zero and then divide by the same number, you get the number you started with.

Source: Adapted from Carpenter, T. P., Franke, M. L., and Levi, L. (2003). *Thinking Mathematically: Integrating Arithmetic & Algebra in Elementary School.* Portsmouth, NH: Heinemann.

Justifying Conjectures

Attempting to justify that a conjecture is true is a significant form of algebraic reasoning and is at the heart of what it means to do mathematics. How young students attempt to prove that something is always true is a relatively new and interesting area of research (Ball & Bass, 2003; Carpenter, Franke, & Levi, 2003; Schifter, 1999; Schifter, Monk, Russell, & Bastable, 2007). These researchers all believe that there is a real value in challenging students even as early as second grade to justify that the conjectures they make are always true. Therefore, when conjectures are made in class, rather than respond with an answer, ask, "Do you think that is always true? How can we find out?" Students need to reason through ideas based on their own thinking rather than simply relying on the word of others.

The most common form of justification, especially in elementary school, is the use of examples. Students will try lots of specific numbers in a conjecture. "See, it works for any number you try." They may try very large numbers as substitutes for "any" number and they may try rational fractions or decimal values. Proof by example will hopefully lead to someone asking, "How do we know there aren't some numbers that it doesn't work for?"

Less commonly, students will attempt to use some form of logic. Often these efforts include the use of physical materials to show the reasoning behind the conjecture. For example, a student attempting to prove that $a + b = b + a$ might show two bars of snap cubes, one with 8 cubes and the other with 6. The bars are used to show that the number of blocks does not change when the order of the two bars is reversed. What moves this beyond just an example is the student's statement or explanation that the number of cubes in the bars is not part of the argument: "It would work this way no matter how many blocks are in each bar."

At the elementary level, not all students will be able to create arguments and some may not even follow those constructed by others (Carpenter et al., 2003). However, at all levels it is important to push students to reason using logic and not be content with appeals to authority or the use of examples. Remember that your goal is for students' thinking to be involved in these justifications; there is little value in making a good argument *for* your students.

Odd and Even Relationships

An interesting category of number structures is that of odd and even numbers. Students will often observe that the sum of two even numbers is even, that the sum of two odd numbers is even, or that the sum of an even and an odd number is always odd. Similar statements can be made about multiplication.

❚❚ ——————— *Pause and Reflect*

Before reading on, think for a moment about how you might prove that the sum of two odd numbers is always even.

Students will provide a variety of interesting proofs of odd/even conjectures. As with other conjectures, they typically begin by trying lots of numbers. But here it is a bit easier to imagine that there just might be two numbers "out there" that don't work. Then students turn to the definition or a model that illustrates the definition. For example, if a number is odd and you split it in two, there will be a leftover. If you do this with the second odd number, it will have a leftover also. So if you put these two numbers together, the two leftovers will go together so there won't be a leftover in the sum. Students frequently use models such as bars of snap cubes to strengthen their arguments.

The following calculator activity helps students explore properties of odd and even numbers.

Activity 14.10

Broken Calculator: Can You Fix It?

Explore these two challenges, and afterward ask students for conjectures they might make about odds and evens.

1. If you cannot use any of the even keys (0, 2, 4, 6, 8), can you create an even number in the calculator display? If so, how?
2. If you cannot use any of the odd keys (1, 3, 5, 7, 9), can you create an odd number in the calculator display? If so, how?

It is not important that all students initiate conjectures. It is important that all students actively consider the validity of all conjectures made by classmates. When deciding if a conjecture is always true, have students write their ideas before sharing with the class. If you begin with a class discussion, only a few students are likely to participate, with others content to listen whether or not they are following the arguments. You can then use both what the students write as well as their input in discussions to assess what level of reasoning they are at: authority, use of examples, or an appeal to logic. ◆

Study of Patterns and Functions

Patterns are found in all areas of mathematics. Learning to search for patterns and how to describe, translate, and extend them is part of doing mathematics and thinking algebraically.

Repeating Patterns

The concept of a repeating pattern and how a pattern is extended or continued can be introduced to the full class in several ways. One possibility is to draw simple shape patterns on the board and extend them in a class discussion. Oral patterns can be recited. For example, "do, mi, mi, do, mi, mi" is a simple singing pattern. Body movements such as arm up, down, and sideways provides three movements with which to make patterns: up, side, side, down, up, side, side, down. Boy-girl patterns or stand-sit patterns are also good movement patterns.

Children's books often have repeating patterns. For example, a very long repeating pattern can be found in *If You Give a Mouse a Cookie* (Numeroff, 1985) in which each event eventually leads back to giving a mouse a cookie, with the implication that the sequence would be repeated.

Identifying and Extending Repeating Patterns. An important concept in working with repeating patterns is for students to identify the core of the pattern (Warren & Cooper, 2008). The *core* of a repeating pattern is the string of elements that repeats. In addition, it is important to use knowledge of the core to extend the pattern.

Activity 14.11

Making Pattern Strips

Students can work independently or in groups of two or three to extend patterns made from simple materials: buttons, colored blocks, connecting cubes, toothpicks, geometric shapes—items you can gather easily. For each set of materials, draw two or three complete repetitions of a pattern on strips of tagboard about 5 cm by 30 cm. The students' task is to use actual materials, copy the pattern shown, and extend it as far as they wish. Figure 14.10 illustrates one possible pattern for each of various manipulatives. You can also select one manipulative and make ten different pattern strips so that students can work with partners and then trade and work on identifying the core and extending patterns.

Young children make a significant generalization when they see that two patterns constructed with different materials are actually the same pattern. For example, in creating a repeating pattern with cubes, as in Figure 14.10, you can ask students to find a pattern block pattern with the same pattern (from one of the strips), or ask them to build such a pattern.

"[S]tudents should recognize that the color pattern 'blue, blue, red, blue, blue, red' is the same in form as 'clap, clap, step, clap, clap, step.' This

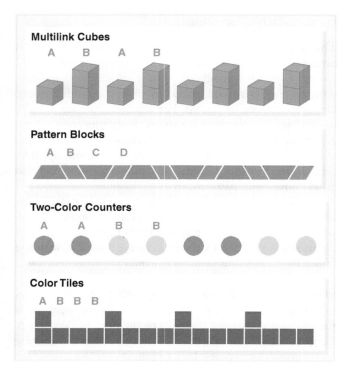

Multilink Cubes

A   B   A   B

Pattern Blocks

A   B   C   D

Two-Color Counters

A   A   B   B

Color Tiles

A   B   B   B

Figure 14.10 Examples of repeating patterns using manipulatives.

recognition lays the foundation for the idea that two very different situations can have the same mathematical features and thus are the same in some important ways. Knowing that each pattern above could be described as having the form AABAAB is for students an early introduction to the power of algebra" (pp. 91–92). ◆

The following activities reflect the powerful algebraic concept of repeating patterns just described in the quotation from *Principles and Standards*.

Activity 14.12

Pattern Match

Using the chalkboard or overhead projector, show six or seven different patterns (e.g., ABAB, ABCABC, etc.) with different materials or pictures (e.g., smileys, arrows pointing in different directions, etc.). Place students in pairs. One in each pair closes his or her eyes while the partner uses the A, B, C scheme to identify the core of a pattern that they have selected.

After hearing the pattern, the students who had their eyes closed examine the patterns and try to decide which pattern was selected. If two of the patterns in the list have the same structure, the discussion can be very interesting.

Conversely, give students the A, B, C label of the core of a pattern (e.g., ABCD or ABB) and ask them to create a pattern of this kind using two or three different models. Translation of a pattern from one medium to another is an alternative way of helping students separate the relationship in a pattern from the materials used to build it.

Predicting with Repeating Patterns: Linking to Divisibility. Prediction is an important part of algebraic thinking. The next activity focuses on prediction as a forerunner to looking at the functions.

Activity 14.13

Predict down the Line

For most repeating patterns, the elements of the pattern can be numbered 1, 2, 3, and so on. Provide students with a pattern to extend. Before students begin to extend the pattern, have them predict exactly what element will be in, say, the fifteenth position. Students should be required to provide a reason for their prediction, preferably in writing.

Notice in an ABC pattern that the third, sixth, ninth, and twelfth terms are the C. Students can use their developing concepts of multiplication and division to predict what the eighteenth and twenty-fifth items would be. Ask them to predict the hundredth item. Since 100 ÷ 3 = 33 remainder 1, it would be the A item in the pattern. If predicting the hundredth element, students will not be able to check the prediction by extending the pattern. Justification focuses on students' knowledge of multiplication and division (Warren & Cooper, 2008).

Using Real Contexts. Though geometric patterns and motions, like clapping, are good ways to introduce patterns, it is important that students see patterns in the world around them. The seasons, days of the week, and months of the year are just a beginning. Students might be able to think of AB patterns in their daily activities, for example "to school, home from school" or "set table before eating, clear table after eating."

Predicting what happens down the line has some interesting real-world contexts appropriate for upper elementary and middle school students. One context is the Olympics (Bay-Williams & Martinie, 2004). The Summer Olympics are held in 2008, 2012, and every four years after that. The Winter Olympics are held in 2010, 2014, and so on. This makes the ABCD or ABAC pattern: No Olympics, Summer Olympics, No Olympics, Winter Olympics.

A second context is the names of hurricanes, which are in an ABCDEF repeating pattern by letter in the alphabet, meaning that for each letter of the alphabet, there are six names that are used and then repeated (except that a name is retired when a major hurricane is given that name, like Katrina) (Fernandez & Schoen, 2008). The A names, for example, are: 2006—Alberto, 2007—Andrea, 2008—Arthur, 2009—Ana, 2010—Alex, and 2011—Arlene. (Good for you if you noticed the ABAB pattern regarding gender!). Assuming the names don't get retired, ask students questions such as:

- In what year will the first hurricane of that year be named Alex?
- What will be the first hurricane's name in the year 2020? 2050?
- Can you describe in words how to figure out the name of a hurricane, given the year?

Number Patterns. In the same way that contexts can be used to predict a number down the line, number patterns can be engaging for students, varying in complexity from simple repeating patterns such as 1, 2, 1, 2 to much more advanced. In this way, they can provide an interesting challenge for gifted students or be part of a learning station and explored by those who finish other work early. Here are a few:

2, 4, 6, 8, 10, . . .   (even numbers; add 2 each time)

1, 4, 7, 10, 13, . . .   (start with 1; add 3 each time)

1, 4, 9, 16, . . .   (squares)

0, 1, 5, 14, 30, . . . (add the next square number)

2, 5, 11, 23, . . .   (double the number and add 1)

2, 6, 12, 20, 30, . . . (multiply pairs of counting numbers)

3, 3, 6, 9, 15, 24, . . . (add the two preceding numbers—an example of a Fibonacci sequence)

For each of these patterns, students predict the thirteenth number or one hundredth number, to eventually find a general rule to produce any number in the sequence.

The calculator provides a powerful approach to patterns.

Growing Patterns

Beginning at about the fourth grade and extending through the middle school years, students can explore patterns that involve a progression from step to step. In technical terms, these are called sequences; we will simply call them *growing patterns*. With these patterns, students not only extend patterns but also look for a generalization or an algebraic relationship that will tell them what the pattern will be at any point along the way. Growing patterns can be functions, and growing patterns used in school textbooks tend to be

functions. Figure 14.11(a) is a growing pattern in which design 1 requires three triangles, design 2 requires six triangles, and so on—so we can say that the number of triangles needed is a function of which design it is (which happens to be the function triangles = 3 × design number). The Border Problem discussed earlier in this chapter can be adapted to be a growing pattern by simply having a swimming pool that is 5 by 5, then 6 by 6, then 7 by 7, and so on.

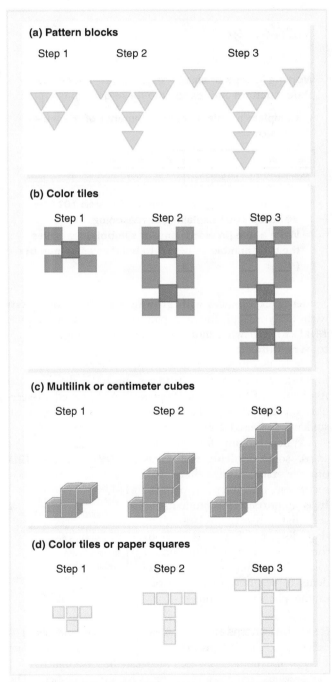

(a) Pattern blocks

Step 1   Step 2   Step 3

(b) Color tiles

Step 1   Step 2   Step 3

(c) Multilink or centimeter cubes

Step 1   Step 2   Step 3

(d) Color tiles or paper squares

Step 1   Step 2   Step 3

Figure 14.11 Geometric growing patterns using manipulatives.

Geometric patterns make good exemplars because the pattern is easy to see and because students can manipulate the objects. Figure 14.11 shows one growing pattern for four different manipulatives, though the possibilities are endless.

The questions in Activity 14.14, mapped to the pattern in Figure 14.11(a), are commonly used (and good ones to use!) to help students begin to think about the functional relationship.

Activity 14.14

Predict How Many

Working in pairs or small groups, have students explore a pattern and respond to these questions:

- Complete a table that shows number of triangles for each step.

Step Number	1	2	3	4	5 ...	10	20
Number of Triangles							

- How many triangles are needed for step 10? Step 20? Step 100? Explain your reasoning.
- Write a rule (in words and/or symbols) that gives the total number of pieces to build any step number (*n*).

Students' experiences with growing patterns should start with fairly straightforward patterns (such as in Figure 14.11) to somewhat more complicated (see Figure 14.12) to very difficult.

It is also important to include fractions and decimals in working with growing patterns. In 2003, the National Assessment of Educational Progress (NAEP) tested 13-year-olds on the item in Figure 14.13. Only 27 percent of students answered correctly (Lambdin & Lynch, 2005).

When looking for relationships, some students will focus on the table and others will focus on the physical pattern. It is important for students to see that whatever relationships they discover, they exist in both forms. So if a relationship is found in a table, challenge students to see how that plays out in the physical version.

myeducationlab

Go to the Building Teaching Skills and Dispositions section of Chapter 14 of MyEducationLab. Click on Videos and watch the video entitled **"Use Symbols"** to see a first-grade class creating patterns.

Recursive Patterns and Formulas. For most students, it is easier to see the patterns from one step to the next. In Figure 14.12(a) the number in each step can be determined from the previous step by adding successive even numbers. The description that tells how a pattern changes from step to step is known as a *recursive* pattern (Bezuszka & Kenney, 2008).

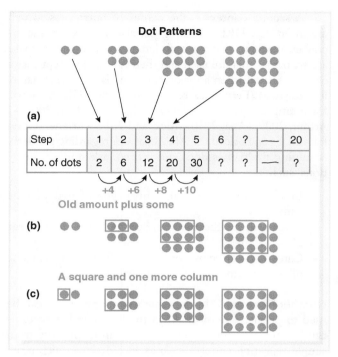

Figure 14.12 Two different ways to analyze relationships in the "dot pattern."

The recursive pattern can also be observed in the physical pattern. In Figure 14.12(b), notice that in each step, the previous step has been outlined. That lets you examine the amount added and see how it creates the pattern of adding on even numbers.

Recursive formulas are equations that show you how to get the next quantity, given the one you have. For example, in Figure 14.11, the first design grows by 3 trian-

Term	1	2	3	4
Fraction	$\frac{1}{2}$	$\frac{2}{3}$	$\frac{3}{4}$	$\frac{4}{5}$

If the list of fractions above continues in the same pattern, which term will be equal to 0.95?

- Ⓐ The 100th
- Ⓑ The 95th
- Ⓒ The 20th
- Ⓓ The 19th
- Ⓔ The 15th

Figure 14.13 NAEP item for 13-year-olds.
Source: Lambdin, D. V., & Lynch, K. (2005). "Examining Mathematics Tasks from the National Assessment of Educational Progress." *Mathematics Teaching in the Middle School, 10*(6), 314–318. Reprinted with permission. Copyright © 2005 by the National Council of Teachers of Mathematics, Inc. www.nctm.org. All rights reserved.

gles each time, so the recursive formula can be written as NEXT = NOW + 3. If NOW is the step 5 quantity, then NEXT is the step 6 quantity. Try to write a recursive formula for the other three patterns in Figure 14.11.

Explicit Formulas. To find the table entry for the hundredth step, the only way a recursive formula can help is to find all of the prior 99 entries in the table. If a formula can be discovered that connects the number of the step to the number of objects in a step, any table entry can be determined without building or calculating all of the previous entries. A rule that determines the number of elements in a step from the step number is called the *explicit formula*. Activities and textbooks in elementary and middle school often call the explicit formula the "rule" for the growing pattern.

❙❙ —————————— *Pause and Reflect*

Can you determine an explicit formula for the pattern in Figure 14.12? How did you find the formula?

There is no single best method for finding this relationship between step number and step, and students are likely to see it different ways. Some will analyze the table and notice that if they multiply the step number by the next step number, they will get the number of circles for that step. This leads the explicit formula: $d = n(n + 1)$, where d is number of dots and n is the step number.

Some will examine the physical pattern to see what is changing. In Figure 14.12(c), a square array is outlined for each step. Each successive square is one larger on a side. In this example, the side of each square is the same as the step number. The column to the right of each square is also the step number. At this point, writing a numeric expression for each step number can help students write the explicit formula. For example, the first four steps in Figure 14.12 are $1^2 + 1$, $2^2 + 2$, $3^2 + 3$, and $4^2 + 4$. The explicit formula is therefore $d = n^2 + n$.

Regardless of whether students use the table or the model, they will likely be able to describe the explicit formula in words before they can write it in symbols. If the goal of your lesson is to be able to find the rule, then stopping with the verbal formula is appropriate. In this case, you may have some students that are ready to represent the formula in symbols and they can be challenged to do so as a form of differentiating your instruction. If your instructional goal is to write formulas using symbols, then ask students to first write the formula, or rule, in words and then think about how they can translate that statement to numbers and symbols.

NCTM Standards "In grades 3–5, students should investigate numerical and geometric patterns and express them mathematically in words or symbols. They should analyze the structure of the pattern and how it grows or changes, organize this information systematically, and use their analysis to develop generalizations about the mathematical relationships in the pattern" (p. 159). ◆

Graphs of Functions. So far, growing patterns have been represented by (1) the physical materials or drawings, (2) a table, (3) words, and (4) symbols. A graph adds a fifth representation. Figure 14.14 shows the graph for the Border Problem and the Dot Pattern. Notice that the first is a straight-line (linear) relationship and the other is a curved line that would make half of a parabola if the points were joined. The horizontal axis is always used for the step numbers, the independent variable.

Graphs provide visuals that allow students to readily see relationships among growing patterns. Consider strings of a single color of pattern blocks (Figure 14.15) and the corresponding perimeters. This is a good pattern to explore in the same manner as the Border Problem, beginning with a

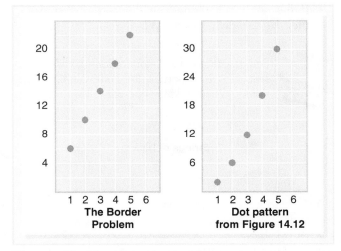

Figure 14.14 Graphs of two growing patterns.

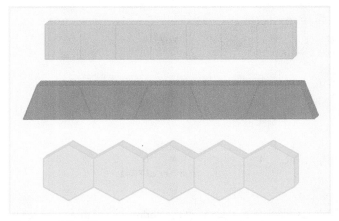

Figure 14.15 For each string of pattern blocks, can you determine the perimeter for *N* pattern blocks?

string of seven or eight blocks and finding ways to determine the perimeter without counting. Again, there are at least five different ways to find the perimeter, each resulting in a general formula that appears on the surface to be different from the others.

Having graphs of three related growing patterns offers the opportunity to compare and connect the graphs to the patterns and to the tables (see Figure 14.16). For example, ask students to discuss how to get from one coordinate to the next (up six, over one) and then ask how that information can be found in the table. Second, you can point at a particular point on the graph and ask what it tells about the pattern.

See if you can answer the following questions, which you can also pose to students to help them understand the graphical representation of the function:

- How does each graph represent each of the string patterns?
- Why is there not a line connecting the dots?
- Why is one line steeper than the others?
- Why is there no dot on the *y*-axis?
- If the dots were plotted on the *y*-axis, what would they be for each string? Why?

 Being able to make connections across representations is important for understanding functions. When asking questions like the ones listed above, look to see if students are able to link the graph to the context, to the table, and to the formula. ◆

Not all functions have straight-line graphs. For example, in building a rectangular pen with 24 yards of fence, if you increase the width, you will decrease the length. The area will vary accordingly (see Figure 14.17). An explicit formula for the width is $w = 12 - l$ (*l* is the length), which decreases at a constant rate, therefore looking like a line. By contrast, the explicit formula for area of the pen is $a = l(12 - l)$—it rises in a curve, reaches a maximum value, and then goes back down.

Graphs and Contexts. It is important for students to be able to interpret and construct graphs related to real situations, including sketching the shape of a graph without using any specific data, equations, or numbers. The advantage of activities such as these is the focus on how a graph can express the relationships involved.

Activity 14.15

Sketch a Graph

Sketch a graph for each of these situations. No numbers or formulas are to be used.

a. **The temperature of a frozen dinner from 30 minutes before it is removed from the freezer until it is removed from the microwave and placed on the table. (Consider time 0 to be the moment the dinner is removed from the freezer.)**
b. **The value of a 1970 Volkswagen Beetle from the time it was purchased to the present. (It was kept by a loving owner and is in top condition.)**
c. **The level of water in the bathtub from the time you begin to fill it to the time it is completely empty after your bath.**
d. **Profit in terms of number of items sold.**
e. **The height of a baseball from when it is thrown to the time it hits the ground.**
f. **The speed of the baseball in the situation in item e.**

⏸ ——————— *Pause and Reflect*

Stop for a moment and sketch graphs for each situation in the last activity.

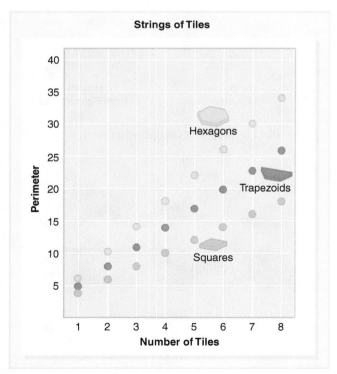

Figure 14.16 Graphs of the perimeters of three different pattern-block strings. The lines are not drawn because for this context, there are no solutions between the points.

In a classroom, it is fun to have students sketch their graphs on transparencies without identifying which situation they selected (no labels on the graphs). Let students examine the graph to see if they can determine which situation goes with each graph that is presented. Figure 14.18 contains six graphs that match the six situations described in

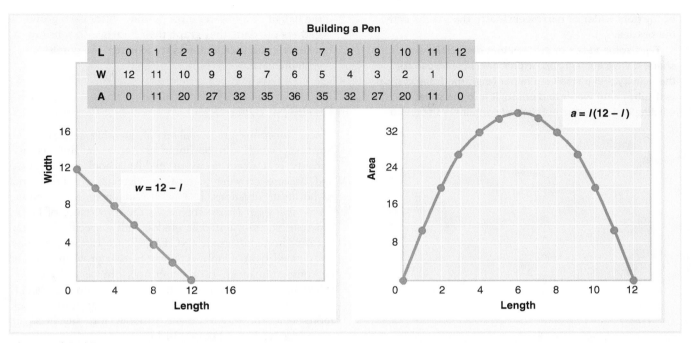

Building a Pen

L	0	1	2	3	4	5	6	7	8	9	10	11	12
W	12	11	10	9	8	7	6	5	4	3	2	1	0
A	0	11	20	27	32	35	36	35	32	27	20	11	0

$w = 12 - l$

$a = l(12 - l)$

Figure 14.17 The width and area graphs as functions of the length of a rectangle with a fixed perimeter of 24 units.

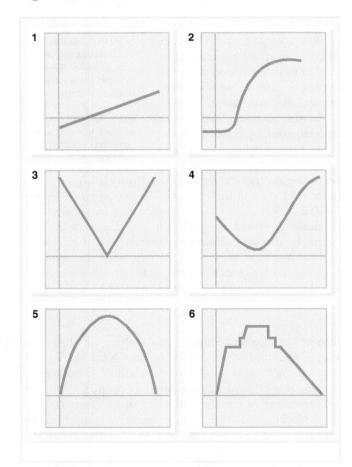

Figure 14.18 Match each graph with the situations described in Activity 14.15. Talk about what change is happening in each case.

the "Sketch a Graph" activity. Can you match these graphs with the six situations?

Graphs and Rate of Change. Notice that the analysis of the graphs focuses on how the graphs increase or decrease and how steeply or gradually. A graph is a picture of the rate of change of one variable in terms of the other. Essentially, graphs can only have one of the seven characteristics shown in Figure 14.19 or some combination of these. These types of change will be seen in the following activity.

Figure 14.19 Seven ways that graphs can change. A graph often has combinations of these characteristics.

Activity 14.16

Bottles and Volume Graphs

Figure 14.20 shows six vases and six graphs. Assume that the bottles are filled at a constant rate. Because of their shapes, the height of the liquid in the bottles will increase either more slowly or more quickly as the

bottle gets wider or narrower. Match the graphs with the bottles.

Find some vases or glasses that have different shapes. Give each group or pair one vase to use for the activity. Fill a small container (e.g., medicine cup or test tube) with water and empty it into the vase, recording in a table the number of containers used and the height of the water after pouring. After each group gathers the data, they graph their findings. Graphs are collected and then students try to match the graph with the vase.

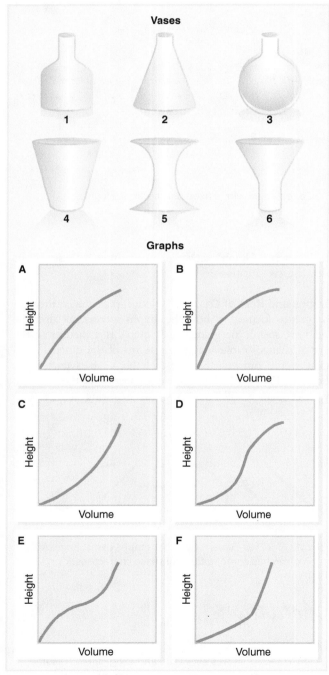

Figure 14.20 Assuming bottles are filled at a constant rate, match the graphs with the vases.

Linear Functions

Linear functions are a subset of growing patterns and functions, which can be linear or nonlinear. But because linearity is a major focus of middle school mathematics, and because growing patterns in elementary school tend to be linear situations, it appears here in its own section. *Curriculum Focal Points* emphasizes the importance of linear functions across the middle grades, with a specific focus on linearity in eighth grade (NCTM, 2006). Linear functions are defined quite simply as functions that grow in a linear or constant manner. In a graph, this can be easily established by seeing that the plotted points lie on one line.

Linearity can be established by looking at the other representations. If you make a table for the hexagon perimeter task in Figure 14.15 you will notice that the recursive pattern is +4 each time. The rate of change from one step to the next is constant (+4). You can always look at the recursive relationship to determine whether the function is growing at a constant rate and therefore linear.

In the equation, linearity can be determined by looking at the part of the expression that changes. Compare the two formulas from the rectangular pen problem. One was $w = 12 - l$ and the other was $a = l(12 - l)$ or $a = 12l - l^2$. Notice that in the first case the change is related to l and each time l changes by 1, w changes by the same amount—a constant rate of change, as in linear situations. In the area formula, when l changes by the same amount, the area changes in varying amounts. In fact, this is a quadratic situation. Figure 14.17 shows these graphs.

Rate of Change and Slope. An analysis of change is one of the four components in the NCTM Algebra standard (see Appendix). Rate, whether constant or varying, is a type of change often associated with how fast something is traveling. Rate is an excellent context for exploring linearity, because constant rates can be seen in a wide range of contexts, such as the geometric model of the pattern block perimeter pattern or the rate of growth of a plant. Other rate contexts in numerical situations include hourly wages, gas mileage, profit, and even the cost of an item, such as a bus ticket.

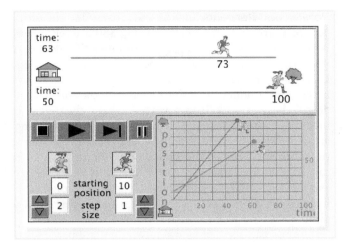

Figure 14.21 Applet 5.2, "Understanding Distance, Speed, and Time Relationships Using Simulation Software." Used with permission from NCTM e-Standards. Copyright © 2003 by the National Council of Teachers of Mathematics, Inc. All rights reserved. The presence of the screenshot from NCTM e-Standards, http://standards.nctm.org/document/eexamples/chap5/5.2/index.htm, does not constitute or imply an endorsement by NCTM.

The NCTM e-Examples has two applets that target rate, making the connection between a real-world context and graphs. In Applet 5.2 students can adjust the speed, direction, and starting position of two runners. As the runners are set in motion, a time–distance graph is generated dynamically for each runner (see Figure 14.21). ◆

The NCTM applet compares two rates through two representations (visual model and the graph). Many real-world situations can be similarly described. Another NCTM applet (6.2), for example, explores phone call rates in this manner. Another example is shown by Figure 14.16. The three graphs are increasing at different rates. Notice each slant or slope is different. *Slope* is the numeric value that describes the rate of change for a linear function.

One of the explicit formulas for the hexagon growing pattern is $y = 4x + 2$. Note that the rate of change is 4 because the perimeter increases by 4 with each new piece. All linear functions can be written in this form: $y = mx + b$ (including $y = mx$ when $b = 0$). The value m in this formula is the rate of change or the slope of the line.

Conceptually, then, slope signifies how much y increases when x increases by 1. If a line contains the points $(2, 4)$ and $(3, -5)$, then you can see that as x increases by 1, y decreases by 9. So the rate of change, or slope, is -9. For the points $(4, 3)$ and $(7, 9)$, you can see that when x increases by 3, y increases by 6. Therefore, an increase of 1 in x results in a change of 2 in y (dividing 6 by 3). After further exploration and experiences, your students will begin to notice that you can find the rate of change or slope by finding the difference in the y values and dividing by the difference in the x values.

Sometimes an equation may not look like the familiar form $y = mx + b$. For example, in the rectangular pen problem, if the l and w represent the length and width and the perimeter is 24, then $2l + 2w = 24$ is an equation that relates the length to the width, but can be simplified to $w = -1l + 12$, a linear equation with a slope of -1 and an initial value of 12.

Zero Slope and No Slope. Understanding these two easily confused slopes requires contexts, such as walking rates. Consider this story:

You walk for 10 minutes at a rate of 1 mile per hour, stop for 3 minutes to watch a nest of baby birds, then walk for 5 more minutes at 2 miles per hour.

What will the graph look like for the 3 minutes when you stop? What is your rate when you stop? In fact, your rate is 0 and since you are at the same distance for 3 minutes, the graph will be a horizontal line.

Let's say that you see a graph of a walking story that includes a vertical line. What would this mean? That you traveled a distance with no time passing! Now, even if you were a world record sprinter, this would be impossible, and therefore a vertical line has no slope. Remember rate is based a change of 1 in the x value, and a vertical line will never have a change in the x variable.

Proportional and Nonproportional Situations. Linear functions can be proportional or nonproportional. The rate example just described is *proportional*. The distance you walk is proportional to how much time you have walked. As another example, your paycheck is proportional to the hours you work. But it is not the case that the perimeter of the pattern block growing problem is proportional to the number of blocks used. Although you have a constant increase factor of 4, there is an extra 2 units of perimeter. Said another way, you cannot get from the input (number of blocks) to the perimeter by multiplying by a factor, as you can in proportional situations.

All proportional situations, then, are equations in the form $y = mx$. Notice that the graphs of all proportional situations are straight lines that pass through the origin. Students will find that the slope of these lines is also the rate of change between the two variables.

This distinction is important from a teaching perspective because proportional situations are easier to generalize; you should be careful to select growing patterns that are proportional before moving to ones that are not. Figure 14.11(a)–(c) show proportional representations. However, if you slightly altered the patterns, they would become nonproportional. For example, in the first pattern, if the triangles were added on to only two of the prongs, like an upside-down V, then you could no longer find the *n*th term simply by multiplying the step number by a factor. Pattern (d) demonstrates such a situation—it grows by three with an initial value of 4 squares.

❚❚ ——————— *Pause and Reflect*

Can you determine the explicit formula for the upside-down V pattern? Its first steps require 3, 5, 7, and 9 triangles, respectively.

Typical proportion problems can be adapted for an algebraic approach. Consider the following example:

Two out of every three students who eat in the cafeteria drink a pint of white milk. If 450 students eat in the cafeteria, how many pints of milk are consumed?

As the problem is stated, there are a fixed number of students (450) and a single answer to the problem. Students would be expected to set up a proportion and solve for the unknown. But if only the first sentence of the problem is provided, students can be asked to find a rule (explicit formula) that shows the amount of milk in terms of the number of students, $m = \frac{2}{3}s$, where *s* is number of students and *m* is the number of pints of milk.

In nonproportional situations, one value is constant. In the perimeter pattern problem, for example, no matter which step number you are on, there are 2 units (one on each end that must be included). Similarly, the Border Problem always has the 4 corners. If you were walking, but had a head start of 50 meters, or if you were selling something and had an initial expense, those values are constants in the linear function that make it not proportional. The constant value, or initial value, of a linear function ends up being where the graph crosses the *y*-axis. We can find out the initial value in the table by using 0 as a step number, in the equation by using $x = 0$ and simplifying, or on the graph by seeing where the line would cross the *y*-axis.

Nonproportional situations are more challenging for students to generalize. Students want to use the recursive value (e.g., +4) as the factor (×4), without considering what constant or initial values are part of the situation. Students often make the common error of using the table to find the tenth step and doubling it to find the twentieth step, which works in proportional situations but not in nonproportional situations. Mathematics education researchers have found that having students analyze their errors is essential in helping support their learning of mathematics concepts (Lannin, Arbaugh, Barker, & Townsend, 2006).

Parallel and Perpendicular Lines. Consider the situation of Larry and Mary, each earning $30 a week for the summer months. Mary starts the summer $50 dollars in the hole and Larry already has $20. When will Mary and Larry have the same amount of money? In week 3, how much more money does Larry have? How much more does he have in week 7? In any week, what is the difference in their wealth? The rate for Larry and Mary's earnings are the same—and the graphs would therefore go up at the same rate; that is, the slopes would be the same. We can tell that the graphs of $y = 30x + 20$ (Larry's money) and $y = 30x - 50$ (Mary's money) are parallel without even making the graphs because the rates (or slopes) are the same.

Slopes can also tell us when two lines are perpendicular, but it is less obvious. A little bit of analysis using similar triangles will show that for perpendicular lines, the slope of one is the negative reciprocal of the other.

Mathematical Modeling

Kaput (1999) defines modeling as the process of beginning with real phenomena and attempting to mathematize them. Mathematical models, or equations, are used to predict other phenomena. Mathematical models are not to be confused with the models that use manipulatives or visuals for building a pattern (such as a pattern block).

We have already seen many examples of mathematical models. How is modeling used to predict? Take the example of selling widgets marked up at some percentage over wholesale. Once a formula is derived for a given price and markup, it can be used to determine the profit at different sales levels. Furthermore, it is relatively easy to make adjustments in the price and markup percentage, allowing for further predictions. That is, the equation, or mathematical model, allows us to find values that cannot be observed in the real phenomenon.

Consider creating a mathematical model to describe the depreciation of a car at 20 percent each year. Determining the model might progress in the following steps: If the car loses 20 percent of its value in 1 year, then it must be worth 80 percent of its value after a year. So after 1 year, the $15,000 car is worth $15,000 × 0.8. In the second year, it loses 20 percent of that value, so it will be worth only 80 percent of its value at the end of year one, which was $15,000 × 0.8. The value at the end of year 2 would be ($15,000 × 0.8) × 0.8, and so on. At the end of *y* years, the value of the car can be expressed in this equation: value = $15,000 × 0.8^y. Figure 14.22 shows the graph and the table of values on a graphing calculator.

The next activity provides another context appropriate for developing a mathematical model.

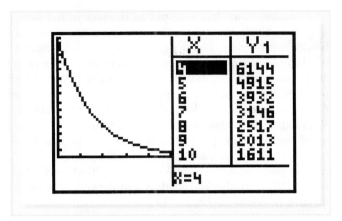

Figure 14.22 The graph and table for $V = 15{,}000 \times 0.8^y$. Years, the independent variable, are shown under X and value, the dependent variable, is shown under Y1.

Activity 14.17

How Many Gallons Left?

A car gets 23 miles per gallon of gas. It has a gas tank that holds 20 gallons. Suppose that you were on a trip and had filled the tank at the outset. Determine a mathematical model that describes the gallons left given number of miles traveled?

Notice that the word *rule* could replace "mathematical model." In this case, one possible equation is $g = 20 - \frac{m}{23}$. Use the model, or equation, to make predictions. For example, "How can you tell from the model how much gas will be left after driving 300 miles?" "How many miles can you drive before the gas tank has only 3 gallons left?" Two more engaging contexts are provided in Figure 14.23.

Sometimes a model is provided and the important task is for students to understand and use the formula. Consider the following pumping water problem and related equation from the Michigan Algebra Project (Herbel-Eisenmann & Phillips, 2005):

Suppose you turn a pump on and let it run to empty the water out of a pool. The amount of water in the pool (W, measured in gallons) at any time (T, measured in hours) is given by the following equation: $W = -350\,(T - 4)$.

⏸ ———————— *Pause and Reflect*

What questions might you pose to middle school students to help them make sense of this equation? Try to think of three.

1. Pleasant's Hardware buys widgets for $4.17 each, marks them up 35 percent over wholesale, and sells them at that price. Create a mathematical model to relate widgets sold (*w*) to profit (*p*). The manager asks you to determine the formula if she were to put the widgets on sale for 25 percent off. What is your formula or mathematical model for the sale, comparing widgets sold (*s*) to profit (*p*)?

2. In Arches National Park in Moab, Utah, there are sandstone cliffs. A green coating of color, called cyanobacteria, covers some of the sandstone. Bacteria grow by splitting into two (or doubling) in a certain time period. If the sandstone started with 50 bacteria, create a mathematical model for describing the growth of cyanobacteria on the sandstone.

Figure 14.23 Mathematical modeling problems for further exploration.
Source: Adapted from Buerman, M. (2007). "The Algebra of the Arches." *Mathematics Teaching in the Middle School, 12*(7), 360–365.

In the Michigan Algebra Project, students were asked to solve several problems and explain how the equation was used to find the answer. Those questions and one student's responses are provided in Figure 14.24.

🌀 Teaching Considerations

It is important to emphasize some key considerations that will lead students to feel empowered to do algebra. Some of these ideas have already been implied in the previous discussions of algebraic concepts.

Emphasize Appropriate Algebra Vocabulary

A large part of understanding mathematics is the ability to communicate mathematically, so it is important to use appropriate terminology in teaching algebra. This is far more than a vocabulary list; it is the practice of consistently using, and having students use, appropriate words for situations. Creating word walls and keeping a journal of terms are ways to help all students but especially English language learners (ELLs). Having graphs, models, or tables to illustrate the words is essential. Here we briefly share some important vocabulary terms.

Independent and Dependent Variables. Although the meanings of "independent" and "dependent" variables are implied by the words themselves, they can still be challenging for students. The independent variable is the step number, or the input, or whatever value is being used to

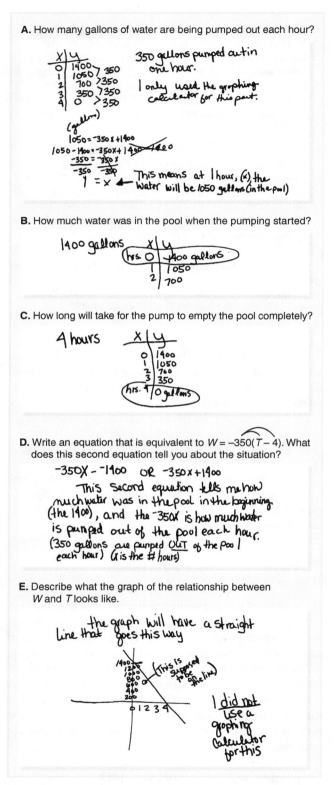

A. How many gallons of water are being pumped out each hour?

B. How much water was in the pool when the pumping started?

C. How long will take for the pump to empty the pool completely?

D. Write an equation that is equivalent to $W = -350(T - 4)$. What does this second equation tell you about the situation?

E. Describe what the graph of the relationship between W and T looks like.

Figure 14.24 One student's explanations of questions regarding what a mathematical model means.

Source: Figure 3 from Herbel-Eisenmann, B. A., & Philips, E. D. (2005). "Using Student Work to Develop Teachers' Knowledge of Algebra." *Mathematics Teaching in the Middle School, 11*(2), p. 65. Reprinted with permission. Copyright © 2005 by the National Council of Teachers of Mathematics, Inc. www.nctm.org. All rights reserved.

find another value. For example, in the case of the strings of pattern blocks the independent variable is the number of blocks in the string. The dependent variable is the number of objects needed, the output, or whatever value you get from using the independent variable. In the pattern block problem, it is the perimeter. You can say that the perimeter of the block structure depends on the number of blocks. Recall the two equations and graphs representing a pen of 24 meters in Figure 14.17. In this case, the length has been selected as the independent variable (though it could have as easily been the width) and the dependent variable is width. What are the independent and dependent variables for the problem in Figure 14.24?

Discrete and Continuous. In elementary school, the discussion of functions, especially graphical representations, should include a discussion of whether the points plotted on the graph should be connected or not and why. In the pattern block perimeter problem, the answer is no because you will only have whole number values. When isolated or selected values are the only ones appropriate for a context, the function is *discrete*. If all values along a line or curve are solutions to the function, then it is *continuous*. The pen example is continuous—the length can be any value up to a certain maximum and the width (or area) would change accordingly.

Domain and Range. The *domain* of a function comprises the possible values for the independent variable. If it is discrete, like the pattern block perimeter problem, it may include all positive whole numbers. For the 24-meter rectangular pen, the domain is all real numbers between 0 and 12. The *range* is the corresponding possible values for the dependent variable. In the pattern block perimeter problem, the range is the positive whole numbers; in the rectangular pen, the range for the length is the same as the domain—real numbers between 0 and 12.

Multiple Representations

Functions can be represented in any of five ways: (1) the pattern itself, which we can refer to as the context; (2) the table; (3) the verbal description; (4) the symbolic equation; and (5) the graph. In both the repeating and the growing pattern sections, each example has included at least two representations (e.g., context and the table) and as many as all five (e.g., the dot pattern in Figure 14.12). It is important to see that each representation is a way of looking at the function, each providing a different way of looking at or thinking about the function. The value of each representation is in the way that it helps us see and understand the function in a different manner than the others do. To illustrate this point, we will use the context of a hot dog vendor.

Brian is trying to make money to help pay for college by selling hot dogs from a hot dog cart at the coliseum during major performances and ball games. He pays the cart owner $35 per night for the use of the cart. He sells hot dogs for $1.25 each. His costs for the hot dogs, condiments, napkins, and other paper products are about 60 cents per hot dog on average. The profit from a single hot dog is, therefore, 65 cents.

Context. This function begins with a context: selling hot dogs and the resulting profit. We are interested in Brian's profit in terms of the number of hot dogs sold. The more hot dogs Brian sells, the more profit he will make. Brian does not begin to make a profit immediately because he must pay the $35 rent on the vending cart. Nonetheless, Brian's profit is dependent on—is a function of—the number of hot dogs he sells.

The context helps students make sense of what changes (number of hot dogs sold) and what stays the same ($35 rental), which can help them figure out the explicit formula. The context supports students' conceptual understanding of the other more abstract representations and illustrates that algebra is a tool for describing real-world phenomena. The context alone, though, is not sufficient—carefully selected prompts to connect the context to other representations are needed to support students' algebraic thinking (Earnest & Balti, 2008).

Table. Brian might well sit down and calculate some possible income figures based on anticipated sales. This will give him some idea of how many hot dogs he must sell to break even and what his profit might be for an evening. A table of values might resemble Table 14.2.

The number of hot dogs shown in the table is purely a matter of choice. One could calculate the profit for 10,000 hot dogs (10,000 × 0.65 – 35), even though it is not reasonable in this context. The table provides a concise way to look at the recursive pattern and the explicit pattern. The recursive pattern can lead to seeing what changes, if it changes at a constant rate, and how that can help find the explicit formula.

Verbal Description. In the hot dog vendor situation, Brian's profit depends on the number of hot dogs that are sold. In functional language, we can say, "Profit is a function of the number of hot dogs sold." The phrase "is a function of" expresses the dependent relationship. The profit depends on—is a function of—the hot dog sales. The verbal description of the explicit formula for the hot dog stand might be stated by students as, "You multiply each hot dog sold by $0.65; then you subtract the $35 for the cart."

The verbal explanation of the explicit formula provides a connection from the context to the symbolic representation. Students may struggle with using variables, and being able to first describe the formula in words is an important stepping-stone for being able to use symbols (Lannin, Townsend, Armer, Green, & Schneider, 2008).

Symbols. Suppose that we pick a letter—say, h—to represent the number of hot dogs Brian sells. Brian's profit is represented by the equation $p = (0.65 \times h) - 35$, where p is the letter selected to stand for profit. This equation defines a mathematical relationship between two values or two variables, profit and hot dogs.

By expressing a function as an equation, it is possible to find the profit for any number of hot dogs. Conversely, if Brian wants to make $100, he can figure out how many hot dogs he needs to sell. Because it is abstract, it is particularly important that students explain what each number and each variable represents.

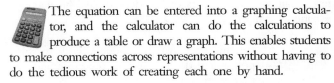 The equation can be entered into a graphing calculator, and the calculator can do the calculations to produce a table or draw a graph. This enables students to make connections across representations without having to do the tedious work of creating each one by hand.

Graphs. In Figure 14.25, four different values of hot dog sales are plotted on a graph. The horizontal axis represents the number of hot dogs sold, and the vertical axis, the profit. As we have already established, the profit goes up as the sales go up. There is, in this situation, a linear pattern to the six values. In this context it means that the profit is going up at a constant rate, namely at 0.65 per hot dog.

The graphical representation allows one to see "at a glance" that the relationship between sales and profits is linear—a straight line—and is increasing. It also can be used to get quick approximate answers to questions about Brian's profits, such as, "How many hot dogs must be sold to break even?" "How many will need to be sold to earn $100?" (It looks to be near 210 or 215.) The context gives meaning to the graph, and the graph adds understanding to the context.

The graph indicates the pattern in the data, but in terms of the context, all values may not make sense for the context. In this case, it would not make sense to extend the

Table 14.2

Number of Hot Dogs Sold (Independent Variable) and the Profit (Dependent Variable)	
Hot Dogs Sold	**Profit**
0	−35.00
50	−2.50
100	30.00
150	62.50

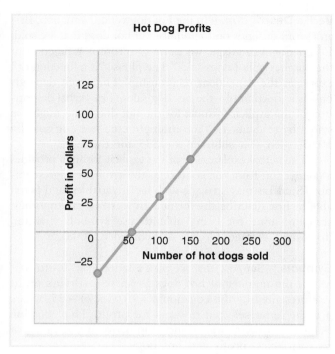

Hot Dog Profits

Figure 14.25 A graph showing profit as a function of hot dogs sold.

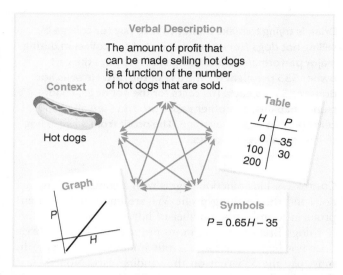

Figure 14.26 Five different representations of a function. For any given function, students should see that all these representations are connected and illustrate the same relationship.

line to the left of the vertical axis, as this would mean selling a negative quantity of hot dogs. Nor is it reasonable to talk about sales of millions of hot dogs (unless he develops a national chain!).

 In the past, when students had to plot points and do by hand all the computations that were involved, functions were limited to examples using whole numbers to avoid the tedium of computing and plotting fractional values. Thanks to technology, we can now explore realistic contexts involving more precise and "messy" numbers. ◆

Connect Representations

Figure 14.26 illustrates the five representations of functions for the hot dog context. The most important idea is to see that, for a given function, each of these representations illustrates the same relationship and that students should be able to explain connections across representations in a conceptual manner. This is a different experience than you might have experienced in an Algebra I textbook that gave instructions such as, "Graph the function, given the equation," along with a set of steps to follow. The difference lies in whether the movement among representations is about following a rote procedure or about making sense of the function. The latter is your goal as a teacher.

The seventh-grade *Connected Mathematics Project* (CMP II) has an entire unit titled "Variables and Patterns," in

which students explore and use different representations of functions in real contexts. The excerpt on the next page is a lesson focused on tables and graphs.

 "By the middle grades, students should be able to understand the relationships among tables, graphs, and symbols and to judge the advantages and disadvantages of each way of representing relationships for practical purposes. As they work with multiple representations of functions—including numeric, graphic, and symbolic—they will develop a more comprehensive understanding of functions" (p. 38). ◆

 A good formative or summative assessment prompt for the hot dog problem (which can be adapted to any task) is: "Can you show me how to use each representation to find the profit for selling 225 hot dogs?" ◆

Algebraic Thinking Across the Curriculum

One reason the phrase "algebraic thinking" is used instead of "algebra" is that the practice of looking for patterns and generalizations goes beyond curriculum topics that are usually categorized as algebra topics. You have already experienced some of this integration—looking at geometric growing patterns and working with perimeter and area. In fact, in *Curriculum Focal Points* (NCTM, 2006), many of the focal points that include algebra connect it to other content areas. In the sections that follow, the emphasis of the content moves to be on the other content areas, with algebraic

Connected Mathematics

Grade 7, *Variables and Patterns*
Investigation 3: Analyzing Graphs and Tables

Context

Much of this unit is built on the context of a group of students who take a multiday bike trip from Philadelphia to Williamsburg, Virginia, and who then decide to set up a bike tour business of their own. Students explore a variety of functional relationships between time, distance, speed, expenses, profits, and so on. When data are plotted as discrete points, students consider what the graph might look like between points. For example, what interpretations could be given to each of these five graphs showing speed change from 0 to 15 mph in the first 10 minutes of a trip?

Task Description

In this investigation, the fictional students in the unit began gathering data in preparation for setting up their tour business. As their first task, they sought data from two different bike rental companies as shown here, given by one company in the form of a table and by the other in the form of a graph. The task is interesting because of the firsthand way in which students experience the value of one representation over another, depending on the need of the situation. In this unit students are frequently asked whether a graph or a table is the better source of information.

In the tasks that follow, students are given a table of data showing results of a phone poll that asked at which price former tour riders would take a bike tour. Students must find the best way to graph this data. After a price for a bike tour is established, graphs for estimated profits are created with corresponding questions about profits depending on different numbers of customers.

The investigations use no formulas at this point. The subsequent investigation is called "Patterns and Rules"

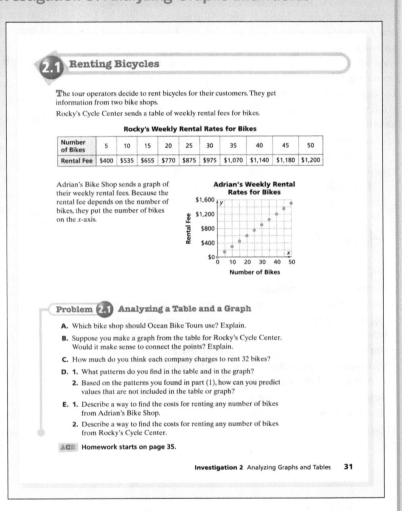

2.1 Renting Bicycles

The tour operators decide to rent bicycles for their customers. They get information from two bike shops.

Rocky's Cycle Center sends a table of weekly rental fees for bikes.

Rocky's Weekly Rental Rates for Bikes

Number of Bikes	5	10	15	20	25	30	35	40	45	50
Rental Fee	$400	$535	$655	$770	$875	$975	$1,070	$1,140	$1,180	$1,200

Adrian's Bike Shop sends a graph of their weekly rental fees. Because the rental fee depends on the number of bikes, they put the number of bikes on the *x*-axis.

Adrian's Weekly Rental Rates for Bikes

Problem 2.1 Analyzing a Table and a Graph

A. Which bike shop should Ocean Bike Tours use? Explain.

B. Suppose you make a graph from the table for Rocky's Cycle Center. Would it make sense to connect the points? Explain.

C. How much do you think each company charges to rent 32 bikes?

D. 1. What patterns do you find in the table and in the graph?

    2. Based on the patterns you found in part (1), how can you predict values that are not included in the table or graph?

E. 1. Describe a way to find the costs for renting any number of bikes from Adrian's Bike Shop.

    2. Describe a way to find the costs for renting any number of bikes from Rocky's Cycle Center.

ACE Homework starts on page 35.

Investigation 2 Analyzing Graphs and Tables **31**

and begins the exploration of connecting equations or rules to the representations of graphs and tables. In the final investigation, students use graphing calculators to explore how graphs change in appearance when the rules that produce the graphs change.

thinking used as a tool for discovery. This brief discussion will be developed more fully in later chapters.

Measurement and Algebra. Soares, Blanton, and Kaput (2006) describe how to "algebrafy" the elementary curriculum. One measurement example they give uses *Spaghetti and Meatballs for All*, looking at the increasing number of chairs needed given the number of tables put together.

Geometric formulas relate various dimensions, areas, and volumes of shapes. Each of these formulas involves at least one functional relationship. Consider any familiar formula for measuring a geometric shape. For example, the circumference of a circle is $c = 2\pi r$. The radius is the independent variable and circumference is the dependent variable. We can say that the circumference is dependent on the radius. Even nonlinear formulas like volume of a cone ($V = 1/3\pi r^2 h$) are functions. Here the volume is a function of both the height of the cone and the radius. If the radius is held constant, the volume is a function of the height. Similarly, for a fixed height, the volume is a function of the radius.

The following activity explores how the volume of a box varies as a result of changing the dimensions.

Activity 14.18

Designing the Largest Box

Begin with a rectangular sheet of cardstock, and from each corner, cut out a square. Fold up the four resulting flaps, and tape them together to form an open box. The volume of the box will vary depending on the size of the squares (see Figure 14.27). Write a formula that gives the volume of the box as a function of the size of the cutout squares. Use the function to determine what size the squares should be to create the box with the largest volume.

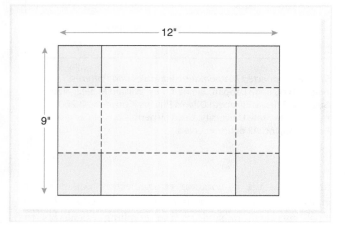

Figure 14.27 If squares are cut from a 9-by-12-inch piece of cardboard so that the four flaps can be folded up, what size squares should be cut so that the volume of the box is the largest possible?

Data and Algebra. Data can be obtained from sports records, census reports, the business section of the newspaper, and many other sources. Students can gather data such as measurement examples or survey data. The Internet has many sites where data can be found.

 "When doing experiments or dealing with real data, students may encounter 'messy data,' for which a line or a curve may not be an exact fit. They will need experience with such situations and assistance from the teacher to develop their ability to find a function that fits the data well enough to be useful as a prediction tool" (p. 228). ◆

Experiments. There are many experiments that students can explore to see the functional relationships, if any, that exist between two variables. Gathering real data is an excellent way to engage a range of learners and to see how mathematics can be used to describe real phenomena.

Data should be collected and then represented in a table or on a graph. The goal is to determine if there is a relationship between the independent and dependent variables, and if so, whether it is linear or nonlinear, as in the following engaging experiments:

- How long would it take for 100 students standing in a row to complete a wave similar to those seen at football games? Experiment with different numbers of students from 5 to 25. Can the relationship predict how many students it would take for a given wave time?
- How far will a Matchbox car roll off of a ramp, based on the height the ramp is raised?
- How is the flight time of a paper airplane affected by the number of paper clips attached to the nose of the plane?
- What is the relationship between the number of dominoes in a row and the time required for them to fall over? (Use multiples of 100 dominoes.)
- Make wadded newspaper balls using different numbers of sheets of newspaper, using rubber bands to help hold the paper in a ball. What is the relationship between the number of sheets and the distance the ball can be thrown?
- What is the relationship between the number of drops of colored water dropped on a paper towel and the diameter of the spot? Is the relationship different for different brands of towels?
- How much weight can a toothpick bridge hold? Lay toothpicks in a bunch to span a 2-inch gap between two boards. From the toothpicks, hang a bag or other container into which weights can be added until the toothpicks break. Begin with only one toothpick (McCoy, 1997).

Experiments like these are fun and accessible to a wide range of learners. They also provide an opportunity for students to engage in experimental design. Students need practice in identifying independent and dependent variables, controlling experiments for other variables, measuring and recording results, and analyzing data. This is a perfect blend of mathematics and science.

Scatter Plots. Often in the real world, phenomena are observed that seem to suggest a functional relationship but not necessarily as clean or as well defined as some of the situations we have described so far. Certainly this would be true of the experiments described above. However, even in the case of measuring the increasing height of a stack of identical books as each new one is added—a linear situation—measuring error will lead to values that are not exactly on a line. In such cases, the data are generally plotted on a graph to produce a scatter plot of points.

A visual inspection of the graphed data may suggest what kind of relationship, if any, exists. If a linear relationship seems to exist, for example, students can approximate a line of best fit or use graphing technology to do a linear regression to find the line of best fit (along with the equation). They do not need to understand what linear regression is to use this function on the graphing calculator—just that it is a statistical method for finding the line of best fit.

Not all scatter plots will show a straight-line relationship. Suppose students were figuring out the time it takes for balloons of various diameters to deflate (another engaging experiment!). A parabolic or cubic function might better approximate the shape of the data. Graphing calculators can also find best-fitting curves. These brief examples of algebraic thinking in other content areas illustrate the importance of algebra in the K–8 curriculum

Reflections

Writing to Learn

1. Kaput lists five types of algebraic thinking. Rather than list each of these, describe algebraic thinking in no more than three sentences in a manner that encompasses Kaput's main ideas and the spirit of this chapter.
2. What misconceptions do students have regarding the equal sign? What causes these misconceptions and how can instruction clear these up?
3. What misconceptions do students have regarding variables? What causes these misconceptions and how can instruction clear these up?
4. Explain how to solve the equation $4x + 3 = x + 12$ on the pan balance.
5. What is a recursive relationship? Where in a table for a growing pattern would you look for the recursive relationship? What would it mean in terms of the pattern itself?
6. How can you tell from the recursive relationship whether the graph of the growing pattern will be straight or curved?

7. How can you determine if a function is linear in each of the five representations?

For Discussion and Exploration

1. The idea of having students make connections from arithmetic to algebra is a relatively new idea for the elementary curriculum. What examples can you find in the number strand for taking an algorithm and presenting it in a way that it becomes a process for generalizing a rule? (See the "Generalization with Addition" section for an example.)
2. Explore some of the online applets that focus on functions (see "Online Resources" at the end of the chapter). For each consider what the technology provides in terms of learning opportunities. How might the technology be used to support the diversity in a classroom?

Resources

Literature Connections

Many teachers find pattern explorations sufficiently interesting that they may not think of using literature to provide a springboard for student explorations. However, the following three examples of books are excellent beginnings for patterns and chart building.

Anno's Magic Seeds *Anno, 1994*

Anno's Magic Seeds has several patterns. A wise man gives Jack two magic seeds, one to eat and one to plant. The planted seed will produce two new seeds by the following year. Several years later, Jack decides to plant both seeds. Then he has a family and starts to sell seeds.

At each stage of the story, there is an opportunity to develop a chart and extend the current pattern into the future. Austin and Thompson (1997) describe how they used the story to develop patterns and charts with sixth- and seventh-grade students.

Bats on Parade *Appelt, 1999*

This story includes the pattern of bats walking 1 by 1, then 2 by 2, and so on. One activity from this enjoyable book is determining the growing pattern of the number of bats given the array length (e.g., 3 for the 3-by-3 array). There is also one mouse, so this can be included in a second investigation. Activity sheets for these two ideas and two others can be found in Roy and Beckmann, 2007.

Pattern *Pluckrose, 1988*

This book brings pattern from the real world to the classroom in the form of brilliantly colored photographs. Pattern is seen in the soles of tennis shoes, dishes, butterflies, leaves, and flowers. The book provides a jumping-off point for an exploration of repeating patterns in the world around us.

Two of Everything: *A Chinese Folktale*
Hong, 1993

The magic pot discovered by Mr. Haktak doubles whatever goes in it, including his wife! This idea of input–output is great for exploring functions from grades 2 through 8; just vary the rule of the magic pot from doubling to something more complex. For more details and handouts, see Suh (2007) and Wickett, Kharas, and Burns (2002).

Recommended Readings

Articles

Joram, E., Hartman, C., & Trafton, P. R. (2004). "As people get older, they get taller": An integrated unit on measurement, linear relationships, and data analysis. *Teaching Children Mathematics, 10*(7), 344–351.
This is a wonderful unit for second grade showing students using real data to answer the question of how much taller students in the fourth grade were compared to students in the second grade. They used a best-fit line to create a function from the scatter plot data.

Kalman, R. (2008). Teaching algebra without algebra. *Mathematics Teaching in the Middle School, 13*(6), 334–339.
This article includes three contexts that involve simplifying equations and effectively explains how to make sense of the simplification by relating it to the context. An excellent resource for helping middle school students make sense of symbols and properties.

Molina, M., & Ambrose, R. C. (2006). Fostering relational thinking while negotiating the meaning of the equals sign. *Teaching Children Mathematics, 13*(2), 111–117.
This article helps us understand the conceptual considerations related to the equal sign while simultaneously illustrating the value of errors and misconceptions in creating opportunities for learning.

Books

Carpenter, T. P., Franke, M. L., & Levi, L. (2003). *Thinking mathematically: Integrating arithmetic and algebra in elementary school.* Portsmouth, NH: Heinemann.
This book is a detailed look at helping children in the primary grades develop the thinking and create the generalizations of algebra. The included CD shows classroom-based examples of the ideas discussed. Many of the ideas about equality, true/false sentences, and generalizations discussed in this chapter were influenced by this book.

Driscol, M. (1999). *Fostering algebraic thinking: A guide for teachers, grades 6–10.* Portsmouth, NH: Heinemann.
Driscol's book is one of the most popular algebra resources—full of rich problems to use and helpful for expanding the reader's understanding of algebra.

Greenes, C. E., & Rubenstein, R. (Eds.). (2008). *Algebra and algebraic thinking in school mathematics.* NCTM 70th Yearbook. Reston, VA: NCTM.
NCTM Yearbooks are always excellent collections of articles for grades pre-K–12. This one is no exception, offering a wealth of thought-provoking and helpful articles about algebraic thinking.

NCTM's Navigations Series

Cuevas, G. J., & Yeatts, K. (2001). *Navigating through algebra in grades 3–5.* Reston, VA: NCTM.

Friel, S., Rachlin, S., & Doyle, D. (2001). *Navigating through algebra in grades 6–8.* Reston, VA: NCTM.

Greenes, C., Cavanagh, M., Dacey, L., Findell, C., & Small, M. (2001). *Navigating through algebra in prekindergarten–grade 2.* Reston, VA: NCTM.
These books offer high-quality algebra activities that reflect the Principles and Standards. Each book includes a CD-ROM with blackline masters for the activities, applets, and selected articles.

Online Resources

Algebra Balance Scales and Algebra Balance Scales—Negative
http://nlvm.usu.edu/en/nav/frames_asid_324_g_3_t_2.html
Linear equations are presented on a two-pan balance with variables on each side. The user can solve equations in the same way as described in the text. The negative version uses balloons for negative values and negative variables.

Graph Sketcher
www.shodor.org/interactivate/activities/GraphSketcher
Works very much like a graphing calculator for graphing functions of any type. A good demonstration tool for making graphs of equations.

Learning about Rate of Change (e-Example)
http://standards.nctm.org/document/eexamples/chap6/6.2/index.htm
A nice interactive lesson in which the cost per minute to make a phone call (the slope) can be adjusted and then the graph of the cost can be displayed. A slider helps connect points on the two graphs.

Pan Balance—Shapes
http://illuminations.nctm.org/ActivityDetail.aspx?id=33

With each problem, four shapes are assigned unknown values. By stacking shapes on the two balance pans, the user attempts to balance the scale and then create additional balances. A numbers version and an expressions version are extensions of this applet.

Patterns, Relations and Functions (eNLVM module)
http://enlvm.usu.edu/ma/nav/toc.jsp?sid=__shared&cid=
emready@patterns_relations_functions&bb=course

This site encourages students to generate rules and functions for geometric sequences, describing relationships between the pattern number and characteristics of the pattern.

Slope Slider
www.shodor.org/interactivate/activities/slopeslider

A good interactive tool for illustrating the meaning of slope and the y-intercept for a linear equation of the form $y = mx + b$. The user can use a slider to change the value of m or b and see the graph change dynamically.

Function Machine Applets

Function Machine (NLVM)
http://nlvm.usu.edu/en/nav/frames_asid_191_g_3_t_1.html

Function Machine (Math Playground)
www.mathplayground.com/functionmachine.html

This is a nice, Flash-based tool.

Stop That Creature! (PBS Kids' CyberChase)
http://pbskids.org/cyberchase/games/functions/
functions.html

In this fun game, figure out the rule that runs the game to shut down the creature cloning machine.

Function Machine (Shodor Project Interactivate)
www.shodor.org/interactivate/activities/FunctionMachine

The functions on this site have one of the following forms: $y = x \times \_\_$, $y = x + \_\_$, $y = x - \_\_$, where the underline can be any integer between -10 and 10.

Linear Function Machine (Shodor Project Interactivate)
www.shodor.org/interactivate/activities/LinearFunct
Machine

Field Experience Guide Connections

The focus on multiple representations and meaning in this chapter are a good match for FEG Field Experiences 1.2 and 4.1. Number patterns and geometric growing patterns are the focus of FEG Expanded Lessons 9.12 and 9.13 and FEG Activity 10.8. Expanded Lesson 9.14 for grades 6–8 connects graphs to stories—an excellent integration of writing. In addition, Activities 10.9 ("Compensation Decision") and 10.10 ("Solving the Mystery") are excellent applications of algebra. Balanced Assessment Item 11.2 ("Grocery Store") is an excellent assessment for finding a rule to describe a growing pattern.

Developing Fraction Concepts

From Chapter 15 of *Elementary and Middle School Mathematics: Teaching Developmentally*, 7/e. John A. Van de Walle. Karen S. Karp. Jennifer M. Bay-Williams. Copyright © 2010 by Pearson Allyn and Bacon. All rights reserved.

Developing Fraction Concepts

Fractions have always represented a considerable challenge for students, even into the middle grades. Results of NAEP testing have consistently shown that students have a weak understanding of fraction concepts (Sowder & Wearne, 2006; Wearne & Kouba, 2000). This lack of understanding is then translated into difficulties with fraction computation, decimal and percent concepts, and the use of fractions in other content areas, particularly algebra (NMP, 2008).

Curriculum Focal Points (NCTM, 2006) places initial development of foundational fraction concepts in grade 3 as one of three focal points: *Developing an understanding of fractions and fraction equivalence.* Fraction concepts are also emphasized at each grade following grade 3, focusing on topics such as computation and proportional reasoning. Elementary and middle school programs must provide students with adequate time and experiences to develop a deep conceptual understanding of this important area of the curriculum. This chapter explores conceptual development of fraction concepts in order to help students construct a firm foundation.

Big Ideas

1. For students to really understand fractions, they must experience fractions across many constructs, including part of a whole, ratios, and division.

2. Three categories of models exist for working with fractions—area (e.g., $\frac{1}{3}$ of a garden), length (e.g., $\frac{3}{4}$ of an inch), and set or quantity (e.g., $\frac{1}{2}$ of the class).

3. Partitioning and iterating are ways for students to understand the meaning of fractions, especially numerator and denominator.

4. Students need many experiences estimating with fractions.

5. Understanding equivalent fractions is critical. Two equivalent fractions are two ways of describing the same amount by using different-sized fractional parts. For example, in the fraction $\frac{6}{8}$, if the eighths are taken in twos, then each pair of eighths is a fourth. Six-eighths then can be seen to be equivalent to three-fourths.

Mathematics Content Connections

What students bring to the topic of fractions is an understanding of fair sharing. Other whole-number ideas actually interfere in early fraction development, as discussed later in this chapter. However, fraction concepts are intimately connected to other areas of the curriculum. In addition to the clear content connections just listed, fractions are used frequently in measurement and in probability.

- **Algebraic Thinking:** As described in Chapter 14, fractions are a part of algebra. Equations with variables often involve fractions or can be solved using fractions. For example, $\frac{x}{4} = \frac{5}{16}$ is an equation involving equivalent fractions.

- **Fraction Computation:** Without a firm conceptual understanding of fractions, computation with fractions is relegated to rules without reasons.

- **Decimals and Percents:** A key idea for students is that decimal notation and percent notation are simply two other representations of fractions. By making the connections among these three representations, the load of new ideas to be learned is significantly reduced.

- **Ratio and Proportion:** A part-to-whole concept of a fraction is just one form of ratio. The same fraction notation can be used for part-to-part ratios (e.g., the ratio of boys to girls in the room is 3 to 5 or $\frac{3}{5}$).

Meanings of Fractions

Fractions are a critical foundation for students, as they are used in measurement across various professions, and they are essential to the study of algebra and more advanced mathematics. This understanding must go well beyond recognizing that $\frac{3}{5}$ of a region is shaded. This chapter begins with a look at the multiple concepts related to fractions and how these relate to students' knowledge of whole numbers.

Fraction Constructs

Understanding fractions means understanding all the possible concepts that fractions can represent. One of the commonly used meanings of fraction is part-whole, including examples when part of a whole is shaded. In fact, part-whole is so ingrained in elementary textbooks as the way to represent fractions, it may be difficult for you to think about what else fractions might represent. Although the part-whole model is the most used in textbooks, many who research fraction understanding believe students would understand fractions better with more emphasis across other meanings of fractions (Clarke, Roche, & Mitchell, 2008; Siebert & Gaskin, 2006).

II ———————— *Pause and Reflect*

Beyond shading a region of a shape, how else are fractions modeled? Try to name three ideas.

Part-Whole. Part-whole is one meaning of fractions and in fact goes beyond shading a region. For example, it could be part of a group of people ($\frac{3}{5}$ of the class went on the field trip) or it could be part of a length (we walked $3\frac{1}{2}$ miles). Cramer, Wyberg, and Leavitt (2008), researchers on rational numbers, note that the circle model is particularly effective in illustrating the part-whole relationship. Perhaps these were among the ideas you listed in responding to the Pause and Reflect. The following paragraphs present some other meanings that are important for students to experience to achieve a deep understanding with many connections among ideas.

Measure. Measurement involves identifying a length and then using that length as a measurement piece to determine the length of an object. For example, in the fraction $\frac{5}{8}$, you can use the unit fraction $\frac{1}{8}$ as the selected length and then count or measure to show that it takes five of those to reach $\frac{5}{8}$. This concept focuses on how much rather than how many parts, which is the case in part-whole situations (Behr, Lesh, Post, & Silver, 1983; Martinie, 2007).

Division. Consider the idea of sharing $10 with 4 people. This is not a part-whole scenario, but it still means that each person will receive one-fourth ($\frac{1}{4}$) of the money, or $2\frac{1}{2}$ dollars. Division is often not connected to fractions, which is unfortunate. Students should understand and feel comfortable with the example here written as $\frac{10}{4}$, $4\overline{)10}$, $10 \div 4$, $2\frac{2}{4}$, and $2\frac{1}{2}$ (Flores, Samson, & Yanik, 2006). Division of fractions is addressed in detail in the next chapter.

Operator. Fractions can be used to indicate an operation, as in $\frac{4}{5}$ of 20 square feet or $\frac{2}{3}$ of the audience was holding banners. These situations indicate a fraction of a whole number, and students may be able to use mental math to determine the answer. Researchers note that this construct is not emphasized enough in school curricula (Usiskin, 2007) and that just knowing how to represent fractions doesn't mean students will know how to operate with fractions, such as when working in other areas of the curriculum where fractions occur (Johanning, 2008).

Ratio. The concept of ratio is yet another context in which fractions are used. For example, the fraction $\frac{1}{4}$ can mean that the probability of an event is one in four.

Ratios can be part-part or part-whole. For example, the ratio $\frac{3}{4}$ could be the ratio of those wearing jackets (part) to those not wearing jackets (part); or it could be part-whole, meaning those wearing jackets (part) to those in the class (whole). When working with ratios, students have to attend to part-part and part-whole relationships, which requires attention to the context.

Building on Whole-Number Concepts

Students build on their prior knowledge, meaning that when they encounter situations with fractions, they naturally use what they know about whole numbers to solve the problems. Their prior knowledge of whole numbers both supports and inhibits their work with fractions. It is important for a teacher to help students see how fractions are like and different from whole numbers. The following list shows some common misapplications of whole numbers to fractions:

1. Students think that the numerator and denominator are separate values. It is hard for them to see that $\frac{3}{4}$ is one number. Finding fraction values on a number line or ruler can help students develop this notion. Also, avoid the phrase "three *out of* four" (unless talking about ratios or probability) or "three over four" and instead say "three *fourths*" (Siebert & Gaskin, 2006).

2. In thinking of the numbers separately, students may think that $\frac{2}{3}$ means any two parts, not equal-sized parts. For example, students may think that the shape below shows $\frac{3}{4}$ green, rather than $\frac{1}{2}$ green.

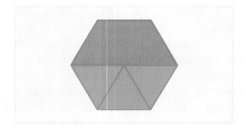

3. Students think that a fraction such as $\frac{1}{5}$ is smaller than a fraction such as $\frac{1}{10}$ because 5 is less than 10. Many visuals and contexts that show parts of the whole are essential in helping students understand. For example, ask students if they would rather go outside for $\frac{1}{2}$ of an hour, $\frac{1}{4}$ of an hour, or $\frac{2}{10}$ of an hour.

4. Students mistakenly use the operation "rules" for whole numbers to compute with fractions, for example, $\frac{1}{2} + \frac{1}{2} = \frac{2}{4}$. The explorations in the estimation section of this chapter can help students understand that this answer is not reasonable.

Only One Size for the Whole. A key idea about fractions that students must come to understand is that a fraction does not say anything about the size of the whole or the size of the parts. A fraction tells us only about the *relationship between* the part and the whole. Consider the following situation.

> Mark is offered the choice of a third of a pizza or a half of a pizza. Because he is hungry and likes pizza, he chooses the half. His friend Jane gets a third of a pizza but ends up with more than Mark. How can that be?

The visual illustrates how Mark got misdirected in his choice. The point of the "pizza fallacy" is that whenever two or more fractions are discussed in the same context, one cannot assume (as Mark did in choosing a half of a pizza) that the fractions are all parts of the same size whole.

Comparisons with any model can be made only if both fractions are parts of the same size whole. For example,

when using Cuisenaire rods, $\frac{2}{3}$ of a light green strip cannot be compared to $\frac{2}{5}$ of an orange strip.

 The *Standards* supports a strong conceptual development of fractions in grades 3 to 5, with computation primarily a middle school topic. "During grades 3–5, students should build their understanding of fractions as parts of a whole and as division. They will need to see and explore a variety of models of fractions, focusing primarily on fractions such as halves, thirds, fourths, fifths, sixths, eighths, and tenths" (p. 150). ◆

Models for Fractions

There is substantial evidence to suggest that the use of models in fraction tasks is important (Cramer & Henry, 2002; Siebert & Gaskin, 2006). Unfortunately, even teachers who use models do not always employ manipulatives or spend adequate time for students to make sense of fractions in light of the model. Properly used, however, models can help students clarify ideas that are often confused in a purely symbolic mode. Sometimes it is useful to do the same activity with two quite different models; from the viewpoint of the students, the activities will be quite different.

Different models offer different opportunities to learn. For example, an area model helps students visualize parts of the whole. A linear model shows that there is always another fraction to be found between any two fractions—an important concept that is underemphasized in the teaching of fractions. Also, some students are able to make sense of one model, but not another. Using appropriate models and using models of each type broaden and deepen students (and teachers) understanding of fractions. This section focuses on three categories of models: region/area, length, and set.

Region or Area Models

In the discussion of sharing, all of the tasks involved sharing something that could be cut into smaller parts. The fractions are based on parts of an area or region. This is a good place to begin and is almost essential when doing sharing tasks. There are many good region models, as shown in Figure 15.1.

Circular fraction piece models are the most commonly used area model. (See Blackline Masters 24–26.) One advantage of the circular region is that it emphasizes the part-whole concept of fractions and the meaning of the relative size of a part to the whole (Cramer, Wyberg, & Leavitt, 2008). The other models in Figure 15.1 demonstrate how different shapes can be the whole. Paper grids, several of which can be found in the Blackline Masters,

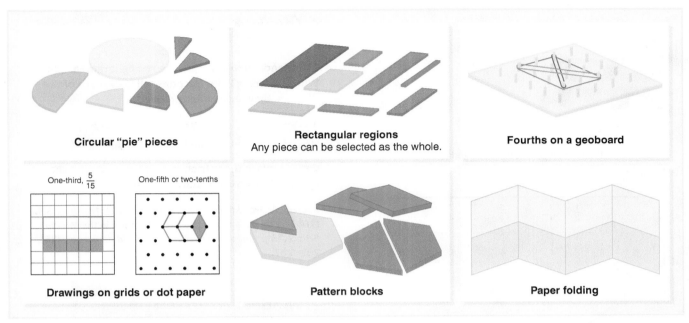

Figure 15.1 Area or region models for fractions.

are especially flexible and do not require management of materials. Commercial versions of area models are available in a wide variety, including circular and rectangular regions. The following activity is an example of how area models can be used to help students develop concepts of equal shares.

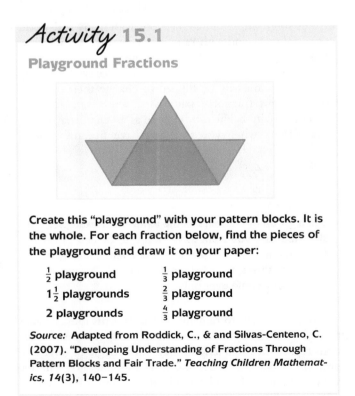

Activity 15.1

Playground Fractions

Create this "playground" with your pattern blocks. It is the whole. For each fraction below, find the pieces of the playground and draw it on your paper:

$\frac{1}{2}$ playground	$\frac{1}{3}$ playground
$1\frac{1}{2}$ playgrounds	$\frac{2}{3}$ playground
2 playgrounds	$\frac{4}{3}$ playground

Source: Adapted from Roddick, C., & and Silvas-Centeno, C. (2007). "Developing Understanding of Fractions Through Pattern Blocks and Fair Trade." *Teaching Children Mathematics, 14*(3), 140–145.

Length Models

With length models, lengths or measurements are compared instead of areas. Either lines are drawn and subdivided, or physical materials are compared on the basis of length, as shown in Figure 15.2.

Cuisenaire rods have pieces in lengths of 1 to 10 measured in terms of the smallest strip or rod. Each length is a different color for ease of identification. Strips of paper or adding-machine tape can be folded to produce student-made fraction strips.

Rods or strips provide flexibility because any length can represent the whole. For example, if you wanted students to work with $\frac{1}{4}$s and $\frac{1}{8}$s, select the brown Cuiseniare rod, which is 8 units long. Therefore, the four rod (purple) becomes $\frac{1}{2}$, the two rod (red) becomes $\frac{1}{4}$ and the one rod (white) becomes $\frac{1}{8}$. For exploring twelfths, put the orange rod and red rod together to make a whole that is 12 units long.

Cuisenaire rods consist of the following colors and lengths:

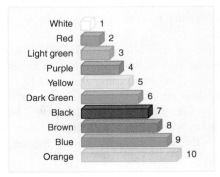

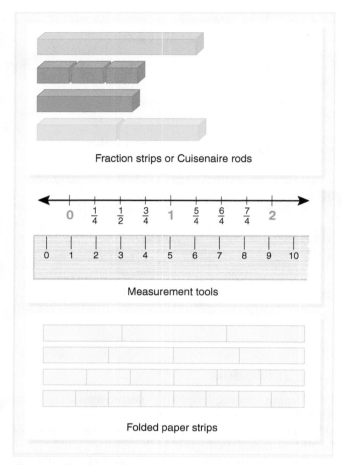

Figure 15.2 Length or measurement models for fractions.

The number line is a significantly more sophisticated measurement model (Bright, Behr, Post, & Wachsmuth, 1988). In fact, many researchers in mathematics education have found it to be an essential model that should be emphasized more in the teaching of fractions (Clarke, Roche, & Mitchell, 2008; Flores, Samson, & Yanik, 2006; Middleton, van den Heuvel-Panhuizen, & Shew, 1998; Usiskin, 2007; Watanabe, 2006). Linear models are closely connected to the real-world contexts in which fractions are commonly used—measuring. Music, for example, is an excellent opportunity to explore $\frac{1}{2}$s, $\frac{1}{4}$s, $\frac{1}{8}$s, and $\frac{1}{16}$s (Goral & Wiest, 2007).

The number line also emphasizes that a fraction is one number as well as its relative size to other numbers, which is not as clear when using area models. Importantly, the number line reinforces that there is always one more fraction to be found between two fractions. The following activity is a fun way to use a real-world context to engage students in thinking about fractions through a linear model.

Activity 15.2
Who Is Winning?

The friends below are playing red light–green light. Who is winning? The fractions tell how much of the distance they have already moved.

Mary—$\frac{3}{4}$ Harry—$\frac{1}{2}$ Larry—$\frac{5}{6}$

Han—$\frac{5}{8}$ Miguel—$\frac{5}{9}$ Angela—$\frac{2}{3}$

Can you place these friends on a line to show where they are between the start and finish?

Source: Adapted from Bay-Williams, J. M., & Martinie, S. L. (2003). "Thinking Rationally about Number in the Middle School." *Mathematics Teaching in the Middle School, 8*(6), 282–287.

Set Models

In set models, the whole is understood to be a set of objects, and subsets of the whole make up fractional parts. For example, 3 objects are one-fourth of a set of 12 objects. The set of 12, in this example, represents the whole or 1. The idea of referring to a collection of counters as a single entity makes set models difficult for some children. Students will frequently focus on the size of the set rather than the number of equal sets in the whole. For example, if 12 counters make a whole, then a set of 4 counters is one-*third*, not one-fourth, since 3 equal sets make the whole. However, the set model helps establish important connections with many real-world uses of fractions and with ratio concepts. Figure 15.3 illustrates several set models for fractions.

Counters in two colors on opposite sides are frequently used. They can easily be flipped to change their color to model various fractional parts of a whole set.

The activity below can be done as an energizer or as a quick activity when you find you have five minutes.

Activity 15.3
Class Fractions

Use a group of students as the whole—for example, six students if you want to work on $\frac{1}{3}$s, $\frac{1}{2}$s, and $\frac{1}{6}$s. Ask students, "What fraction of our friends [are wearing tennis shoes, have brown hair, etc.]?" Change the number of people over time.

It is important to remember that students must be able to explore fractions across models. If they never see fractions represented as a length, they will struggle to solve any problem or context that is linear. As a teacher, you will not know if they really understand the meaning of a fraction

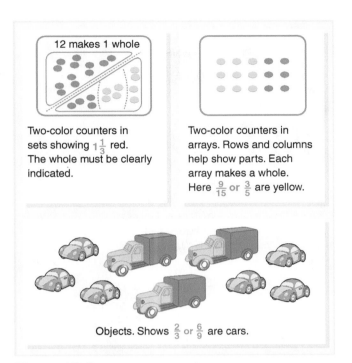

Two-color counters in sets showing $1\frac{1}{3}$ red. The whole must be clearly indicated.

Two-color counters in arrays. Rows and columns help show parts. Each array makes a whole. Here $\frac{9}{15}$ or $\frac{3}{5}$ are yellow.

Objects. Shows $\frac{2}{3}$ or $\frac{6}{9}$ are cars.

Figure 15.3 Set models for fractions.

such as $\frac{1}{4}$ unless you have seen a student model one-fourth using different contexts and models.

A straightforward way to assess students' knowledge of a fractional amount is to give them a piece of paper, fold it into thirds, and at the top of each section write *area, length,* and *set* and have them show you a picture and write a sentence for the fraction (e.g., $\frac{3}{4}$) in all three ways (NCTM, 2007, p. 32). This can be done exactly for commonly used fractions or can be an estimation activity with fractions like $\frac{31}{58}$.

Concept of Fractional Parts

The first goal in the development of fractions should be to help children construct the idea of *fractional parts of the whole*—the parts that result when the whole or unit has been partitioned into *equal-sized portions* or *fair shares.*

Children seem to understand the idea of separating a quantity into two or more parts to be shared fairly among friends. They eventually make connections between the idea of fair shares and fractional parts. Sharing tasks are, therefore, good places to begin the development of fractions.

Sharing Tasks

Considerable research has been done with children from first through eighth grades to determine how they go about the process of forming fair shares and how the tasks posed to students influence their responses (e.g., Empson, 2002; Lamon, 1996; Mack, 2001; Pothier & Sawada, 1983).

Sharing tasks are generally posed in the form of a simple story problem. *Suppose there are four square brownies to be shared among three children so that each child gets the same amount. How much (or show how much) will each child get?* Task difficulty changes with the numbers involved, the types of things to be shared (regions such as brownies, discrete objects such as pieces of chewing gum), and the presence or use of a model.

Students initially perform sharing tasks (division) by distributing items one at a time. When this process leaves leftover pieces students must think of how to subdivide so that every group (or person) gets a fair share. Contexts that lend to subdividing an area include brownies (rectangles), sandwiches, pizzas, crackers, cake, candy bars, and so on. The problems and variations that follow are adapted from Empson (2002).

Four children are sharing ten brownies so that each one will get the same amount. How much can each child have?

Problem difficulty is determined by the relationship between the number of things to be shared and the number of sharers. Because children's initial strategies for sharing involve halving, a good place to begin is with two, four, or even eight sharers. For ten brownies and four sharers, many children will deal out two to each child and then halve each of the remaining brownies (see Figure 15.4).

Consider these variations in numbers:

5 brownies shared with 2 children
2 brownies shared with 4 children
5 brownies shared with 4 children
7 brownies shared with 4 children
4 brownies shared with 8 children
3 brownies shared with 4 children

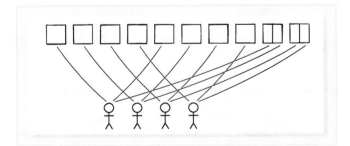

Figure 15.4 Ten brownies shared with four children.

Pause and Reflect

Try drawing pictures for each of the preceding sharing tasks. Which do you think is most difficult? Which of these represent essentially the same degree of difficulty?

The last example, three brownies shared with four children, was significantly more challenging. Figure 15.5 shows how one third-grader, who easily solved the first three, worked hard to solve this problem. Her guess and check strategy involved first subdividing each brownie in two parts, five parts, six parts, seven parts, and then dropping back to four parts.

When the numbers allow for some items to be distributed whole (five shared with two), some students will first share whole items and then cut up the leftovers. Others will slice every piece in half and then distribute the halves. When there are more sharers than items, some partitioning must happen at the beginning of the solution process.

When students who are still using a halving strategy try to share five things among four children, they will eventually get down to two halves to give to four children. For some, the solution is to cut each half in half; that is, "each child gets a whole (or two halves) and a half of a half."

As always, it is important to meet the needs of the range of learners in your classroom. The level of difficulty of these tasks varies, so a tiered lesson can be implemented to provide appropriate tasks for different students, while still enabling all students to learn the important mathematics of the lesson (fair sharing as a meaning of fractions). Figure 15.6 shows how one teacher offers these three tiers for her lesson on sharing brownies (Williams, 2008, p. 326).

As students report their answers, it is important to emphasize the equivalence of different representations (Flores & Klein, 2005). For example, in the case of three people sharing four brownies the answer might be noted on the board this way:

$$\frac{4}{3} = 1\frac{1}{3} = 1 + \frac{1}{3}$$

It is a progression to move to three or six sharers because this will force children to confront their halving strategies.

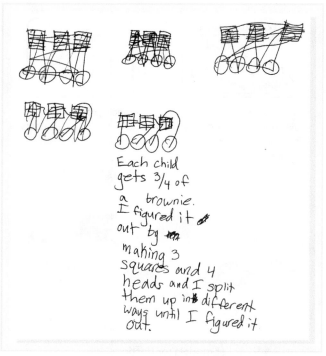

Each child gets 3/4 of a brownie.
I figured it out by making 3 squares and 4 heads and I split them up into different ways until I figured it out.

Figure 15.5 Elizabeth partitions to find the fair shares for 3 brownies shared with 4 people.

Pause and Reflect

Try solving the following variations using drawings. Can you do them in different ways?

4 pizzas shared with 6 children
7 pizzas shared with 6 children
5 pizzas shared with 3 children
5 pizzas shared with 4 children

Subdividing a region into a number of parts other than a power of two (four, eight, etc.) is more challenging for students. Figure 15.7 shows how a student partitioned to solve the third pizza problem. This took much guess and check, at which point the teacher asked, "Can you see a pattern in how you have divided the pizza and how many

Tier 1 task: for students who still need experience with halving	Tier 2 task: for students comfortable with halving and ready to try other strategies.	Tier 3 task: for students ready to solve tasks where students combine halving with new strategies
How can 2 people share 3 brownies? How can 2 people share 5 brownies? How can 4 people share 3 brownies? How can 3 people share 4 brownies?	How can 4 people share 3 brownies? How can 3 people share 4 brownies? How can 3 people share 5 brownies? How can 6 people share 4 brownies?	How can 3 people share 5 brownies? How can 3 people share 2 brownies? How can 6 people share 4 brownies? How can 5 people share 4 brownies?

Figure 15.6 Example of a tiered lesson for the sharing brownies problem.

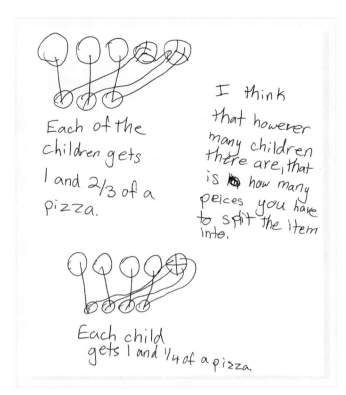

Figure 15.7 Student explains a pattern for finding equal shares of a pizza.

people are eating?" At this point the student noticed a pattern: if there are three people, the remaining pizzas need to be partitioned into thirds. She used this fact to quickly solve the fourth problem. This points out the importance of a teacher not telling students what to think, but rather asking questions that lead students to pause and analyze their work. Notice that the context and the model match—both are circles. It is important to use a range of contexts and to encourage a range of representations across the different types of models (area, length, and set).

Fraction bars, Cuisenaire rods, and fraction circles can be subdivided. Another possibility is to cut out construction paper circles or squares. Some students may need to cut and physically distribute the pieces. Students can use connecting cubes to make bars that they can separate into pieces. Or they can use more traditional fraction models such as circular "pie" pieces.

Fraction Language

During the discussions of students' solutions (and discussions are essential!) is a good time to introduce the vocabulary of fractional parts. When a brownie or other region has been broken into equal shares, simply say, "We call these *fourths*. The whole is cut into four parts. All of the parts are the same size—fourths."

When partitioning a whole, children need to be aware of two aspects or components of fractional parts: (1) the

number of parts determines the fractional amount (e.g., partitioning into 4 parts, means each part is $\frac{1}{4}$ of the unit) and (2) the parts must be the same size, though not necessarily the same shape. Emphasize that the number of parts that make up a whole determines the name of the fractional parts or shares. They will be familiar with halves but should quickly learn to describe thirds, fourths, fifths, and so on.

In addition to helping children use the words *halves*, *thirds*, *fourths*, *fifths*, and so on, be sure to make regular comparison of fractional parts to the whole. Make it a point to use the terms *whole*, or *one whole*, or simply *one* so that students have a language that they can use regardless of the model involved.

A physical model, like color tiles, can mislead students to believe that fractional parts must be the same *shape* as well as the same size. For example:

Class discussions that challenge students' thinking and expose their ideas are the best ways to both help students develop accurate concepts and to find out what they understand.

Equivalent Size of Fraction Pieces

Too often students see shapes that are already all the same shape and size when they are asked questions about what fraction is shaded. The result is that students think that equal shares might need to be the same shape, which is not the case. Young children, in particular, tend to focus on shape, when the focus should be on equal-*sized* parts.

The following activity focuses on this, having examples that are (1) same shape, same size; (2) different shape, same size; (3) different shape, different size; and (4) same shape, different size. The first two categories are then examples of fair shares, or equivalent shares. The activity is a simple extension of the sharing tasks. It is important that students can tell when a region has been separated into a particular type of fractional part.

Activity 15.4

Correct Shares

Draw regions like the ones in Figure 15.8, showing examples and nonexamples of fractional parts. Have students identify the wholes that are correctly divided into requested fractional parts and those that are not. For each response, have students explain their reasoning. The activity should be done with a variety of models, including length and set models.

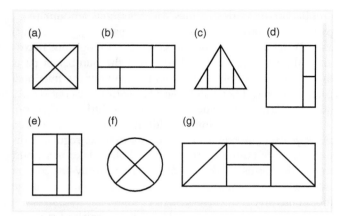

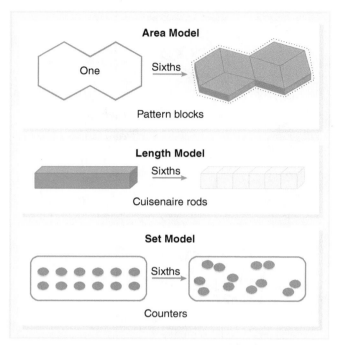

Figure 15.8 Students learning about fractional parts should be able to tell which of these figures are correctly partitioned in fourths. They should also be able to explain why the other figures are not showing fourths.

In the "Correct Shares" activity, it is important to have students explain why they do or do not think the shape is partitioned correctly. The diagrams in the task fall in each of the following categories:

1. Same shape, same size: (a) and (f) [equivalent]
2. Different shape, same size: (e) and (g) [equivalent]
3. Different shape, different size: (b) and (c) [not equivalent]
4. Same shape, different size: (d) [not equivalent]

The "Correct Shares" task is a good formative assessment to see whether students understand that it is the *size* that matters, not the shape. If students only miss (e) and (g), they do not have this concept and you need to plan future tasks that focus on equivalence—for example, asking students to take a square and subdivide a picture themselves, as in Activity 15.5. ◆

Activity 15.5

Finding Fair Shares

Give students dot paper and have them find halves, fourths, or other fractional parts of an enclosed region. The activity is especially interesting when different shapes represent equivalent areas.

Partitioning

Sectioning a shape into equal-sized pieces is called *partitioning*, a major part of developing fraction concepts with young children. In the previous section you were partitioning regions or shapes, which fall under area models. It is also important to partition lengths and quantities. The number line with only 0 and 1 can be used, as well as paper

Figure 15.9 Given a whole, find fractional parts.

strips. Students can partition sets of objects such as coins, counters, or baseball cards.

Notice when partitioning sets that children may confuse the number of counters in a share with the name of the share. In the example in Figure 15.9, the 12 counters are partitioned into 6 sets—*sixths*. Each share or part has two counters, but it is the number of shares that makes the partition show *sixths*.

Using Fraction Language and Symbols

Fraction symbols represent a fairly complex convention that is often misleading to children. It is well worth your time to help students develop a strong understanding of what the numerator and denominator of a fraction tell us.

Counting Fraction Parts: Iteration

Counting fractional parts to see how multiple parts compare to the whole creates a foundation for the two parts of a fraction. Students should come to think of counting fractional parts in much the same way as they might count apples or any other objects. If you know the kind of part you are counting, you can tell when you get to one, when you get to two, and so on.

This counting or repeating a piece is called *iterating*. Like partitioning, iterating is an important part of being able to understand and use fractions. There is evidence that an iterative notion of fractions, one that views a fraction such as $\frac{3}{4}$ as a count of three parts called *fourths*, is an important idea for children to develop (Post, Wachsmuth, Lesh, & Behr, 1985; Siebert & Gaskin, 2006; Tzur, 1999). The iterative concept is most clear when focusing on these two ideas about fraction symbols:

- The top number *counts.* (numerator)
- The bottom number tells *what is being counted.* (denominator)

The *what* of fractions are the fractional parts. They can be counted. Fraction symbols are just a shorthand for saying *how many* and *what.*

Iterating makes sense with length models because iteration is much like measuring. Consider that you have a $2\frac{1}{2}$ feet of ribbon and are trying to figure out how many fourths you have. You can draw a strip and start counting (iterating) the fourths:

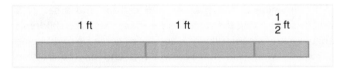

Using a ribbon that is $\frac{1}{4}$ of a foot long as a measuring tool, a student marks off ten-fourths:

Students can participate in many tasks that involve iterating lengths, progressing in increasing difficulty. For example, give the students a strip of paper and tell them that it is $\frac{3}{4}$ of the whole. Ask them to find: $\frac{1}{2}$, $1\frac{1}{2}$, $2\frac{1}{4}$, 3, and so on. To find these, students should partition the piece into three sections to find $\frac{1}{4}$ and then iterate the $\frac{1}{4}$ to find the fractions listed.

Iterating can be done with area models as well. Display some circular fractional pieces in groups as shown in Figure 15.10. For each collection, tell students what type of piece is being shown and simply count them together: "*one*-fourth, *two*-fourths, *three*-fourths, *four*-fourths, *five*-fourths." Ask, "If we have five-fourths, is that more than one whole, less than one whole, or the same as one whole?" To reinforce the piece size even more, you can slightly alter your language to say, "one $\frac{1}{4}$, two $\frac{1}{4}$s, three $\frac{1}{4}$s," and so on.

As students count each collection of parts, discuss the relationship to one whole. Make informal comparisons between different collections. "Why did we get almost two wholes with seven-fourths, and yet we don't even have one whole with ten-twelfths?"

Also take this opportunity to lay verbal groundwork for mixed fractions. "What is another way that we could say seven-thirds?" (Two wholes and one more third or one whole and four-thirds.)

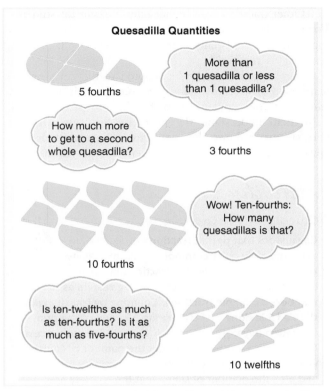

Figure 15.10 Iterating fractional parts in an area model. (See Blackline Masters 24–26.)

With this introduction, students are ready for the following task.

Activity 15.6

More, Less, or Equal to One Whole

Give students a collection of fractional parts (all the same size pieces) and indicate the kind of fractional part they have. Parts can be drawn on a worksheet or physical models can be placed in plastic baggies with an identifying card. For example, if done with Cuisenaire rods or fraction strips, the collection might have seven light green rods/strips with a caption or note indicating "each piece is $\frac{1}{8}$." The task is to decide if the collection is less than one whole, equal to one whole, or more than one whole. Ask students to draw pictures or use symbols to explain their answer.

Try Activity 15.6 with several different fraction models and then with no model, using mental imagery only. Iteration can also be done with set models, although this can be confusing for students. For example, show a collection of two-color counters and ask questions such as, "If 5 counters is one-fourth, how much is 15 counters?"

Other questions can be engaging puzzles for students. For example: "Three counters represent $\frac{1}{8}$ of my set; how big is my set?" "Twenty counters represents $\frac{2}{3}$ of my set; how big is my set?"

Similar activities can be adapted to meet a range of learners. For example, adding a context such as people, candy, crayons, or an item familiar to students will help them understand the problem. Students who are very strong at doing these puzzles can create their own "puzzle statements" and pose them to the class.

Activity 15.7

Calculator Fraction Counting

Calculators that permit fraction entries and displays are now quite common in schools. Many, like the TI-15, now display fractions in correct fraction format and offer a choice of showing results as mixed numbers or simple fractions. Counting by fourths with the TI-15 is done by first storing $\frac{1}{4}$ in one of the two operation keys: [Op1] [+] 1 [n] 4 [d] [Op1]. To count, press 0 [Op1] [Op1] [Op1], repeating to get the number of fourths wanted. The display will show the counts by fourths and also the number of times that the [Op1] key has been pressed. Ask students questions such as the following: "How many $\frac{1}{4}$s to get to 3?" "How many $\frac{1}{5}$s to get to 5?" These can get increasingly more challenging: "How many $\frac{1}{4}$s to get to $4\frac{1}{2}$?" "How many $\frac{2}{3}$s to get to 6? Estimate and then count by $\frac{2}{3}$s on the calculator." Students should coordinate their counts with fraction models, adding a new fourths piece to the pile with each count. At any time, the display can be shifted from mixed form to simple fractions with a press of a key. The TI-15 can be set so that it will not simplify fractions automatically, the appropriate setting prior to the introduction of equivalent fractions.

Fraction calculators provide a powerful way to help children develop fractional symbolism. A variation on Activity 15.7 is to show children a mixed number such as $3\frac{1}{8}$ and ask how many counts of $\frac{1}{8}$ on the calculator it will take to count that high. The students should try to stop at the correct number ($\frac{25}{8}$) before pressing the mixed-number key.

Fraction Notation

After experiences with partitioning and iterating, students are ready to learn the symbolic notations for fractions. The way that we write fractions with a top and a bottom number and a bar between is a convention—an arbitrary agreement for how to represent fractions, so it is one of the concepts that you simply tell students. However, understanding of the convention can be clarified by giving a demonstra-

tion that will encourage students to tell *you* what the top and bottom numbers stand for. The following procedure is recommended even if your students have been "using" symbolic fractions for several years.

Display several collections of fractional parts in a manner similar to those in Figure 15.10. Have students count the parts together. After each count, write the correct fraction, indicating that this is how it is written as a symbol. Include sets that are more than one, but write them as simple or "improper" fractions and not as mixed numbers. Include at least two pairs of sets with the same numerators such as $\frac{4}{8}$ and $\frac{4}{3}$. Likewise, include sets with the same denominators. After the class has counted and you have written the fraction for at least six sets of fractional parts, pose the following questions:

What does the bottom number in a fraction tell us? What does the top number in a fraction tell us?

❚❚ —————————— *Pause and Reflect*

Imagine counting a set of 5 eighths and a set of 5 fourths and writing the fractions for these sets. Use children's language in your formulations and try to come up with a way to explain what the numbers on top and on the bottom mean.

Here are some likely explanations for the top and bottom numbers from second or third graders.

- *Top number:* This is the counting number. It tells how many shares or parts we have. It tells how many have been counted. It tells how many parts we are talking about. It counts the parts or shares.
- *Bottom number:* This tells what is being counted. It tells how big the part is. If it is a 4, it means we are counting *fourths;* if it is a 6, we are counting *sixths;* and so on.

This formulation of the meanings of the numerator and denominator may seem unusual to you. It is often said that the top number tells "how many." (This phrase seems unfinished. How many *what?*) The bottom number is said to tell "how many parts it takes to make a whole." This may be correct but can be misleading. For example, a $\frac{1}{6}$ piece is often cut from a cake without making any slices in the remaining $\frac{5}{6}$ of the cake. That the cake is only in two pieces does not change the fact that the piece taken is $\frac{1}{6}$. Or if a pizza is cut in 12 pieces, two pieces still make $\frac{1}{6}$ of the pizza. In neither of these instances does the bottom number tell how many pieces make a whole.

Fractions Greater Than 1

In the previous section, fractions less than and greater than 1 were mixed together. This was done intentionally and should similarly be done with students as they are learning fractions. Too often students aren't exposed to numbers greater than one (e.g., $\frac{5}{2}$ or $4\frac{1}{4}$) and then when they are added into the mix (no pun intended!), students find them confusing.

The term *improper fraction* is used to describe fractions such as $\frac{5}{2}$ that are greater than one. This term can be a source of confusion as the word *improper* implies that this representation is not acceptable, which is not the case at all—in fact, in algebra it is often the preferred representation. Instead, try not to use this phrase and instead use "fractions" or "fractions greater than 1." If you do use the term (because it is in the state standards, for example), then be sure to share with students that it is really not improper to write fractions greater than one as a single fraction.

In the fourth National Assessment of Educational Progress, about 80 percent of seventh graders could change a mixed number to an improper fraction, but fewer than half knew that $5\frac{1}{4}$ was the same as $5 + \frac{1}{4}$ (Kouba et al., 1988a). The result indicates that many children are using procedures without understanding them.

If you have counted fractional parts beyond a whole, as in the previous section, your students already know how to write $\frac{13}{6}$ or $\frac{13}{5}$. Ask students to use a model to illustrate these values and find equivalent representations. Neumer (2007), a fifth-grade teacher, found that using Unifix cubes (Multilink cubes could also be used) was the most effective way to help students see both forms for recording fractions greater than 1. Figure 15.11 illustrates how to use Unifix cubes. Students identify one cube as the unit fraction ($\frac{1}{5}$) for the problem ($\frac{12}{5}$). They count out 12 fifths and build wholes. Conversely, they could start with the mixed number, build it, and find out how many total cubes (or fifths) were used. This procedure is an example of a length model. Repeated experiences in building and solving these tasks will lead students to see a pattern of multiplication and division that closely resembles the algorithm for moving between these two forms.

Context can help students understand the equivalency of these two ways to record fractions, which is the focus of Activity 15.8.

Activity 15.8

Pitchers and Cups

Show students a pitcher that can hold enough to fill six cups with juice. You can even use an actual pitcher and actual cups for sharing with the class. Ask questions such as the following: "If I have $3\frac{1}{2}$ pitchers, how many cups will I be able to fill?" "If we have 16 students in our class, how many pitchers will I need?" Alter the amount the pitcher can hold to involve other fractions.

After a while, challenge students to figure out the two equivalent forms without using models. A good explanation for $3\frac{1}{4}$ might be that there are 4 fourths in one whole, so there are 8 fourths in two wholes and 12 fourths in three wholes. The extra fourth makes 13 fourths in all, or $\frac{13}{4}$. (Note the iteration concept playing a role.)

Do not push the traditional algorithm (multiply the bottom by the whole number and add the top) as it can interfere with students making sense of the relationship between the two and their equivalency. This procedure can readily be developed by the students in their own words and with complete understanding by looking at patterns in their work.

Assessing Understanding

Present exercises that ask students to demonstrate their understanding of fractional parts as well as the meanings of the top and bottom numbers in a fraction. Models are used to represent wholes and parts of wholes. Examples of each type of exercise are provided in Figures 15.12 and 15.13. Each figure includes examples with a region model (freely drawn rectangles), a length model (Cuisenaire rods or fraction strips), and set model (counters).

❚❚ ——————————— *Pause and Reflect*

Work through the exercises in Figure 15.2 and 15.3. If you do not have access to rods or counters, just draw lines or circles. What can you learn about student understanding if they are able to solve problems in 15.12 but not 15.13? What if students are able to use paper but not the Cuisenaire rods? If students are stuck, what contexts for each model can be used to support their thinking?

Two or three challenging parts-and-whole questions can make an excellent performance assessment. The tasks should be presented to the class in just the same form as in the figures. Physical models are often the best way to present the tasks so that students can use a trial-and-error approach to determine their results. As with all tasks, it should be clear that an explanation is required to justify each answer. As students build their solutions, you can walk

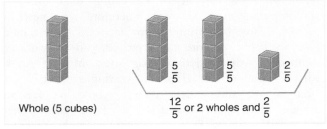

Figure 15.11 Unifix cubes are used to represent the equivalence of $\frac{12}{5}$ and $2\frac{2}{5}$.

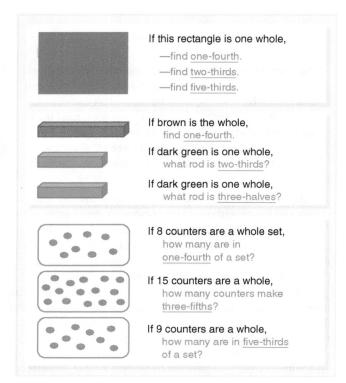

Figure 15.12 Given the whole and the fraction, find the part.

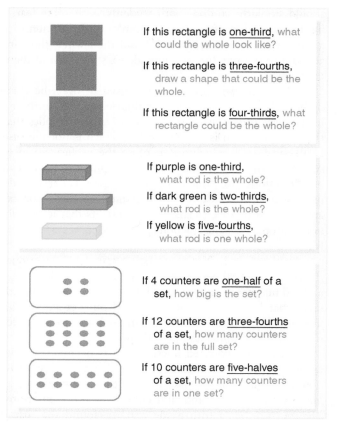

Figure 15.13 Given the part and the fraction, find the whole.

around observing and asking questions to assess students' understanding.

As noted throughout this book, it is a good idea to create simple story problems or contexts that ask the same questions.

Mr. Samuels has finished $\frac{3}{4}$ of his patio. It looks like this:

Draw a picture that might be the shape of the finished patio.

Questions involving unit fractions are generally the easiest. The hardest questions usually involve fractions greater than 1. For example, *If 15 chips are five-thirds of one whole set, how many chips are in a whole set?* However, in every question, the unit fraction plays a significant role. If you have $\frac{5}{3}$ and want the whole, you first need to find $\frac{1}{3}$.

The parts-and-whole questions are challenging yet very effective at helping students reflect on the meanings of the numerator and denominator. They also are a good diagnostic assessment to see if students really understand the meanings of the numerator and denominator since the tasks require students to *use* those meanings, not simply recite a definition.

Estimating with Fractions

The focus on fractional parts is an important beginning, but number sense with fractions demands more—it requires that students have some intuitive feel for fractions. They should know "about" how big a particular fraction is and be able to tell easily which of two fractions is larger.

Like with whole numbers, students are less confident and less capable of estimating than they are at computing exact answers. Therefore, you need to provide many opportunities for students to estimate. Even in daily classroom conversations, you can work on estimation with fractions, asking questions like "About what fraction of our class are wearing sweaters?" Or, after tallying survey data about a topic like favorite dinner, ask, "About what fraction of our class picked spaghetti?" Activity 15.9 offers some examples of visual estimating activities.

Activity 15.9

About How Much?

Draw a picture like one of those in Figure 15.14 (or prepare some ahead of time for the overhead). Have each student write down a fraction that he or she thinks is a good estimate of the amount shown (or the indicated mark on the number line). Listen to the ideas of several students, and ask them whether a particular estimate is a good one. There is no single correct answer, but estimates should be "in the ballpark." If children have difficulty coming up with an estimate, ask whether they think the amount is closer to 0, $\frac{1}{2}$, or 1.

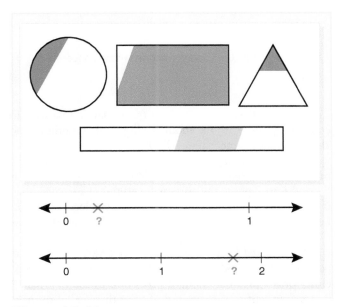

Figure 15.14 About how much? Name a fraction for each drawing and explain why you chose that fraction.

Benchmarks of Zero, One-Half, and One

As suggested in Activity 15.9, the most important reference points or benchmarks for fractions are 0, $\frac{1}{2}$, and 1. For fractions less than 1, simply comparing them to these three numbers gives quite a lot of information. For example, $\frac{3}{20}$ is small, close to 0, whereas $\frac{3}{4}$ is between $\frac{1}{2}$ and 1. The fraction $\frac{9}{10}$ is quite close to 1. Since any fraction greater than 1 is a whole number plus an amount less than 1, the same reference points are just as helpful: $3\frac{3}{7}$ is almost $3\frac{1}{2}$.

Activity 15.10

Zero, One-Half, or One

On a set of cards, write a collection of 10 to 15 fractions, one per card. A few should be greater than 1

($\frac{9}{8}$ or $\frac{11}{10}$), with the others ranging from 0 to 1. Let students sort the fractions into three groups: those close to 0, close to $\frac{1}{2}$, and close to 1. For those close to $\frac{1}{2}$, have them decide if the fraction is more or less than $\frac{1}{2}$. The difficulty of this task largely depends on the fractions. The first time you try this, use fractions such as $\frac{1}{20}$, $\frac{53}{100}$, or $\frac{9}{10}$ that are very close to the three benchmarks. On subsequent days, mostly use fractions with denominators less than 20. You might include one or two fractions such as $\frac{2}{8}$ or $\frac{3}{4}$ that are exactly in between the benchmarks. Ask students to explain how they are using the numerator and denominator to decide.

The next activity is also aimed at developing the same three reference points for fractions. In "Close Fractions," however, the students must come up with the fractions rather than sort fractions already provided.

Activity 15.11

Close Fractions

Have your students name a fraction that is close to 1 but not more than 1. Next have them name another fraction that is even closer to 1 than the first. For the second response, they have to explain why they believe the fraction is closer to 1 than the previous fraction. Continue for several fractions in the same manner, each one being closer to 1 than the previous fraction. Similarly, try close to 0 or close to $\frac{1}{2}$ (either under or over). The first several times you try this activity, let the students use models to help with their thinking. Later, see how well their explanations work when they cannot use models or drawings.

Focus discussions on the important idea that there are infinitely many fractions, so they can always find one in between.

Using Number Sense to Compare

The ability to tell which of two fractions is greater is another aspect of number sense with fractions. That ability is built around concepts of fractions, not on an algorithmic skill or symbolic tricks. In the 2000 NAEP test, only 21 percent of fourth-grade students could explain why one unit fraction was larger or smaller than another—for example, $\frac{1}{5}$ and $\frac{1}{4}$ (Kloosterman et al., 2004). For eighth graders, only 41 percent were able to correctly order three fractions given in simplified form (Sowder, Wearne, Martin, & Strutchens, 2004). As these researchers note, "How students can work meaningfully with fractions if they do not have a sense of the relative size of the fractions is difficult to imagine" (p. 116).

Comparing Unit Fractions. Children have a tremendously strong mind-set about numbers, which can cause difficulties with the relative size of fractions. In their experience, larger numbers mean "more," which can translate to: "Seven is more than four, so sevenths should be bigger than fourths" (Mack, 1995). The inverse relationship between number of parts and size of parts cannot be told but must be a creation of each student's own thought process through many experiences.

Activity 15.12

Ordering Unit Fractions

List a set of unit fractions such as $\frac{1}{3}$, $\frac{1}{8}$, $\frac{1}{5}$, and $\frac{1}{10}$. Ask children to put the fractions in order from least to most. Challenge children to defend the way they ordered the fractions. The first few times you do this activity, have them illustrate their ideas by using models.

Students may notice that larger bottom numbers mean smaller fractions, but this is not a rule to be memorized. Revisit this basic idea periodically. Children will seem to understand one day and revert to their more comfortable ideas about big numbers a day or two later. Repeat Activity 15.12 with all numerators equal to some number other than 1. You may be surprised to see that this is much harder for students.

Comparing Any Fractions. You have probably learned rules or algorithms for comparing two fractions. The usual approaches are finding common denominators and using cross-multiplication. These rules can be effective in getting correct answers but require no thought about the size of the fractions. If children are taught these rules before they have had the opportunity to think about the relative sizes of various fractions, there is little chance that they will develop any familiarity with or number sense about fraction size. Comparison activities (which fraction is more?) can play a significant role in helping children develop concepts of relative fraction sizes. Reflective thought is the goal, not an algorithmic method of choosing the correct answer.

❙❙ ─────────── *Pause and Reflect*

Assume for a moment that you do not know the common denominators or cross-multiplication techniques. Now examine the pairs of fractions in Figure 15.15 and select the larger of each pair using a reasoning approach that a fourth grader might use.

The following numbered list shows ways that the fractions in Figure 15.15 might have been compared:

Which fraction in each pair is greater?
Give one or more reasons. Try not to use drawings or models.
Do not use common denominators or cross-multiplication.

A. $\frac{4}{5}$ or $\frac{4}{9}$		G. $\frac{7}{12}$ or $\frac{5}{12}$	
B. $\frac{4}{7}$ or $\frac{5}{7}$		H. $\frac{3}{5}$ or $\frac{3}{7}$	
C. $\frac{3}{8}$ or $\frac{4}{10}$		I. $\frac{5}{8}$ or $\frac{6}{10}$	
D. $\frac{5}{3}$ or $\frac{5}{8}$		J. $\frac{9}{8}$ or $\frac{4}{3}$	
E. $\frac{3}{4}$ or $\frac{9}{10}$		K. $\frac{4}{6}$ or $\frac{7}{12}$	
F. $\frac{3}{8}$ or $\frac{4}{7}$		L. $\frac{8}{9}$ or $\frac{7}{8}$	

Figure 15.15 Comparing fractions using concepts.

1. *More of the same-size parts* (same denominators). To compare $\frac{3}{8}$ and $\frac{5}{8}$, think about having 3 of something and also 5 of the same thing. (B, G)

2. *Same number of parts but parts of different sizes* (same numerators). Consider the case of $\frac{3}{4}$ and $\frac{3}{7}$. If a whole is divided into 7 parts, the parts will certainly be smaller than if divided into only 4 parts. Children may select $\frac{3}{7}$ as larger because 7 is more than 4 and the top numbers are the same. (A, D, H)

3. *More and less than one-half or one whole.* The fraction pairs $\frac{3}{7}$ versus $\frac{5}{8}$ and $\frac{5}{4}$ versus $\frac{7}{8}$ do not lend themselves to either of the previous thought processes. In the first pair, $\frac{3}{7}$ is less than half of the number of sevenths needed to make a whole, and so $\frac{3}{7}$ is less than a half. Similarly, $\frac{5}{8}$ is more than a half. Therefore, $\frac{5}{8}$ is the larger fraction. The second pair is determined by noting that one fraction is less than 1 and the other is greater than 1. (A, D, F, G, H)

4. *Closeness to one-half or one whole.* Why is $\frac{9}{10}$ greater than $\frac{3}{4}$? Each is one fractional part away from one whole, and tenths are smaller than fourths. Similarly, notice that $\frac{5}{8}$ is smaller than $\frac{4}{6}$ because it is only one-eighth more than a half, while $\frac{4}{6}$ is a sixth more than a half. Can you use this basic idea to compare $\frac{3}{5}$ and $\frac{5}{9}$? (*Hint:* Each is half of a fractional part more than $\frac{1}{2}$.) Also try $\frac{5}{7}$ and $\frac{7}{9}$. (C, E, I, J, K, L)

How did your reasons for choosing fractions in Figure 15.15 compare to these ideas? It is important that you are comfortable with these informal comparison strategies as a major component of your own number sense as well as for helping children develop theirs. Notice that some of the comparisons, such as D and H, could have been solved using more than one of the strategies listed.

Tasks you design for your students should assist them in developing these and possibly other methods of comparing two fractions. It is important that the ideas come from your students and their discussions. To teach "the four ways to compare fractions" would be adding four more mysterious rules and defeats the purpose of encouraging students to apply their number sense.

To develop these methods for comparing fractions, select pairs of fractions that will likely elicit desired comparison strategies. On one day, for example, you might have two pairs with the same denominators and one with the same numerators. On another day, you might pick fraction pairs in which each fraction is exactly one part away from a whole. Try to build strategies over several days by the strategic choice of fraction pairs.

The use of a region or number-line model may help students who are struggling to reason mentally. Place greater emphasis on students' reasoning and connect it to the visual models.

The next activity extends the comparison task a bit more.

Activity 15.13

Line 'Em Up

Select four or five fractions for students to put in order from least to greatest. Have them indicate approximately where each fraction belongs on a number line labeled only with the points 0 and 1. Adding-machine paper can be used as the number line. Students can compare their lines with others and explain how they decided where to place the fractions.

To place fractions on the number line, students must also make estimates of fraction size in addition to simply ordering the fractions.

Including Equivalent Fractions. The discussion to this point has somewhat artificially ignored the idea that students might use equivalent-fraction concepts in making comparisons. Equivalent-fraction concepts are such an important idea that the entire following section is devoted to the development of that idea. However, equivalent-fraction concepts need not be put off until last and certainly should be embedded in the discussions of which fraction is more.

Smith (2002) suggests that the comparison question to ask is "Which of the following two (or more) fractions is greater, *or are they equal*?" (p. 9, emphasis added). He points out that this question leaves open the possibility that two fractions that may look different can, in fact, be equal.

In addition to this point, with equivalent fraction concepts, students can adjust how a fraction looks so that they can use ideas that make sense to them. Burns (1999) describes how fifth graders compared $\frac{6}{8}$ to $\frac{4}{5}$. (You might want to stop for a moment and think how you would compare these fractions.) One child changed the $\frac{4}{5}$ to $\frac{8}{10}$ so that

both fractions would be two parts away from the whole and he reasoned from there. Another changed both fractions to a common *numerator* of 12.

Be absolutely certain to revisit the comparison activities and include pairs such as $\frac{8}{12}$ and $\frac{2}{3}$ in which the fractions are equal but do not appear to be.

Equivalent-Fraction Concepts

Equivalence is a critical but often poorly misunderstood concept. This is particularly true with fraction equivalence.

Conceptual Focus on Equivalence

 *Pause and Reflect*

How do you know that $\frac{4}{6} = \frac{2}{3}$? Before reading further, think of at least two different explanations.

Here are some possible answers to the above question.

1. They are the same because you can simplify $\frac{4}{6}$ and get $\frac{2}{3}$.
2. If you have a set of 6 items and you take 4 of them, that would be $\frac{4}{6}$. But you can make the 6 into 3 groups and the 4 would be 2 groups out of the 3 groups. That means it's $\frac{2}{3}$.

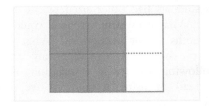

3. If you start with $\frac{2}{3}$, you can multiply the top and the bottom numbers by 2, and that will give you $\frac{4}{6}$, so they are equal.
4. If you had a square cut into 3 parts and you shaded 2, that would be $\frac{2}{3}$ shaded. If you cut all 3 of these parts in half, that would be 4 parts shaded and 6 parts in all. That's $\frac{4}{6}$, and it would be the same amount.

All of these answers are correct. But let's think about what they tell us. Responses 2 and 4 are conceptual, although not as efficient. The procedural responses, 1 and 3, are efficient but do not indicate conceptual understanding. All students should eventually be able to write an equivalent fraction for a given fraction. At the same time, the procedures should never be taught or used until the students understand what the result means. Consider how different the procedure and the concept appear to be.

Concept: Two fractions are equivalent if they are representations for the same amount or quantity—if they are the same number.

Algorithm: To get an equivalent fraction, multiply (or divide) the top and bottom numbers by the same nonzero number.

In a problem-based classroom, students can develop an understanding of equivalent fractions and also develop from that understanding a conceptually based algorithm. As with most algorithms, it is a serious instructional error to rush too quickly to the rule. Be patient! Intuitive methods are always best at first.

Equivalent-Fraction Models

The general approach to helping students create an understanding of equivalent fractions is to have them use contexts and models to find different names for a fraction. Consider that this is the first time in their experience that a fixed quantity can have multiple names (actually an infinite number). The following activities are possible starting places.

Activity 15.14

Different Fillers

Using a region model for fractions that is familiar to your students, prepare a worksheet with two or at most three outlines of different fractions, as in Figure 15.16. Do not limit yourself to unit fractions. For example, if the model is circular fraction pieces, you might draw an outline for $\frac{2}{3}$, $\frac{1}{2}$, and $\frac{3}{4}$. The students' task is to use their own fraction pieces to find as many equivalent fractions for the region as possible. After completing the three examples, have students write about the ideas or patterns they may have noticed in finding the names. Follow the activity with a class discussion.

In the class discussion following the "Different Fillers" activity, a good question to ask involves what names could be found if students had other sized pieces. For example, ask students "What equivalent fractions could you find if we had sixteenths in our fraction kit? What names could you find if you could have a piece of any size at all?"

The following activity is a variation of "Different Fillers." Instead of using a manipulative, the task is constructed on dot paper.

Activity 15.15

Dot Paper Equivalencies

Create a worksheet using a portion of either isometric or square dot grid paper (see Blackline Masters 37–40).

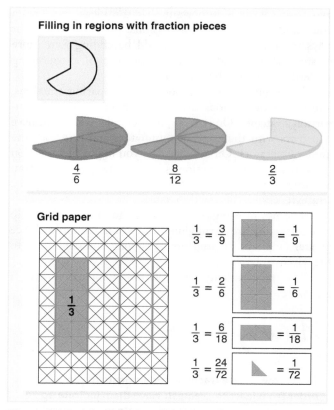

Figure 15.16 Area models for equivalent fractions.

On the grid, draw the outline of a region and designate it as one whole. Draw a part of the region within the whole. The task is to use different parts of the whole determined by the grid to find names for the part. See Figure 15.16, which includes an example drawn on an isometric grid. Students should draw a picture of the unit fractional part that they use for each fraction name. The larger the size of the whole, the more names the activity will generate.

The "Dot Paper Equivalencies" activity is a form of what Lamon (2002) calls "unitizing," that is, given a quantity, finding different ways to chunk the quantity into parts in order to name it. She points out that this is a key ability related not only to equivalent fractions but also to proportional reasoning, especially in the comparison of ratios. (See also Lamon, 1999a,b.)

Length models can be used to create activities similar to the "Different Fillers" task. For example, as shown in Figure 15.17, rods or paper strips can be used to designate both a whole and a part. Students use smaller rods to find fraction names for the given part. To have larger wholes and,

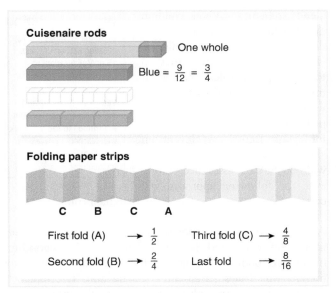

Figure 15.17 Length models for equivalent fractions.

thus, more possible parts, use a train of two or three rods for the whole and the part. Folding paper strips is another method of creating fraction names. In the example shown in Figure 15.17, one-half is subdivided by successive folding in half. Other folds would produce other names and these possibilities should be discussed if no one tries to fold the strip in an odd number of parts.

The following activity is also a unitizing activity in which students look for different units or chunks of the whole in order to name a part of the whole in different ways. This activity utilizes a set model.

Activity 15.16

Apples and Bananas

Have students set out a specific number of counters in two colors—for example, 24 counters, 16 of them red (apples) and 8 yellow (bananas). The 24 make up the whole. The task is to group the counters into different fractional parts of the whole and use the parts to create fraction names for the fractions that are apples and fractions that are bananas. In Figure 15.18, 24 counters are arranged in different groups. You might also suggest arrays (see Figure 15.19).

In Lamon's version of the latter activity, she prompts students with questions such as "If we make groups of four, what part of the set is red?" With these prompts you can suggest fraction names that students are unlikely to think of.

In the activities so far, there has only been a hint of a rule for finding equivalent fractions. The following activity

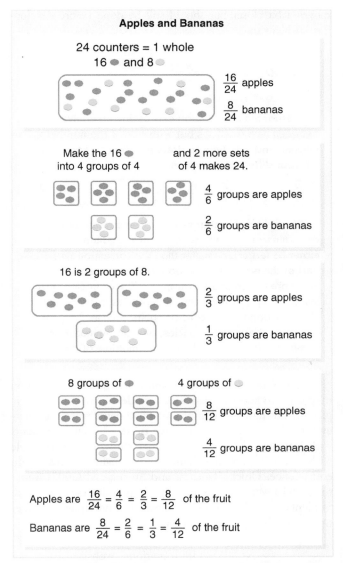

Figure 15.18 Set models for illustrating equivalent fractions.

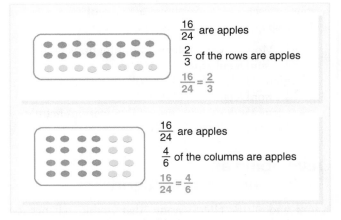

Figure 15.19 Arrays for illustrating equivalent fractions.

moves a bit closer but should still be done before developing an algorithm.

Activity 15.17

Missing-Number Equivalencies

Give students an equation expressing an equivalence between two fractions but with one of the numbers missing and ask them to draw a picture to solve. Here are four different examples:

$$\frac{5}{3} = \frac{\square}{6} \qquad \frac{2}{3} = \frac{6}{\square} \qquad \frac{8}{12} = \frac{\square}{3} \qquad \frac{9}{12} = \frac{3}{\square}$$

The missing number can be either a numerator or a denominator. Furthermore, the missing number can either be larger or smaller than the corresponding part of the equivalent fraction. (All four possibilities are represented in the examples.) The examples shown involve simple whole-number multiples between equivalent fractions. Next, consider pairs such as $\frac{6}{8} = \frac{\square}{12}$ or $\frac{9}{12} = \frac{6}{\square}$. In these equivalencies, one denominator or numerator is not a whole number multiple of the other.

When doing "Missing-Number Equivalencies" you may want to specify a particular model, such as sets or pie pieces. Alternatively, you can allow students to select whatever methods they wish to solve these problems. Students with learning disabilities and other students who struggle with mathematics may benefit from using clocks to do equivalence. Chick, Tierney, and Storeygard (2007) found that clocks were very helpful in a highly diverse classroom. Students were able to use the clocks to find equivalent fractions for $\frac{10}{12}$, $\frac{3}{4}$, $\frac{4}{6}$, and so on.

 NCTM's Illuminations website offers an excellent set of three units called "Fun with Fractions." Each unit uses one of the model types (set, region, or length) and focuses on comparing and ordering fractions and equivalency. The five to six lessons in each unit incorporate a range of manipulatives and engaging activities to support student learning.

> Set Model Unit: http://illuminations.nctm.org/ LessonDetail.aspx?id=U112
> Region Model Unit: http://illuminations.nctm.org/ LessonDetail.aspx?id=U113
> Length Model Unit: http://illuminations.nctm.org/ LessonDetail.aspx?id=U152 ◆

Developing an Equivalent-Fraction Algorithm

Kamii and Clark (1995) argue that undue reliance on physical models does not help children construct equivalence schemes. When children understand that fractions can have different names, they should be challenged to develop a method for finding equivalent names. It might also be argued that students who are experienced at looking for patterns and developing schemes for doing things can invent an algorithm for equivalent fractions without further assistance. However, the following approach will certainly improve the chances of that happening.

A Region Model Approach. Using a rectangular region is a good visual and is closely linked to the algorithm: multiplying both the top and bottom numbers by the same number will always get an equivalent fraction. The approach suggested here is to look for a pattern in the way that the fractional parts in both the part as well as the whole are counted. Activity 15.18 is a beginning, but a good class discussion following the activity will also be required.

Activity 15.18

Slicing Squares

Give students a worksheet with four squares in a row, each approximately 3 cm on a side. Have them shade in the same fraction in each square using vertical dividing lines. You can use the context of a garden or farm. For example, slice each square in fourths and shade three-fourths as in Figure 15.20. Next, tell students to slice each square into equal-sized horizontal slices. Each square must be partitioned differently, using from one to eight slices. For each sliced square, they record an equation showing the equivalent fractions. Have them examine their equations and drawings to look for any patterns. You can repeat this with four more squares and a different fraction.

Following this activity, write on the board the equations for four or five different fraction names found by the students. Discuss any patterns they discovered. To focus the discussion, show on the overhead a square illustrating $\frac{4}{5}$ made with vertical slices as in Figure 15.21. Turn off the overhead and slice the square into six parts in the opposite direction. Cover all but two edges of the square as shown in the figure. Ask, "What is the new name for my $\frac{4}{5}$?"

The reason for this exercise is that many students simply count the small regions and never think to use multiplication. With the covered square, students can see that there are four columns and six rows to the shaded part, so there must be 4×6 parts shaded. Similarly, there must be

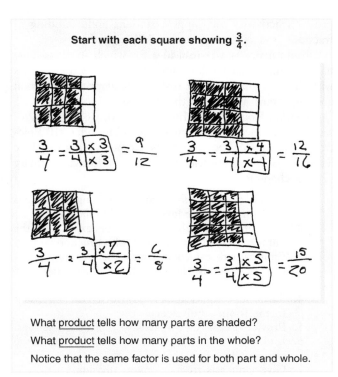

Start with each square showing $\frac{3}{4}$.

What <u>product</u> tells how many parts are shaded?

What <u>product</u> tells how many parts in the whole?

Notice that the same factor is used for both part and whole.

Figure 15.20 A model for developing the equivalent-fraction algorithm.

5×6 parts in the whole. Therefore, the new name for $\frac{4}{5}$ is $\frac{4 \times 6}{5 \times 6}$, or $\frac{24}{30}$.

Using this idea, have students return to the fractions on their worksheet to see if the pattern works for other fractions.

Examine examples of equivalent fractions that have been generated with other models, and see if the rule of multiplying top and bottom numbers by the same number holds there also. If the rule is correct, how can $\frac{6}{8}$ and $\frac{9}{12}$ be equivalent?

Writing Fractions in Simplest Terms. The multiplication scheme for equivalent fractions produces fractions with larger denominators. To write a fraction in *simplest*

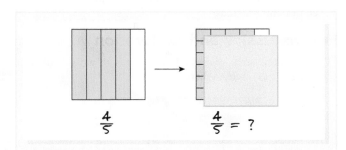

Figure 15.21 How can you count the fractional parts if you cannot see them all?

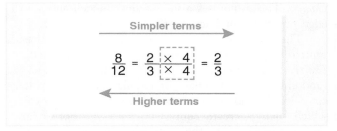

Figure 15.22 Using the equivalent-fraction algorithm to write fractions in simplest terms.

terms means to write it so that numerator and denominator have no common whole-number factors. (Some texts use the name *lowest terms* instead of *simplest terms*.) One meaningful approach to this task of finding simplest terms is to reverse the earlier process, as illustrated in Figure 15.22. The search for a common factor or a simplified fraction should be connected to grouping.

Two additional notes:

1. Notice that the phrase *reducing fractions* was not used. This terminology implies making a fraction smaller and is rarely used anymore in textbooks. Fractions are simplified, not reduced.
2. Teachers may tell students that fraction answers are incorrect if not in simplest or lowest terms. This also misinforms students about the equivalency of fractions. When students add $\frac{1}{6} + \frac{1}{2}$ both $\frac{2}{3}$ and $\frac{4}{6}$ are correct. It is best to reinforce that they are both correct and are equivalent.

Multiplying by One. Many middle school textbooks use a strictly symbolic approach to equivalent fractions. It is based on the multiplicative property that says that any number multiplied by 1 remains unchanged. Any fraction of the form $\frac{n}{n}$ can be used as the identity element. Therefore, $\frac{3}{4} = \frac{3}{4} \times 1 = \frac{3}{4} \times \frac{2}{2} = \frac{6}{8}$. Furthermore, the numerator and denominator of the identity element can also be fractions. In this way, $\frac{6}{12} = \frac{6}{12} \times \left(\frac{1/6}{1/6}\right) = \frac{1}{2}$.

This explanation relies on an understanding of the multiplicative identity property, which most students in grades 4 to 6 do not fully appreciate. It also relies on the procedure for multiplying two fractions. Finally, the argument uses solely deductive reasoning based on an axiom of the rational number system. It does not lend itself to intuitive modeling. A reasonable conclusion is to delay this important explanation until at least seventh or eighth grade in an appropriate prealgebra context and not as a method or a rationale for producing equivalent fractions.

 In the NCTM e-Examples (http://standards .ctm.org/document/eexamples/index.htm), there is a motivating fraction game for two players (Applet 5.1, *Communicating about Mathematics Using*

Games). The game uses a number-line model, and knowledge of equivalent fractions plays a significant role.

The NLVM website (http://nlvm.usu.edu) has a limited applet tool for exploring equivalent fractions, *Fractions—Equivalent.* Proper fractions are presented randomly in either square or circular formats. Students can slice the model in as many parts as they wish to see which slicings create equivalent fractions. For squares, the new slices go in the same direction as the original slices. For circles, it is a bit hard to distinguish new slices from old. Students enter an equivalent fraction and then click a button to check their response. ◆

Teaching Considerations for Fraction Concepts

Because the teaching of fractions is so important, and because fractions are often not well understood even by adults, a recap of the big ideas is needed. Hopefully you have recognized that one reason fractions are not well understood is that there is a lot to know about them— from part-whole relationships to division. In addition, building understanding means representing across area, length, and set models—and including contexts that fit these models. Using es-

> **myeducationlab**
>
> Go to the Building Teaching Skills and Dispositions section of Chapter 15 of MyEducationLab. Click on Videos and watch the video entitled "**A Lesson on Fractions**" to see a class use fraction pieces to learn about equivalent fractions.

timation activities can support student understanding of fractions and is an important skill in and of itself.

Equivalence is a central idea for which students must have sound understanding and skill. Connecting visuals with the procedure and not rushing the algorithm too soon are important aspects of the process.

Clarke, Roche, and Mitchell (2008), well-known researchers of fraction teaching and learning, offer "10 Practical Tips for Making Fractions Come Alive and Make Sense." These tips are listed here as an effective summary of this chapter:

1. Give a greater emphasis to the meaning of fractions than on the procedures for manipulating them.
2. Develop a generalizable rule for explaining the numerator and denominator of a fraction.
3. Emphasize that fractions are numbers, making extensive use of number lines in representing fractions and decimals.
4. Take opportunities early to focus on improper fractions and equivalencies.
5. Provide a variety of models to represent fractions.
6. Link fractions to key benchmarks and encourage estimation.
7. Give emphasis to fractions as division.
8. Link fractions, decimals, and percents wherever possible.
9. Take the opportunity to interview several students one on one . . . to gain awareness of their thinking strategies.
10. Look for examples and activities that can engage students in thinking about fractions in particular and rational number ideas in general. (pp. 374–378)

Reflections

Writing to Learn

1. Describe what is meant by sharing activities. What is the goal of these activities? When would you implement them?
2. Give examples of manipulatives within each of the three categories of fraction models.
3. What does partitioning mean? Explain and illustrate.
4. What does iteration mean? Explain and illustrate.
5. Describe how a student might explain what the numerator and denominator mean.
6. What are two ways you can support students' development of estimating with fractions?
7. Describe two ways to compare $\frac{5}{12}$ and $\frac{5}{8}$ (not common denominator or cross-product methods).
8. What are two ways to build the conceptual relationship between $\frac{11}{4}$ and $2\frac{3}{4}$?

9. What contexts might you use to develop the concept of equivalence within each of the models—area, length, and set?
10. How can you help children develop the algorithm for equivalent fractions?

For Discussion and Exploration

1. A common error that children make is to write $\frac{3}{5}$ for the fraction represented here:

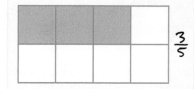

Why do you think that they do this? What activity or strategy would you use to try to address this misconception?

2. Fractions are often named by adults and in cartoons as a dreaded math topic. Why do you think this is true? How might your fraction instruction alter this perception for your students?

Resources

Literature Connections

Context takes children away from rules and encourages them to explore ideas in a more open and meaningful manner. The way that children approach fraction concepts in these contexts may surprise you.

How Many Snails? A Counting Book   *Giganti, 1988*

Each page of this book has a similar pattern of questions. For example, "I went walking and I wondered: How many clouds were there? How many clouds were big and fluffy? How many were big and fluffy and gray?" Students can look at the pictures and find the fraction of the objects (e.g., clouds) that have the particular characteristic (big and fluffy). Whitin and Whitin (2006) describe how a class used this book to write their own stories in this pattern and record the fractions for each subset of the objects.

The Doorbell Rang   *Hutchins, 1986*

Often used to investigate whole-number operations of multiplication and division, this book is also an excellent early introduction to fractions. The story is a simple tale of two children preparing to share a plate of 12 cookies. Just as they have figured out how to share the cookies, the doorbell rings and more children arrive. You can change the number of children to create a sharing situation that requires fractions (e.g., 5 children).

The Man Who Counted: A Collection of Mathematical Adventures   *Tahan, 1993*

This book contains a story, "Beasts of Burden," about a wise mathematician, Beremiz, and the narrator, who are traveling together on one camel. They are asked by three brothers to solve an argument. Their father has left them 35 camels to divide among them: half to one brother, one-third to another, and one-ninth to the third. The story provides an excellent context for discussing fractional parts of sets and how fractional parts change as the whole changes. However, if the whole is changed from 35 to, say, 36 or 34, the problem of the indicated shares remains unresolved. The sum of $\frac{1}{2}$, $\frac{1}{3}$, and $\frac{1}{9}$ will never be one whole, no matter how many camels are involved. Bresser (1995) describes three days of activities with his fifth graders.

Recommended Readings

Articles

Clarke, D. M., Roche, A., & Mitchell, A. (2008). Ten practical tips for making fractions come alive and make sense. *Mathematics Teaching in the Middle School, 13*(7), 373–380.
This article has the ten suggestions listed in the summary of this chapter. Each is discussed and favorite activities are shared. An excellent overview of teaching fractions.

Flores, A., & Klein, E. (2005). From students' problem-solving strategies to connections in fractions. *Teaching Children Mathematics, 11*(9), 452–457.
This article offers a very realistic view (complete with photos of student work) of how children develop initial fraction concepts and an understanding of notation as they engage in sharing tasks like those described in this chapter.

Reys, B. J., Kim, O., & Bay, J. M. (1999). Establishing fraction benchmarks. *Mathematics Teaching in the Middle School, 4*(8), 530–532.
This short article describes a simple three-question interview administered to 20 fifth-grade students. The results are both sad and surprising. A significant conclusion is that the teaching of benchmarks for fractions, specifically 0, $\frac{1}{2}$, and 1, is generally neglected in the standard curriculum.

Stump, S. (2003). Designing fraction counting books. *Teaching Children Mathematics, 9*(9), 546–549.
This article describes the work of several preservice teachers whose students created counting books in which they count by unit fractions.

Books

Burns, M. (2001). *Teaching arithmetic: Lessons for introducing fractions, grades 4–5.* Sausalito, CA: Math Solutions Publications.
Typical of Marilyn Burns, this book offers well-designed lessons with lots of details, sample student dialogue, and Blackline Masters. These are introductory ideas for fraction concepts. Five lessons cover one-half as a benchmark. Assessments are also included.

Online Resources

Cyberchase (PBS)
www.pbs.org/teachers/search/results.html?q=fractions&x= 0&y=0&num=100&loggedin=0&loggedin=0&active=audio video

Cyberchase is a very popular television series targeting important mathematics. The site offers videos that model fractions with real-world connections. Also offered are activities such as "Make a Match" (http://pbskids.org/cyberchase/games/equivalentfractions/index.html), in which students examine the concept of equivalent fractions and match a fraction with a graphic representation of that fraction. Another activity is "Thirteen Ways of Looking at a Half" (http://pbskids.org/cyberchase/games/fractions/index.html), in which students explore fractions of geometric shapes—in particular, the thirteen ways half of an eight-piece square can be arranged.

Fraction Bars (Math Playground)
http://mathplayground.com/Fraction_bars.html
The user sets the total parts and then the shaded parts for each bar. Explore fractional parts, the concept of numerator and denominator, and equivalency. The user can turn the numbers on or off.

Fraction Concepts (eNLVM Module)
http://enlvm.usu.edu/ma/nav/toc.jsp?sid=__shared&cid=emready@fraction_concepts&bb=published
These part-whole activities provide practice in writing and comparing fractions. A full lesson plan with NCTM standards correlations and worksheets is provided, and the teacher can log in to see how students performed.

Fraction Track
http://standards.nctm.org/document/eexamples/chap5/5.1/index.htm
Players position fractions on number lines with different denominators. Fractions can be split into parts. A challenging game involving equivalent-fraction concepts.

Fraction Pointer
www.shodor.org/interactivate/activities/FractionPointer
A good applet for connecting an area model with the number line. After creating area models for two fractions, the user must then create a new fraction between the first two. Similar to the *Illuminations* applet, "Equivalent Fractions."

National Library of Virtual Manipulatives
http://nlvm.usu.edu
This site offers numerous models for exploring fractions, including fraction bars and fraction pieces. Also there is an applet for comparing and visualizing fractions.

Field Experience Guide Connections

Because fractions are not as well understood as whole numbers, they are a good content area for the Chapter 3 field experiences, especially 3.1, 3.4, 3.5, and 3.6, which target conceptual and procedural understanding. FEG Expanded Lesson 9.6 is a dot paper activity focused on fraction equivalencies. FEG Expanded Lesson 9.10 and FEG Activity 10.6 ("Fraction Find") target an important concept of fractions—the idea that you can always find one more fraction between any two fractions.

Developing Strategies for Fraction Computation

A fifth-grade student asks, "Why is it when we times 29 times two-ninths that the answer goes down?" (Taber, 2002, p. 67). Although generalizations from whole numbers can confuse students, you should realize that their ideas about the operations were developed with whole numbers. Students need to build on their ideas of whole-number operations. We can use their prior understanding of the whole-number operations to give meaning to fraction computation. This, combined with a firm understanding of fractions, provides the foundation for understanding fraction computation. Without this foundation, your students will almost certainly be learning rules without reasons, an unacceptable goal.

Big Ideas

1. The meanings of each operation on fractions are the same as the meanings for the operations on whole numbers. Operations with fractions should begin by applying these same meanings to fractional parts.

   - For addition and subtraction, the numerator tells the number of parts and the denominator the type of part. It is the parts that are added or subtracted.

   - For multiplication by a fraction, repeated addition and area models support development of the algorithm for multiplication of fractions.

   - For division by a fraction, the two ways of thinking about the operation—partition and measurement—will lead to two different thought processes for division. Both are important.

2. Estimation in fraction computation is tied almost entirely to concepts of the operations and relative sizes of fractions. A computation algorithm is not required for making estimates. Estimation should be an integral part of computation development to keep students' attention on the meanings of the operations and the expected sizes of the results.

Mathematics Content Connections

As just noted, computation with fractions is built on an understanding of the operations for whole numbers and on fraction sense. Understanding fraction computation has connections in these areas as well.

- **Algebraic Thinking:** Equations with variables often involve fractions or can be solved using fractions. For example, $\frac{3}{4}x = 15$ could be solved mentally, if fraction multiplication is understood *and* the procedure for solving it requires multiplication (or division) of fractions.

- **Decimals and Percents:** Because decimals and percents are alternative representations for fractions, they can often help with computational fluency, especially in the area of estimation. For example, 2.452×0.513 is about $2\frac{1}{2} \times \frac{1}{2}$ or $1\frac{1}{4} = 1.25$. Twenty-five percent off of the $132 list price is easily computed as $\frac{1}{4}$ of 132.

- **Proportional Reasoning:** Fraction multiplication helps us to think about fractions as operators. This in turn is connected to the concepts of ratio and proportion, especially the ideas of scaling and scale factors.

- **Measurement:** Not only does measuring often involve adding, subtracting, multiplying, and dividing with fractions, but the models for understanding the operations include a measurement interpretation (How many $\frac{1}{2}$″ segments can you get from 5″ of string?).

Number Sense and Fraction Algorithms

Today it is important to be able to compute with fractions, primarily for the purpose of making estimates and for understanding computations in algebra, measurement, and other mathematics strands.

Conceptual Development Takes Time

It is important to give students ample opportunity to develop fraction number sense prior to and during instruction about common denominators and other procedures for computation. Even in grade 7 or 8 it makes sense to delay computation and work on concepts if students are not conceptually ready.

Premature attention to rules for fraction computation has a number of serious drawbacks. None of the algorithms helps students think about the operations and what they mean. When students follow a procedure they do not understand, they have no means of assessing their results to see if they make sense. Second, mastery of the poorly understood algorithm in the short term is quickly lost. When mixed together, the differing procedures for each operation soon become a meaningless jumble. Students ask, "Do I need a common denominator, or do I just add or multiply the bottom numbers?" "Which one do I invert, the first or the second number?" When the numbers in a problem are altered slightly, for example, a mixed number appears, students think the algorithm does not apply.

 Principles and Standards suggests that the main focus on fractions and decimals in grades 3–5 should be on the development of number sense and informal approaches to addition and subtraction. In grades 6–8, students should expand their skills to include all operations with fractions, decimals, and percents. ◆

A Problem-Based Number Sense Approach

Even if your curriculum guidelines call for teaching all four of the operations with fractions, you must still delay a rush to algorithmic procedures until it becomes clear that students are ready. Students can become adequately proficient using informal student-invented methods that they understand.

The following guidelines should be kept in mind when developing computational strategies for fractions:

1. *Begin with simple contextual tasks.* This should seem like déjà vu, as this recommendation applies to nearly every topic. Huinker (1998) makes an excellent case for using contextual problems and letting students develop their own methods of computation with fractions. Problems or contexts need not be elaborate. What you want is a context for both the meaning of the operation and the fractions involved.

2. *Connect the meaning of fraction computation with whole-number computation.* To consider what $2\frac{1}{2} \times \frac{3}{4}$ might mean, we should ask, "What does 2×3 mean?" Follow this with "What might $2 \times 3\frac{1}{2}$ mean?," slowly moving to a fraction times a fraction. The concepts of each operation are the same, and benefits can be had by connecting to whole number operations, explicitly discussing what is similar and what is different.

3. *Let estimation and informal methods play a big role in the development of strategies.* "Should $2\frac{1}{2} \times \frac{1}{4}$ be more or less than 1? More or less than 2?" Estimation keeps the focus on the meanings of the numbers and the operations, encourages reflective thinking, and helps build informal number sense with fractions. Can you reason to get an exact answer without using the standard algorithm? One way is to apply the distributive property, splitting the mixed number and multiplying both parts by $\frac{1}{4}$: $(2 \times \frac{1}{4}) + (\frac{1}{2} \times \frac{1}{4})$. Two $\frac{1}{4}$s is $\frac{2}{4}$ or $\frac{1}{2}$ and a half of a fourth is $\frac{1}{8}$. So, add an eighth to a half and you have $\frac{5}{8}$.

4. *Explore each of the operations using models.* Use a variety of models. Have students defend their solutions using the models, including simple student drawings. You will find that sometimes it is possible to get answers with models that do not seem to help with pencil-and-paper approaches. That's fine! The ideas will help children learn to think about the fractions and the operations, contribute to mental methods, and provide a useful background when you eventually do get to the standard algorithms.

These four steps are embedded in each of the sections in this chapter.

Computational Estimation

A frequently quoted result from the Second National Assessment of Educational Progress (Post, 1981) concerns the following item:

> Estimate the answer to $\frac{12}{13} + \frac{7}{8}$. You will not have time to solve the problem using paper and pencil.

Here is how 13-year-olds answered:

Response	Percent of 13-Year-Olds
1	7
2	24
19	28
21	27
Don't know	14

A more recent study of sixth- and eighth-grade Taiwanese students included this same item. The results were nearly identical to those in the NAEP study (Reys, 1998).

In the Taiwanese study, a significantly higher percentage of students (61 percent and 63 percent) were able to correctly compute the sum, a process that requires finding the common denominator of thirteenths and eighths! Notice that to estimate this sum requires no skill whatsoever with computation—only a feeling for the size of the two fractions.

Addition and Subtraction. The development of fraction number sense should most certainly include estimation of fraction sums and differences—even before computational strategies are introduced. The following activity can be done regularly as a short full-class warm-up for any fraction lesson.

Activity 16.1

First Estimates

Tell students that they are going to estimate a sum or difference of two fractions. They are to decide only if the exact answer is more or less than 1. On the overhead projector, for no more than about 10 seconds, show a fraction addition or subtraction problem involving two fractions. Students write down on paper or a mini whiteboard their choice of more or less than one. Do several problems in a row. Then return to each problem and discuss how students decided on their estimate.

Activity 16.1, estimating to over or under 1, is the beginning of related tasks that are more complicated. When students are ready for a tougher challenge, choose from the following variations:

- Use a target answer that is different than 1. For example, estimate more or less than $\frac{1}{2}$, $1\frac{1}{2}$, 2, or 3.
- Choose fractions both less than and greater than 1. Estimate to the nearest half.

In the discussions following these estimation exercises, ask students if they think that the exact answer is more or less than the estimate that they gave.

Figure 16.1 shows six sample sums and differences that might be used in a "First Estimates" activity.

 Pause and Reflect

Test your own estimation skills with the sample problems in Figure 16.1. Look at each computation for only about 10 seconds and write down an estimate. After writing down all six of your estimates, look at the problems and decide whether your estimate is higher or lower than the actual computation. Don't guess! Have a good reason.

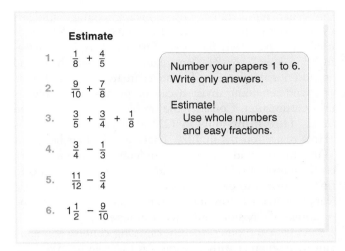

Estimate

1. $\frac{1}{8} + \frac{4}{5}$
2. $\frac{9}{10} + \frac{7}{8}$
3. $\frac{3}{5} + \frac{3}{4} + \frac{1}{8}$
4. $\frac{3}{4} - \frac{1}{3}$
5. $\frac{11}{12} - \frac{3}{4}$
6. $1\frac{1}{2} - \frac{9}{10}$

Number your papers 1 to 6. Write only answers.

Estimate!
Use whole numbers and easy fractions.

Figure 16.1 Example of fraction estimation expressions.

In most cases students' estimates should not be much more than $\frac{1}{2}$ away from the exact sum or difference.

NCTM Standards "The development of rational-number concepts is a major goal for grades 3–5, which should lead to informal methods for calculating with fractions. For example, a problem such as $\frac{1}{4} + \frac{1}{2}$ should be solved mentally with ease because students can picture $\frac{1}{2}$ and $\frac{1}{4}$ or can use decomposition strategies, such as $\frac{1}{4} + \frac{1}{2} = \frac{1}{4} + (\frac{1}{4} + \frac{1}{4})$" (p. 35). ◆

Multiplication and Division. How would you estimate the answer to $3\frac{2}{3} \times 2\frac{1}{4}$? Using the estimation technique of rounding one factor up and the other down, this product might be estimated as 4×2. That simple estimation may be all that is required in a real setting. It is also good enough to help students know if their calculated answer is in the right ballpark.

In the real world, there are many instances when whole numbers times fractions must be multiplied and mental estimates or even exact answers are quite useful. For example, sale items are frequently listed as "$\frac{1}{4}$ off" or we read of a "$\frac{1}{3}$ increase" in the number of registered voters. Also, fractions are excellent substitutes for percents, as you will see in the next chapter. To get an estimate of 60 percent of $36.69, it is useful to think of 60 percent as $\frac{3}{5}$ or as a little less than $\frac{2}{3}$.

These products of fractions and large whole numbers can be calculated mentally by thinking of the meanings of the top and bottom numbers. For example, $\frac{3}{5}$ is 3 *one*-fifths. So if you want $\frac{3}{5}$ of 350, for example, first think about *one*-fifth of 350, or 70. If *one*-fifth is 70, then *three*-fifths is 3×70, or 210. Although this example has very compatible numbers, it illustrates a process for mentally multiplying a large number by a fraction: First determine the unit fractional part, and then multiply by the number of parts you want.

When numbers are not so nice, encourage students to use compatible numbers. To estimate $\frac{3}{5}$ of $36.69, a useful compatible is $35. One-fifth of 35 is 7, so three-fifths is 3 × 7, or 21. Now adjust a bit—perhaps add an additional 50 cents, for an estimate of $21.50.

Understanding division can be greatly supported by using estimation. Consider the problem 12 ÷ 4. This can mean "How many fours in 12?" Similarly, 12 ÷ $\frac{1}{4}$ means "How many fourths in 12?" There are 48 fourths in 12. With this basic idea in mind, students should be able to estimate problems like $4\frac{1}{3} \div \frac{1}{2}$ and $3\frac{4}{5} \div \frac{2}{3}$. Asking students to first use words to describe what these equations are asking (e.g., how many halves in $4\frac{1}{3}$) can help them think about the meaning of division and then estimate.

As with the other operations, using context is important in estimating with division. An example is: "We have 5 submarine sandwiches. A serving for one person is $\frac{2}{5}$ of a sandwich. About how many people will get a full serving?"

Addition and Subtraction

Addition and subtraction of fractions are usually taught together in fifth or sixth grade. *Curriculum Focal Points* (NCTM, 2006) includes addition and subtraction of fractions and decimals as a fifth-grade focal point and stresses ability to model and represent, ability to estimate, and fluency.

As with whole-number computation, provide computational tasks without giving rules or procedures for completing them. Expect that students will use a variety of methods and that the methods will vary widely with the fractions encountered in the problems.

Students should find a variety of ways to solve problems with fractions, and their invented approaches will contribute to the development of the standard algorithms (Huinker, 1998; Lappan & Mouck, 1998; Schifter, Bastable, & Russell, 1999c).

Invented Strategies

Invented strategies are critical for developing an understanding of fractions, as they tend to use a student's number sense. Besides, most of the fractions people add in their adult lives involve halves, fourths, eighths—fractions that can be added mentally in whatever ways people find most comfortable. Apply the same strategies by encouraging students to model the problem or solve it in a way that makes sense to them.

Consider the following problem.

Mark bought $4\frac{1}{4}$ pounds of candy for his mom. The candy looked so good that he ate $\frac{7}{8}$ of a pound of it. How much did he give to his mom?

A fifth-grade class was asked to solve this problem in two ways. Many students attempted or correctly used a standard subtraction algorithm for mixed numbers as one method. However, not a single drawing or other explanation could be found in the class for the algorithm. As shown in Figure 16.2, Christian makes an error with the algorithm but draws a correct picture showing $4\frac{1}{4} = \frac{34}{8}$ and gets a correct answer of $\frac{27}{8}$. However, he is not confident in his drawing and crosses it out. Although many students do not understand their procedural methods, if not asked to justify their methods, they will believe in the algorithm more than their own reasoning.

A drawing method used by many in the class involved taking the $\frac{1}{8}$ left from the $\frac{7}{8}$ and adding it onto the $\frac{1}{4}$ as shown in Brandon's drawing. Only DaQuawn does this first in a symbolic manner. His "second method" is a drawing supporting his work. When DaQuawn shares with the class he says, "I took this from eighths so I could minus it from $\frac{7}{8}$. That leaves $\frac{1}{8}$. Then change [points to quarter circle] to $\frac{1}{8}$. Minus $\frac{1}{8}$ from . . . no, add it to $\frac{1}{8}$ equals $\frac{2}{8}$ plus $\frac{1}{8}$ equals $\frac{3}{8}$."

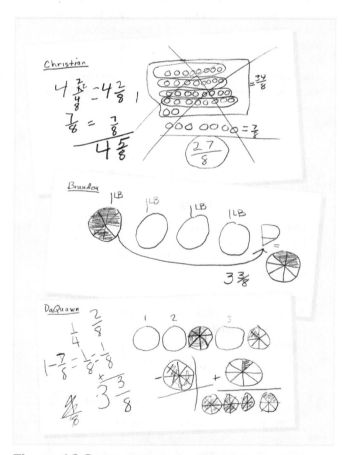

Figure 16.2 Fifth-grade students show how they solved the problem $4\frac{1}{4} - \frac{7}{8}$. For most students, their methods based on drawings have little to do with their symbolic algorithms. The work of DaQuawn, a student who struggles, is an exception.

DaQuawn's teacher notes that he "struggles with reading and writing although he has good number sense." This teacher values students' thinking and carefully distinguishes mathematics learning from students' abilities to express their ideas.

These examples illustrate how written work can provide insights into students' thinking—in this case showing that students have difficulty connecting symbols and pictures.

Fraction Circles. Students seem to have a preference for drawing circles to represent fractions. Perhaps that says something about an overuse of that model. The drawings in Figure 16.2 are not carefully drawn—the partitioning does not show equal parts. However, the students are not making conclusions based on the size of the pieces, but rather they are drawing to count sections. As long as students know that sections should be equivalent, do not be concerned with poorly drawn fraction models.

Cramer, Wyberg, and Leavitt (2008), well-known researchers in the area of rational numbers, have found circles to be the best model for adding and subtracting fractions because circles allow students to develop mental images of the sizes of different pieces (fractions) of the circle. Figure 16.3 shows how students estimate first (including marking a number line), and then explain how they added the fraction using fraction circles.

How you ask students to solve a problem can make a difference in what occurs in the classroom. For example, consider this problem:

Jack and Jill ordered two medium pizzas, one cheese and one pepperoni. Jack ate $\frac{5}{6}$ of a pizza and Jill ate $\frac{1}{2}$ of a pizza. How much pizza did they eat together?

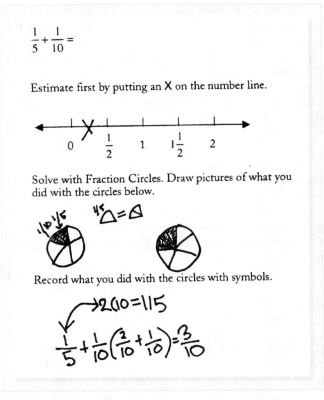

Pause and Reflect

Try to think of two ways that students might solve this problem without using a common-denominator symbolic approach.

If students draw circles as in the earlier example, some will try to fill in the $\frac{1}{6}$ gap in the pizza. Then they will need to figure out how to get $\frac{1}{6}$ from $\frac{1}{2}$. If they can think of $\frac{1}{2}$ as $\frac{3}{6}$, they can use one of the sixths to fill in the gap. Another approach, after drawing the two pizzas, is to notice that there is a half plus 2 more sixths in the $\frac{5}{6}$ pizza. Put the two halves together to make one whole and there are $\frac{2}{6}$ more—1 $\frac{2}{6}$. These are certainly good solutions that represent the type of thinking you want to encourage.

Number Lines. Another helpful model for using invented strategies to add or subtract fractions is the number line. One advantage of the number line is that it can be connected to the ruler, which is a familiar context for exploring

Figure 16.3 A student estimates and then adds fractions using a fraction circle.
Source: Cramer, K., Wyberg, T., & Leavitt, S. (2008). "The Role of Representations in Fraction Addition and Subtraction." *Mathematics Teaching in the Middle School, 13*(8), p. 495. Reprinted with permission. Copyright © 2008 by the National Council of Teachers of Mathematics, Inc. www.nctm.org. All rights reserved.

fraction addition and subtraction. The number line is also a more challenging model than the circle model, because it requires that the student not only understand $\frac{3}{4}$ as 3 out of 4, but as a value between 0 and 1 (Izsak, Tillema, & Tunc-Pekkam, 2008). Using the number line in addition to area representations like the circle can strengthen student understanding (Clarke, Roche, & Mitchell, 2008; Cramer, Wyberg, & Leavitt, 2008; Usiskin, 2007)

Pause and Reflect

Use the ruler as a visual and find the results of these three problems without applying the common denominator algorithm:

$$\frac{3}{4} + \frac{1}{2} \qquad 2\frac{1}{2} - 1\frac{1}{4} \qquad 1\frac{1}{8} + 1\frac{1}{2}$$

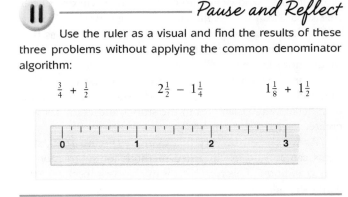

Think about how you solved the problems in Pause and Reflect. Do you think there are other ways? In the first problem, students might use 1 as a benchmark (in the way that 10 or 100 is used as a benchmark with whole numbers). They use $\frac{1}{4}$ from the $\frac{1}{2}$ to get to one whole, and then have $\frac{1}{4}$ more to add on—so $1\frac{1}{4}$. Similarly, they could take the $\frac{1}{2}$ from the $\frac{3}{4}$ to make a whole with the $\frac{1}{2}$ and then add on the $\frac{1}{4}$ or, they might just know that $\frac{1}{2}$ is $\frac{2}{4}$ and then count to get $\frac{5}{4}$ (or $1\frac{1}{4}$).

Adding a context (that fits a linear situation) can also support students' use of invented strategies. In the second problem posed in the Pause and Reflect, for example, one context might be: Desmond runs $2\frac{1}{2}$ miles a day. If he has just passed the $1\frac{1}{4}$ mile marker, how far does he still need to go? Students may first subtract the whole numbers to get $1\frac{1}{2} - \frac{1}{4}$, and then know that $\frac{1}{2} - \frac{1}{4}$ is $\frac{1}{4}$, or they might prefer to change $\frac{1}{2}$ to $\frac{2}{4}$.

Given a different context, stories could be different. For example, Desmond is at mile marker $2\frac{1}{2}$ and James is at mile marker $1\frac{1}{4}$. How far does James need to go to catch up to where Desmond is? In this case, students may use a counting up strategy, noting that it takes $\frac{3}{4}$ to get to 2, then another $\frac{1}{2}$ added to $\frac{3}{4}$ would be $1\frac{1}{4}$. The more students can share strategies and illustrate them on the number line, the more flexible they will become in choosing how to add or subtract a fraction. As with whole numbers, sometimes invented strategies are the best and most efficient, but sometimes the numbers don't lend themselves to a mental strategy, in which case an algorithm can be very useful.

Suppose that you had asked the students to solve the Jack and Jill problem but changed the context to submarine sandwiches, asking students to use Cuisenaire rods or fraction strips to model the problem. The first decision that must be made is what strip to use as the whole. That decision is not required with a circular model. The whole must be the same for both fractions although there is a tendency to use the easiest whole for each fraction. Again, this issue does not arise with circles. In this case, the smallest strip that will work is the 6 rod or the dark green strip. Figure 16.4(a) illustrates a solution.

What if instead, you asked students to compare the quantity that Jack and Jill ate? Figure 16.4(b) illustrates lining up the "sandwiches" to compare their lengths. Recall that subtraction can be thought of as "separate" where the total is known and a part is removed, "comparison" as two amounts being compared to find the difference, and "how many more are needed" as starting with a smaller value and asking how much more to get to the higher value. This sandwich example is a comparison—be sure to include more than "take away" examples in the stories and examples you create.

As we saw in the very first example (Figure 16.2), students can and do use invented methods for subtraction as well as addition. This reasoning is extremely important. Students should become comfortable with different methods

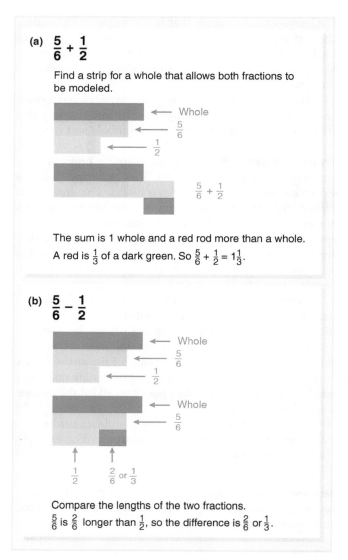

Figure 16.4 Using rods to add and subtract fractions.

of taking simple fractions apart and recombining them in ways that make sense. Keep the fractions in your problems "friendly" with denominators no greater than 12. There is rarely a need to add fifths and sevenths or even fifths and twelfths. With numbers like that, drawings are difficult, as the common denominators are quite large. Although forcing the use of a model such as fraction strips or sets can cause students to prepare for common denominators, it is best to delay that emphasis in the beginning.

Why Are Common Denominators "Required"? Teachers commonly tell students, "In order to add or subtract fractions, you must first get common denominators." The explanation usually goes something like, "After all, you can't add apples and oranges." This well-intentioned statement is essentially false. A correct statement might be, "In order *to use the standard algorithm* to add or subtract fractions, you must first get common denominators." And the explanation is then, "The algorithm is designed to work only with common denominators because it is based on the idea of adding parts that are the same size."

Using their own invented strategies, students will see that many correct solutions are found without ever getting a common denominator. Consider these sums and differences:

$$\frac{3}{4} + \frac{1}{8} \qquad \frac{1}{2} - \frac{1}{8} \qquad \frac{2}{3} + \frac{1}{2} \qquad 1\frac{1}{2} - \frac{3}{4} \qquad 1\frac{2}{3} + \frac{3}{4}$$

Working with the ways different fractional parts are related one to another often provides solutions without common denominators. For example, halves, fourths, and eighths are easily related because $\frac{1}{8}$ is half of $\frac{1}{4}$ and $\frac{1}{4}$ is half of $\frac{1}{2}$. Also, picture three-thirds making up a whole in a circle as in Figure 16.5. Have you ever noticed that one-half of the whole is a third plus a half of a third or a sixth? Similarly, the difference between a third and a fourth is a twelfth.

As noted, the number line is also a tool that can be used mentally to solve addition and subtraction without finding a common denominator. Students instead may start with finding one fraction on the number line or ruler and then "jump" the value of the other fraction. For example, in $3\frac{1}{4} - 1\frac{1}{2}$, students can find $3\frac{1}{4}$, jump down one to $2\frac{1}{4}$, and then jump $\frac{1}{2}$, which takes them to $1\frac{3}{4}$.

Developing an Algorithm

Students can build on their invented strategies and knowledge of equivalence to develop the common-denominator approach for adding and subtracting fractions. Having a strong conceptual foundation of equivalence is important in many other mathematics topics, one of which is computation of fractions. Students that have a level of fluency in moving between $\frac{1}{2}$, $\frac{2}{4}$, $\frac{4}{8}$, and $\frac{8}{16}$, or $\frac{3}{4}$, $\frac{6}{8}$, and $\frac{12}{16}$ can adjust

the fractions as needed to combine or subtract fractions. Whether using an area, length, or set model, establishing equivalence is foundational and needs continued reinforcement during instruction on addition and subtraction of fractions. For example, have students complete a sum such as $\frac{3}{8} + \frac{4}{8}$ and write the finished equation on the board. Then, beneath this equation, write a second sum made of easily seen equivalents for each fraction as shown here:

$$\frac{3}{8} + \frac{4}{8} = \frac{7}{8}$$

$$\frac{6}{16} + \frac{1}{2} = ?$$

Discuss briefly the fact that $\frac{3}{8}$ is equivalent to $\frac{6}{16}$ as is $\frac{4}{8}$ to $\frac{1}{2}$. Now have students write the answer to the second equation and give a reason for their answer. Students should see that the answer is $\frac{7}{8}$. The second sum is the same as the first because although the fractions *look* different, they are actually the same numbers.

Like Denominators. Most lists of objectives first specify addition and subtraction with like denominators. If students have a good foundation with fraction concepts, they should be able to add or subtract fractions with like denominators. Students who are not confident solving problems such as $\frac{3}{4} + \frac{2}{4}$ or $3\frac{7}{8} - 1\frac{3}{8}$ may lack fraction concepts and need more experience manipulating models. The idea that the top number counts and the bottom number tells what is counted makes addition and subtraction of like fractions the same as adding and subtracting whole numbers. When working on adding with like denominators, however, it is important to be sure that students are focusing on the key idea— the units are the same, so they can be combined (Mack, 2004).

 The ease with which students can or cannot add like-denominator fractions should be viewed as an important concept assessment before pushing students forward to an algorithm. As just noted, students who do not see these sums or differences as trivial likely do not understand the meanings of the numerator and denominator. Any further symbolic development will almost certainly be without understanding. ◆

Unlike Denominators. To begin adding and subtracting fractions with unlike denominators, consider a task such as $\frac{5}{8} + \frac{1}{4}$ where only one fraction needs to be changed. Let students use any method. As students explain how they solved it, someone is likely to explain that $\frac{1}{4}$ is the same as $\frac{2}{8}$. Write equations on the board that show the initial equation and the equation rewritten with $\frac{2}{8}$ in place of $\frac{1}{4}$. Ask "Is this still the same equation? Why would we want to change the $\frac{1}{4}$?" Have students use models or drawings to explain why the original problem and also the converted problem should have the same answer.

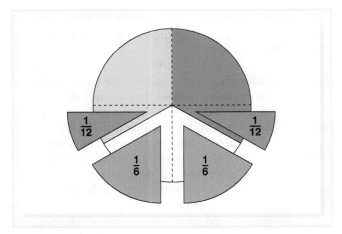

Figure 16.5 There are lots of fractional relationships that can be observed simply by looking at how halves, thirds, fourths, sixths, and twelfths fit into a partitioned circle.

Next try some examples where both fractions need to be changed—for example, $\frac{2}{3} + \frac{1}{4}$. Encourage students to solve these problems without using models or drawings if possible. Suggest (don't require) that the use of equivalent fractions might be an easier tool than a drawing. In the discussion of student solutions, focus attention on the idea of *rewriting the problem* to make it easier to add or subtract. Be certain that students understand that the rewritten problem is the same as the original and, therefore, must have the same answer. If your students express any doubt about the equivalence of the two problems ("Is $\frac{8}{12} + \frac{3}{12}$ really the answer to $\frac{2}{3} + \frac{1}{4}$?"), that should be a clue that the concept of equivalent fractions is not well understood, and more experience using visual or concrete models is needed.

As students continue to explore solutions to sums and differences of fractions, models should remain available for use. The three examples in Figure 16.6 show how models might be used. Note that each model requires students to think about the size of a whole that can be partitioned into the units of both fractions (e.g., fifths and halves require tenths).

The most common error in adding fractions is to add both numerators and denominators. Rather than jump in and attempt to correct this error directly, capitalize on the opportunity for a wonderful class discussion. One idea is to show students the following solution for adding $\frac{1}{2} + \frac{1}{3}$ that you "saw" offered by a fictional student in another class:

$$\frac{1}{2} \, \circ\, \bullet \qquad \frac{1}{3} \, \circ\, \bullet\, \bullet$$

$$\text{add} \;\; \circ\, \circ\, \bullet\, \bullet\, \bullet$$

$$\text{Therefore, } \frac{1}{2} + \frac{1}{3} = \frac{2}{5}.$$

Add tops and bottoms.

Ask students to decide whether the student could be right. If not, what is wrong with the solution?

❚❚ ———— *Pause and Reflect*

Why can't the answer be $\frac{2}{5}$ and what is wrong with the student's reasoning?

Focus first on the answer. The sum of $\frac{2}{5}$ is smaller than $\frac{1}{2}$ when, in fact, $\frac{1}{2} + \frac{1}{3}$ must be more than $\frac{1}{2}$. When students are convinced that the sum cannot be $\frac{2}{5}$, there is real value in letting them decide what is wrong with the reasoning. You must first see where students are in their understanding. For example, Nancy Mack, a researcher and teacher, asked her fifth graders if the following were correct: $\frac{3}{8} + \frac{2}{8} = \frac{5}{16}$. A student correctly replied, "No, because they are eighths (*holds up one-eighth of a fraction circle*). If you put them together you still have eighths (*shows this with the fraction circles*). See, you didn't make them into sixteenths

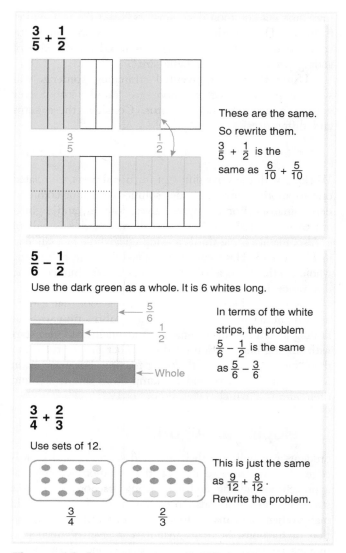

$\frac{3}{5} + \frac{1}{2}$

These are the same. So rewrite them. $\frac{3}{5} + \frac{1}{2}$ is the same as $\frac{6}{10} + \frac{5}{10}$

$\frac{5}{6} - \frac{1}{2}$

Use the dark green as a whole. It is 6 whites long.

In terms of the white strips, the problem $\frac{5}{6} - \frac{1}{2}$ is the same as $\frac{5}{6} - \frac{3}{6}$

$\frac{3}{4} + \frac{2}{3}$

Use sets of 12.

This is just the same as $\frac{9}{12} + \frac{8}{12}$. Rewrite the problem.

Figure 16.6 Rewriting addition and subtraction problems involving fractions so they have a common denominator.

when you put them together. They're still eighths" (Mack, 2004, p. 229).

Common Multiples. Many students have trouble finding common denominators because they are not able to come up with common multiples of the denominators quickly. That is a skill that you may wish to drill. It also depends on having a good command of the basic facts for multiplication. Activity 16.2 is aimed at the skill of finding least common multiples or common denominators. Least common denominators are preferred because the computation is more manageable with smaller numbers, and there is less simplifying to do after adding and subtracting, but *any* common denominator will work, whether it is the smallest or not. Do not require least common multiples—support all common denominators and in discussion students will see that finding the smallest multiple is more efficient.

Activity 16.2

LCM Flash Cards

Make flash cards with pairs of numbers that are potential denominators. Most should be less than 16. For each card, students try to give the least common multiple, or LCM (see Figure 16.7). Be sure to include pairs that are prime, such as 9 and 5; pairs in which one is a multiple of the other, such as 2 and 8; and pairs that have a common divisor, such as 8 and 12.

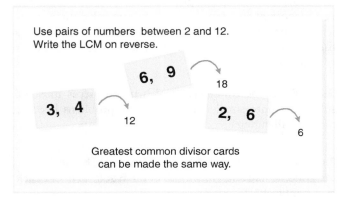

Use pairs of numbers between 2 and 12. Write the LCM on reverse.

6, 9   18

3, 4   12

2, 6   6

Greatest common divisor cards can be made the same way.

Figure 16.7 Least common multiple (LCM) flash cards.

Mixed Numbers and Improper Fractions

A separate algorithm for mixed numbers in addition and subtraction is not necessary even though mixed numbers are often treated as separate topics in traditional textbooks and in some lists of objectives. Include mixed numbers in all of your activities with addition and subtraction, and let students solve these problems in ways that make sense to them. Students will tend to naturally add or subtract the whole numbers and then the fractions. Sometimes this is all that needs to be done, but in other cases regrouping across the whole number and fraction is needed. In subtraction, this happens when the second fraction is larger than the first, and it occurs in addition when the answer of the fraction sum is more than 1.

Dealing with the whole numbers first still makes sense. Consider this problem: $5\frac{1}{8} - 3\frac{5}{8}$. After subtracting 3 from 5, students will need to deal with the $\frac{5}{8}$. Some will take $\frac{5}{8}$ from the whole part, 2, leaving $1\frac{3}{8}$, and then $\frac{1}{8}$ more is $1\frac{4}{8}$. Others may take away the $\frac{1}{8}$ that is there and then take $\frac{4}{8}$ from the remaining 2. A third but unlikely method is to trade one of the wholes for $\frac{8}{8}$, add it to the $\frac{1}{8}$, and then take $\frac{5}{8}$ from the resulting $\frac{9}{8}$. This last method is the same as the traditional algorithm.

One underemphasized technique that is nevertheless a great strategy is to change the mixed numbers to single, or improper, fractions. You may have been taught that this was the process used for multiplication, but that is part of the "rules without reason" approach of having one way to do one procedure. Let's revisit $5\frac{1}{8} - 3\frac{5}{8}$. This can be rewritten as $\frac{41}{8} - \frac{29}{8}$. (See Chapter 15 for conceptual ways for helping students do this.) Because 41 − 29 is 12, the solution is $\frac{12}{8}$ or $1\frac{1}{2}$. This is certainly efficient and will always work. The message here is to provide options to students and you will find that more students understand and are able to solve these problems successfully.

Multiplication

Multiplication of fractions is often taught in middle school, though informal fraction activities that reflect multiplication, such as "What is $\frac{2}{3}$ of 30?" are introduced earlier. *Curriculum Focal Points* (NCTM, 2006) has fluency with multiplication and division of fractions placed at sixth grade. Fluency means that a student can not only do the algorithm, but also understands it and can model problems, solve situations that involve multiplication and division of fractions, and estimate.

It is important to emphasize the application component of fluency, as very few people have learned multiplication and division of fractions such that they are able to do much more than the basic procedure. If you fall in this category, then read the examples in this section carefully and try to solve the problems—many figures are provided to help illustrate the meaning of multiplication of fractions.

When working with whole numbers, we would say that 3 × 5 means "3 sets of 5" (repeated addition) or "3 rows of 5" (area or array). The first factor tells how much of the second factor you have or want. This is a good place to begin using contexts and simple story problems are a significant help in this development.

Developing the Concept

The story problems that you use to pose multiplication tasks to children need not be elaborate, but it is important to think about the numbers that you use in the problems. A possible progression of problem difficulty is developed in the sections that follow.

Fractions of Whole Numbers. Students' first experiences with multiplication should involve finding fractions of whole numbers. A challenging example is, "If the whole is 24, what is $\frac{3}{8}$ of the whole?" These reasoning tasks can lead into discussions of what multiplication of fractions means. Consider the following three problems as good starting tasks:

There are 15 cars in Michael's matchbox car collection. Two-thirds of the cars are red. How many red cars does Michael have?

How might students think through this problem? They might partition 15 into three groups, five in each group, and then see how many are in two groups. Recording this in symbols ($\frac{2}{3}$ of 15) gives the following result: $15 \div 3 \times 2$.

This can be adapted to involve a length context:

The walk from school to the public library takes 15 minutes. When I asked my mom how far we had gone, she said that we had gone $\frac{2}{3}$ of the way. Can you tell me how many minutes we have walked? (Assume constant walking rate.)

Tasks can have lower whole numbers—for example, $\frac{1}{4} \times 2$. What does this mean? How might you solve it? What about $\frac{1}{4} \times 5$? $\frac{3}{4}$ of 5?

Problems in which the first factor or multiplier is a whole number are also important.

Wayne filled 5 glasses with $\frac{2}{3}$ liter of soda in each glass. How much soda did Wayne use?

Notice that this situation is "5 groups of $\frac{2}{3}$" and not "$\frac{2}{3}$ of a group of 5." Although the commutative property means that these numbers can be switched, it is important that students understand each type as representations whose meanings are different. The problem might be solved in a counting-up strategy. It may be solved by repeated addition: $\frac{2}{3} + \frac{2}{3} + \frac{2}{3} + \frac{2}{3} + \frac{2}{3} = \frac{10}{3}$. Students may notice that what they did was multiply the numerator by 5, so $5 \times \frac{2}{3} = (5 \times 2)/3 = \frac{10}{3}$.

This problem may be solved in different ways. Some children will put the thirds together, making wholes as they go. Others will count all of the thirds and then find out how many whole liters are in 10 thirds.

Unit Parts Without Subdivisions. To expand on the ideas just presented, consider these three problems:

You have $\frac{3}{4}$ of a pizza left. If you give $\frac{1}{3}$ of the leftover pizza to your brother, how much of a whole pizza will your brother get?

Someone ate $\frac{1}{10}$ of the loaf of bread, leaving $\frac{9}{10}$. If you use $\frac{2}{3}$ of what is left to make French toast how much of a whole loaf will you have used?

Gloria used $2\frac{1}{2}$ tubes of blue paint to paint the sky in her picture. Each tube holds $\frac{4}{5}$ ounce of paint. How many ounces of blue paint did Gloria use?

Intentionally the units or fractional parts in these problems do not need to be subdivided further. The first problem is $\frac{1}{3}$ of three things, the second is $\frac{2}{3}$ of nine things, and the last is $2\frac{1}{2}$ of four things. The focus remains on the number of unit parts in all, and then the size of the parts determines the number of wholes. Figure 16.8 shows how problems of this type might be modeled. However, it is very important to let students model and solve these problems in their own way, using whatever models or drawings they choose. Require only that they be able to explain their reasoning.

Subdividing the Unit Parts. When the pieces must be subdivided into smaller unit parts, the problems become more challenging.

Zack had $\frac{2}{3}$ of the lawn left to cut. After lunch, he cut $\frac{3}{4}$ of the grass he had left. How much of the whole lawn did Zack cut after lunch?

The zookeeper had a huge bottle of the animals' favorite liquid treat, Zoo Cola. The monkey drank $\frac{1}{5}$ of the bottle. The zebra drank $\frac{2}{3}$ of what was left. How much of the bottle of Zoo Cola did the zebra drink?

❚❚ ———————— *Pause and Reflect*

Pause for a moment and figure out how you would solve each of these problems. Draw pictures to help you, but do not use a computational algorithm.

In Zack's lawn problem, it is necessary to find fourths of two things, the 2 *thirds* of the grass left to cut. In the Zoo Cola problem, you need thirds of four things, the 4 *fifths* of the cola that remain. Again, the concepts of the top number counting and the bottom number naming what is counted play an important role. Figure 16.9 shows a possible solution for Zack's lawn problem. A similar approach can be used

myeducationlab

Go to the Building Teaching Skills and Dispositions section of Chapter 16 of MyEducationLab. Click on Expanded Lessons to download the Expanded Lesson for "Using Visuals to Multiply Fractions" and complete the related activities.

Task	Finding the starting amount	Showing the fraction of the starting amount	Solution
Pizza Find $\frac{1}{3}$ of $\frac{3}{4}$ (of a pizza) or $\frac{1}{3} \times \frac{3}{4}$	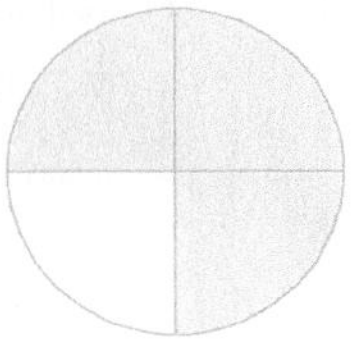	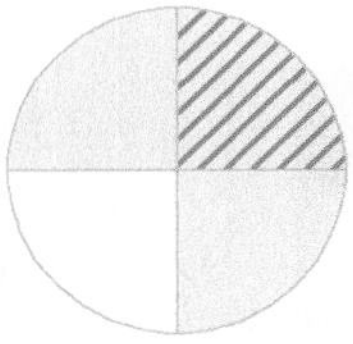	$\frac{1}{3}$ of the $\frac{3}{4}$ is $\frac{1}{4}$ of the original pizza. $\frac{1}{3} \times \frac{3}{4} = \frac{1}{4}$
Bread Find $\frac{2}{3}$ of $\frac{9}{10}$ (of a loaf of bread) or $\frac{2}{3} \times \frac{9}{10}$	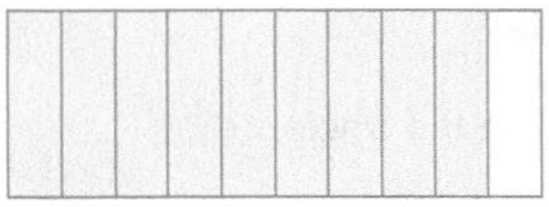	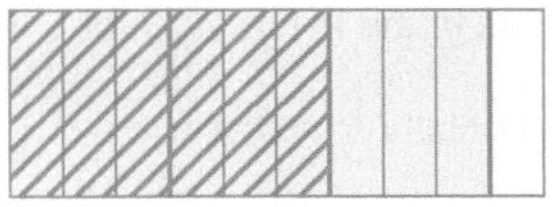	$\frac{2}{3}$ of the $\frac{9}{10}$ is 6 slices of the loaf or $\frac{6}{10}$ of the whole. $\frac{2}{3} \times \frac{9}{10} = \frac{6}{10}$
Paint Find $2\frac{1}{2}$ of $\frac{4}{5}$ (ounces of paint) or $2\frac{1}{2} \times \frac{4}{5}$		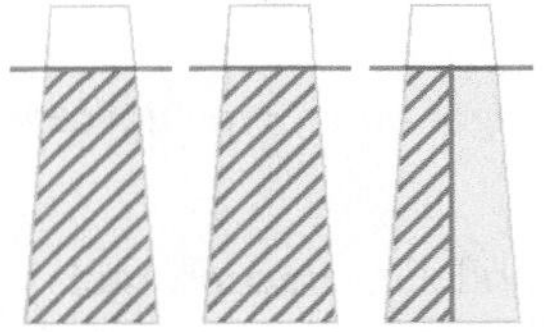	$2\frac{1}{2}$ of the $\frac{4}{5}$ is $\frac{4}{5} + \frac{4}{5} + \frac{2}{5} = \frac{10}{5}$

Figure 16.8 Models that illustrate three problems involving multiplication.

for the Zoo Cola problem. You may have used different drawings, but the ideas should be the same.

Using a paper strip and partitioning it is an effective way to solve multiplication problems, especially when they require additional partitioning (Siebert & Gaskin, 2006). Figure 16.9 illustrates how to use paper strips for the problem $\frac{3}{5} \times \frac{2}{3}$.

(*Three-fifths of $\frac{2}{3}$ of a whole is how much of a whole?*) Solving this problem requires that the thirds be subdivided.

Multiplication of fractions can be modeled with counters (see Figure 16.10). Do not discourage students from using counters, but be prepared to help them find ways to determine the whole.

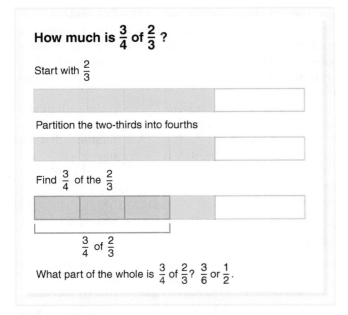

Figure 16.9 Solutions to a multiplication problem when the parts must be subdivided.

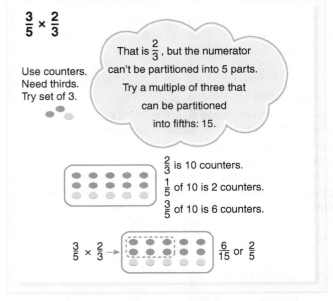

Figure 16.10 Modeling multiplication of fractions with counters.

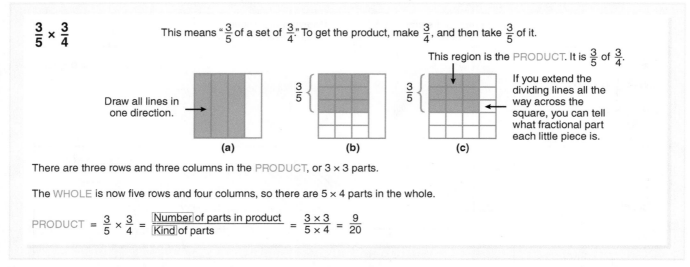

Figure 16.11 Development of the algorithm for multiplication of fractions.

Area Model. The area model for modeling fraction multiplication has several advantages. First, it works for problems where partitioning a length can get tedious. Second, it provides a nice visual to show that a result can be quite a bit smaller than either of the fractions used or that if the fractions are both close to 1, then the result is also close to one. Third, it is a good model for connecting to the standard algorithm for multiplying fractions.

Provide students with a square as in Figure 16.11 and ask them to illustrate the first fraction. For example in $\frac{3}{5} \times \frac{3}{4}$, you are finding $\frac{3}{5}$ of $\frac{3}{4}$, so you first must show $\frac{3}{4}$ (see Figure 16.11(a)). To find fifths of the $\frac{3}{4}$, draw five horizontal lines through the $\frac{3}{4}$ (see Figure 16.11(b)) or all the way across the square so that the whole is in the same-sized partitions (see Figure 16.11(c)).

To introduce the same example in a problem-based manner pose the following task (adapted from Imm, Stylianou, & Chae, 2008, p. 459):

Playground Problem

Two communities, A and B, are building playgrounds in lots that are 50 yards by 100 yards. In community A, they have been asked to convert $\frac{3}{4}$ of their lot to a playground and that $\frac{2}{5}$ of that playground should be covered with blacktop. In community B, they are instructed that they will build their playground on $\frac{2}{5}$ of the lot, and that $\frac{3}{4}$ of the playground should be blacktop. In which park is the playground bigger? In which lot is the blacktop bigger? Illustrate and explain.

Developing the Algorithm

With enough experiences in using the area model (or the linear model), students will start to notice a pattern.

Remember that "enough" is probably a lot more than is usually provided—in other words, this does not mean two or three examples, but several days, even weeks, working with different examples and problems. These exercises will lead students to focus on how the denominators relate to how the grid (or line) is partitioned and how the numerator affects the solution to the problem.

When students are ready to start using the algorithm, ask them to solve three examples such as the following:

$$\frac{5}{6} \times \frac{1}{2} \qquad \frac{3}{4} \times \frac{1}{5} \qquad \frac{1}{3} \times \frac{9}{10}$$

For each one, use a square and partition it vertically and horizontally to model the problems. Ask, "How did you figure out how what the unit of the fraction [the denominator] was?" Or more specifically, on the first problem, you can ask, "How did you figure out that the denominator would be twelfths? Is this a pattern that is true on the other examples?" Then ask students to see if they can find a similar pattern for how the number of parts is determined (the numerator).

As you are helping students focus on the pattern and learn to use the algorithm, do not forget to focus on the meaning of what they are doing. Ask questions that ask them to estimate how big they think the answer will be and why. In the first example here, a student might note that the answer will be slightly less than $\frac{1}{2}$ since $\frac{5}{6}$ is close to, but less than, 1.

Factors Greater Than One

As students are exploring multiplication, begin to include tasks in which one of the factors is a mixed number—for example, $\frac{3}{4} \times 2\frac{1}{2}$. Many textbooks have students change mixed numbers to improper fractions in order to multiply them. In fact, students can make improper fractions or use mixed numbers. Either way, area representations can be used to model the problem, as illustrated in Figure 16.12. This is an efficient way to solve these types of problems, but it is not the only way. Students who understand that $2\frac{1}{2}$ means $2 + \frac{1}{2}$ might multiply $\frac{3}{4} \times 2$ and $\frac{3}{4} \times \frac{1}{2}$ and add the results—the distributive property.

When both factors are mixed numbers, there are four partial products, just as there are when multiplying 2 two-digit numbers.

❚❚ ——————— *Pause and Reflect*

Find the four partial products in this multiplication: $3\frac{2}{3} \times 2\frac{1}{4}$.

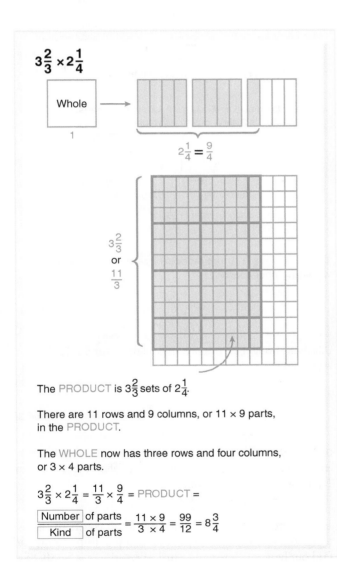

$3\frac{2}{3} \times 2\frac{1}{4}$

Whole
1

$2\frac{1}{4} = \frac{9}{4}$

$3\frac{2}{3}$ or $\frac{11}{3}$

The PRODUCT is $3\frac{2}{3}$ sets of $2\frac{1}{4}$.

There are 11 rows and 9 columns, or 11 × 9 parts, in the PRODUCT.

The WHOLE now has three rows and four columns, or 3 × 4 parts.

$3\frac{2}{3} \times 2\frac{1}{4} = \frac{11}{3} \times \frac{9}{4} = \text{PRODUCT} =$

$\dfrac{\boxed{\text{Number}} \text{ of parts}}{\boxed{\text{Kind}} \text{ of parts}} = \dfrac{11 \times 9}{3 \times 4} = \dfrac{99}{12} = 8\frac{3}{4}$

Figure 16.12 The same approach used to develop the algorithm for fractions less than 1 can be expanded to mixed numbers.

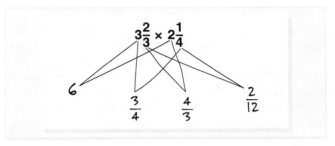

$3\frac{2}{3} \times 2\frac{1}{4}$

6   $\frac{3}{4}$ $\frac{4}{3}$ $\frac{2}{12}$

Figure 16.13 When multiplying two mixed numbers, there will be four partial products. These can then be added up to get the total product or an estimate may be enough. Here the answer is about 8.

Figure 16.13 shows how this product might be worked out by multiplying the individual parts. In most cases, the resulting fractions are not likely to be difficult to work with. More importantly, the process is more conceptual and also lends itself to estimation—either before the partial products are determined or after. Notice that the same four partial products of Figure 16.13 can be found in the rectangle in Figure 16.12.

Division

Invert the divisor and multiply is probably one of the most mysterious rules in elementary mathematics. We want to avoid this mystery at all costs. It makes sense to examine division with fractions from a more familiar perspective.

As with the other operations, go back to the meaning of division with whole numbers. Recall that there are two meanings of division: partitive and measurement (Gregg & Gregg, 2007; Krib-Zalita, 2008; Tirosh, 2000). We will review each briefly and look at some story problems that involve fractions. (Can you make up a word problem right now that would go with the computation $2\frac{1}{2} \div \frac{1}{4}$?)

You should have students explore both measurement and partitive problems. Here we will discuss each type of problem separately for the purpose of clarity. In the classroom, the types of problems should eventually be mixed. As with multiplication, how the numbers relate to each other in the problems tends to affect the difficulty.

Partitive Interpretation of Division

Too often we think of the partition problems strictly as sharing problems: 24 apples to be shared with 4 friends. How many will each friend get? This same sharing structure applies to rate problems: If you walk 12 miles in 3 hours, how many miles do you walk per hour? Both of these problems, in fact, are partition problems, asking the questions, "How much is one?" "How much is the amount for *one* friend?" "How many miles are walked in *one* hour?" The 24 is the amount for the 4 friends. The 12 miles is the amount for the 3 hours.

Whole-Number Divisors. Having the total amount be a fraction with the divisor a whole number is not really a big leap. These problems can still be thought of as sharing situations. However, as you work through these questions, notice that you are answering the question, "How much is the whole?" or "How much for one?"

Cassie has $5\frac{1}{3}$ yards of ribbon to make four bows for birthday packages. How much ribbon should she use for each bow if she wants to use the same length of ribbon for each?

When the $5\frac{1}{3}$ is thought of as fractional parts, there are 16 thirds to share, or 4 thirds for each ribbon. Alternatively, one might think of first allotting 1 yard per bow, leaving $1\frac{1}{3}$ yards. These 4 thirds are then shared, one per bow, for a total of $1\frac{1}{3}$ yards for each bow. The unit parts (thirds) required no further partitioning in order to do the division. In the following problem, the parts must be split into smaller parts.

Mark has $1\frac{1}{4}$ hours to finish his three household chores. If he divides his time evenly, how many hours can he give to each?

Note that the question is "How many hours for one chore?" The 5 fourths of an hour that Mark has do not split neatly into three parts. So some or all of the parts must be partitioned. Figure 16.14 shows three different models for figuring this out. In each case, all of the fourths are subdivided into three equal parts, producing twelfths. There are a total of 15 twelfths, or $\frac{5}{12}$ hour for each chore. (Test this answer against the solution in minutes: $1\frac{1}{4}$ hours is 75 minutes, which divided among 3 chores is 25 minutes per chore.)

Fractional Divisors. The sharing concept appears to break down when the divisor is a fraction. However, it is enormously helpful to keep in mind that for partition and rate problems the fundamental question is "How much is one?" For example, if 18 counters represents $2\frac{1}{4}$ sets, how much is one whole set? In solving these problems, the first task is to find the number in one-fourth and then multiply by 4 to get four-fourths or *one*. Let's see if we can see the same process in the following problem:

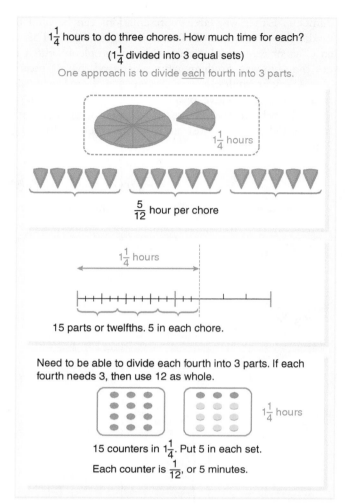

Figure 16.14 Three models of partition division with a whole-number divisor.

Elizabeth bought $3\frac{1}{3}$ pounds of tomatoes for $2.50. How much did she pay per pound?

Pause and Reflect

The given amount of $2.50 is distributed across $3\frac{1}{3}$ pounds. How much is distributed to 1 pound? Solve the problem the same way as you would a parts-and-whole problem. Try it now before reading on.

In $3\frac{1}{3}$ there are 10 thirds. Since the $2.50 covers (or is distributed across) ten-thirds, the first step is to partition and find out how much for one-third. If ten-thirds is $2.50, then one-third is $0.25. There are 3 thirds in one. Therefore, 75 cents must cover 1 pound, or 75 cents per pound.

Try the following problems using a similar strategy.

Dan paid $2.40 for a $\frac{3}{4}$-pound box of cereal. How much is that per pound?

Aidan found out that if she walks really fast during her morning exercise, she can cover $2\frac{1}{2}$ miles in $\frac{3}{4}$ of an hour. She wonders how fast she is walking in miles per hour.

With both problems, first find the amount of one-fourth (partitioning) and then the value of one whole (iterating). Aidan's walking problem is a bit harder because the $2\frac{1}{2}$ miles, or 5 half miles, do not neatly divide into three parts. If this was difficult for you, try dividing each half into three parts. Draw pictures or use models if that will help.

Measurement Interpretation of Division

The measurement interpretation is also called repeated subtraction or equal groups (NCTM, 2006a). In these situations an equal group is taken away from the total repeatedly. For example, *If you have 13 quarts of lemonade, how many canteens holding 3 quarts each can you fill?* Notice that this is not a sharing situation but rather an equal subtraction situation.

Since this is the concept of division that is almost always seen in textbooks and will be used to develop an algorithm for dividing fractions, it is important for students to explore this idea in contextual situations.

Students readily understand problems such as this:

You are going to a birthday party. From Ben and Jerry's ice cream factory, you order 6 pints of ice cream. If you serve $\frac{3}{4}$ of a pint of ice cream to each guest, how many guests can be served? (Schifter, Bastable, & Russell, 1999b, p. 120)

Students typically draw pictures of six items divided into fourths and count out how many servings of $\frac{3}{4}$ can be found. The difficulty is in seeing this as $6 \div \frac{3}{4}$, and that part will require some direct guidance on your part. One idea is to compare the problem to one involving whole numbers (6 pints, 2 per guest) and make a comparison.

Gregg and Gregg (2007) produced a method for developing the concept of division of fractions through servings, a measurement context. In tasks that progress in difficulty, they pose problems and include visuals of the size of the pieces. Figure 16.15 includes a subset of these tasks.

As the figure shows, moving very slowly to more complex examples will enable students to use their whole-number concepts to build an understanding of division with fractions. Over time students will be able to take

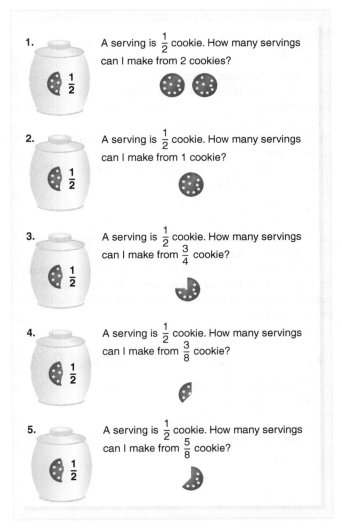

Figure 16.15 Tasks that use the measurement interpretation of "How many servings?" to develop the concept of division.
Source: Gregg, J., & Gregg, D. W. (2007). "Measurement and Fair-Sharing Models for Dividing Fractions." *Mathematics Teaching in the Middle School, 12*(9), p. 491. Reprinted with permission. Copyright © 2008 by the National Council of Teachers of Mathematics, Inc. www.nctm.org. All rights reserved.

on problems that are more complex in context and in the numbers involved, as in the following example.

Farmer Brown found that he had $2\frac{1}{4}$ gallons of liquid fertilizer concentrate. It takes $\frac{3}{4}$ gallon to make a tank of mixed fertilizer. How many tankfuls can he mix?

Try solving this problem yourself. Use any model or drawing you wish to help explain what you are doing. Notice that you are trying to find out *How many sets of 3 fourths are in a set of 9 fourths?* Your answer should be 3 tankfuls (not 3 fourths).

Answers That Are Not Whole Numbers

If Linda had 5 yards of material to make dresses needing $1\frac{1}{6}$ yards each, she could make only four dresses because a part of a dress does not make sense. But suppose that Farmer Brown began with 4 gallons of concentrate. After making five tanks of mix, he would have used $\frac{15}{4}$, or $3\frac{3}{4}$ gallons, of the concentrate. With the $\frac{1}{4}$ gallon remaining he could make a *partial* tank of mix. He could make $\frac{1}{3}$ of a tank of mix, since it takes *3* fourths to make a whole, and he has *1* fourth of a gallon.

Here is another problem to try:

John is building a patio. Each patio section requires $\frac{1}{3}$ of a cubic yard of concrete. The concrete truck holds $2\frac{1}{2}$ cubic yards of concrete. If there is not enough for a full section at the end, John can put in a divider and make a partial section. How many patio sections can John make with the concrete in the truck?

---

ll ———————————— *Pause and Reflect*

You should first try to solve this problem in some way that makes sense to *you*. Stop and do this now.

One way to do this is counting how many thirds in $2\frac{1}{2}$?

Here you can see that you get 3 patio sections from the yellow whole, 3 more from the orange whole, and then you get 1 more full section and $\frac{1}{2}$ of what you need for another patio section. So, the answer is $7\frac{1}{2}$. Students will want to write the "remainder" as $\frac{1}{3}$ since they were measuring in thirds, but the question is how many sections can be made—$7\frac{1}{2}$.

Will common denominators work for multiplication? Let's see. In the problem you just solved, $2\frac{1}{2} \div \frac{1}{3}$, the problem would become $2\frac{3}{6} \div \frac{2}{6}$, or it could be $\frac{15}{6} \div \frac{2}{6}$. The question becomes, *How many sets of 2 sixths are in a set of 15 sixths? Or, How many 2s in 15? 7½.* This is as efficient as the traditional algorithm, and it may make more sense to students to do it this way.

Figure 16.16 shows two division problems solved in this same way, each with a different model. That is, both the dividend or given quantity and the divisor are expressed in the same type of fractional parts. This results in a whole-number division problem. (In the concrete problem, after

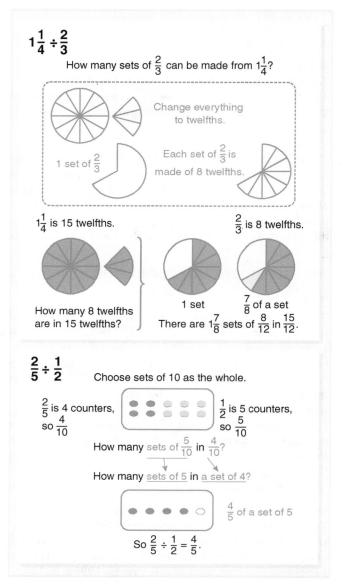

Figure 16.16 Common denominators can be used to solve division of fraction problems.

changing the numbers to twelfths, the answer is the same as $15 \div 8$.) In the classroom, after students have solved problems such as this using their own methods, suggest this common-unit approach.

Developing the Algorithms

There are two different algorithms for division of fractions. Methods of teaching both algorithms are discussed here.

Common-Denominator Algorithm. The common-denominator algorithm relies on the measurement or repeated subtraction concept of division. Consider the problem $\frac{5}{3} \div \frac{1}{2}$. As shown in Figure 16.17, once each number

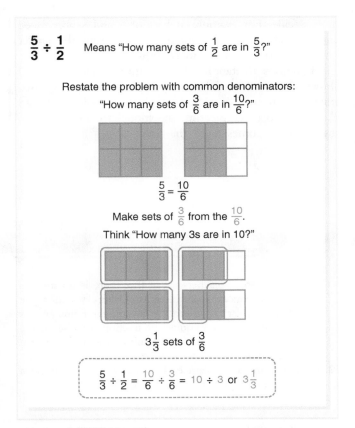

Figure 16.17 Models for the common-denominator method for fraction division.

is expressed in terms of the same fractional part, the answer is exactly the same as the whole-number problem 10 ÷ 3. The name of the fractional part (the denominator) is no longer important, and the problem is one of dividing the numerators. The resulting algorithm, therefore, is as follows: *To divide fractions, first get common denominators, and then divide numerators.* For example, $\frac{5}{3} \div \frac{1}{4} = \frac{20}{12} \div \frac{3}{12} = 20 \div 3 = \frac{20}{3} = 6\frac{2}{3}$.

Try using circular fraction pieces, fraction strips, and then sets of counters to model $1\frac{2}{3} \div \frac{3}{4}$ using a common-denominator approach.

Invert-and-Multiply Algorithm. To invert the divisor and multiply may be one of the most poorly understood procedures in the K–8 curriculum. (Do you know why invert-and-multiply works?) Interestingly, in a much discussed study of Chinese and U.S. teachers, Liping Ma (1999) found that most Chinese teachers not only use and teach this algorithm, but they also understand why it works. U.S. teachers were found to be sadly lacking in their understanding of fraction division.

Providing a series of tasks and having students look for patterns in how they are finding the answers can help students discover the algorithm. For example, consider this

first set, in which the divisor is a unit fraction. Remember to pose the related question that goes with each equation. Servings of food can be the context.

$3 \div \frac{1}{2}$ = (How many servings of $\frac{1}{2}$ in 3 containers?)

$5 \div \frac{1}{4}$ = (How many servings of $\frac{1}{4}$ in 5 containers?)

$3\frac{3}{4} \div \frac{1}{2}$ = (How many servings of $\frac{1}{2}$ in $3\frac{3}{4}$ containers?)

$6 \div \frac{1}{3}$ = (How many servings of $\frac{1}{3}$ in 6 containers?)

$8 \div \frac{1}{5}$ = (How many servings of $\frac{1}{5}$ in $8\frac{1}{2}$ containers?)

In looking across these problems (and more if you are working with students) and looking for a pattern, students will notice they are multiplying by the denominator of the second fraction. For example, in the last example, a student might say, "You get five for every whole container, so 5×8 is 40."

Then take similar problems, but with a second fraction that is not a unit fraction:

$5 \div \frac{3}{4}$ =

$6 \div \frac{2}{3}$ =

$8 \div \frac{2}{5}$ =

Have students compare these responses to the corresponding problems in the first set. Notice that if there are 40 one-fifths in 8, then when you group the fifths in pairs (two-fifths), you will have half as many—20. Stated in servings, if the serving is twice as big, you will have half the number of servings. Similarly, if the fraction is $\frac{3}{4}$, after finding how many fourths, you will group in threes, which means you will get $\frac{1}{3}$ the number of servings. You can see that this means you must divide by 3.

The examples given were measurements because the size of the group (serving) was known, but not the number of groups. Using partitioning, or sharing, examples nicely illustrates the standard algorithm. Consider this example:

You have $1\frac{1}{2}$ oranges, which is $\frac{3}{5}$ of an adult serving. How many oranges (and parts of oranges) make up 1 adult serving? (Kribs-Zaleta, 2008)

You may be thinking that you first need to find what one fifth would be—which would be one-third of the oranges you have—or $\frac{1}{2}$ an orange (notice you are dividing by the numerator). Then, to get the whole serving you multiply $\frac{1}{2}$ by 5 (the denominator) to get $2\frac{1}{2}$ oranges in 1 adult serving.

In either the measurement or the partitive interpretations, the denominator leads you to find out how many fifths, eighths, or sixths you have, and the numerator tells you the size of the serving, so you group according to how many are in the serving. So the process means to multiply by the denominator and divide by the numerator. At some point someone thought, well, if they just flip the fraction, then it would be more straightforward—multiplying by the top and dividing by the bottom—and that is why we have learned to "invert and multiply."

 The NLVM website (http://nlvm.usu.edu/en/nav/NAV/vlibrary.html) has a nice collection of fraction applets. Number Line Bars-Fractions allows the user to place bars of any fractional length along a number line. The number line can be adjusted to have increments from $\frac{1}{2}$ to $\frac{1}{15}$, but the user

must decide. For example, if bars of $\frac{1}{4}$ and $\frac{1}{3}$ are placed end to end, the result cannot be read from the applet until the increments are in twelfths.

Fractions Rectangle Multiplication (also at NLVM) shows the area model for multiplication of any two fractions up to 2 × 2. Although the applet does an excellent job of connecting the model to the equation, the thinking comes from the user. ◆

Reflections

Writing to Learn

1. When should estimation of fraction computation be taught to students? Why is it important to teach computational estimation with fractions?
2. A student adds $\frac{4}{5} + \frac{2}{3}$ and gets $\frac{6}{8}$. How will you help the student understand that this is incorrect and how would you redirect him or her to do it correctly?
3. For the problem $3\frac{1}{4} - 1\frac{1}{2}$ think of a story problem that would be a "take away" situation and one that would be a "comparison" situation.
4. Explain at least one mental method (estimation or mental computation) for each of these:

$$\frac{3}{4} \times 5\frac{1}{2} \qquad 1\frac{1}{8} \text{ of } 40$$

5. Make up a word problem with a fraction as a divisor. Is your problem a measurement problem or a partition problem? Make up a second word problem with fractions of the other type (measurement or partition).

For Discussion and Exploration

1. Imagine teaching fraction computation in the sixth or seventh grade, a subject required by your curriculum. You quickly find that your students have a very weak understanding of fractions. Your textbook primarily targets the

algorithms. Some teachers argue that there is no time to reteach the concepts of fractions. Others would argue that it is necessary to teach the meanings of numerators and denominators and equivalent fractions or else all the computation will be meaningless rules. How will you plan for instruction? Justify your approach.
2. Draw pictures to explain each of these divisions using a measurement approach:

$$\frac{2}{4} \div \frac{1}{4} \qquad 2\frac{1}{3} \div \frac{2}{3} \qquad \frac{3}{4} \div \frac{1}{8} \qquad 2\frac{3}{4} \div \frac{2}{3}$$

In the second and fourth examples, the answer is not a whole number. To help you explain the fractional part of the answer, use a set of counters to explain why $13 \div 5 = 2\frac{3}{5}$, also using a measurement approach. (That is, how many sets of 5 are in a set of 13?) Use the same problems and explain a common-denominator algorithm for division. Use the same rationale to explain why $\frac{13}{79} \div \frac{5}{79} = 13 \div 5 = \frac{13}{5}$.
3. Several calculators are now available that do computations in fractional form as well as in decimal form. Some of these automatically give results in simplest terms. If you have access to such a calculator, discuss how it might be used in teaching fractions and especially fraction computation. If such calculators become commonplace, should we continue to teach fraction computation?

Resources

Literature Connections

Alice's Adventures in Wonderland
Carroll, 1865/1982

This well-known children's story needs no introduction. Because Alice shrinks in the story, there is an opportunity to explore multiplication by fractions. S. B. Taber (2007)

describes in detail how she used this story to engage students in understanding the meaning of multiplication of fractions. She begins by asking if Alice was originally 54" tall, but was shrunk to $\frac{1}{9}$ of her height, how tall would she be? Later, what if she was restored, but to only $\frac{5}{6}$ her original height? The students were then asked to write their own Alice explanations to multiplication equations.

The Man Who Made Parks *Wishinsky, 1999*

This nonfiction novel explains the remarkable story of Frederick Olmsted, who decided he was going to design a park for New York City—what became Central Park. Creating a park design, students can be given fractional amounts for what needs to be included in the park—for example, $\frac{2}{5}$ gardens, $\frac{1}{10}$ playgrounds, $\frac{1}{2}$ natural habitat (streams and forest), and the rest special features (like a baseball arena). Students can build the plan for their park on a rectangular grid. To include multiplication of fractions include guidelines such as that $\frac{3}{4}$ of the park is natural habitat, with $\frac{1}{3}$ of that to be wooded and $\frac{1}{6}$ to be water features, and so on.

Recommended Readings

Articles

Cramer, K., Wyberg, T., & Leavitt, S. (2008). The role of representations in fraction addition and subtraction. *Mathematics Teaching in the Middle School, 13*(8), 490–496.

This article provides illustrations and student work to show how to teach addition using the fraction circle. Essential considerations of effective instruction are emphasized.

Gregg, J., & Gregg, D. U. (2007). Measurement and fair-sharing models for dividing fractions. *Mathematics Teaching in the Middle School, 12*(9), 490–496.

These authors provide specific series of tasks to develop the concept of division of fractions—a must read for a teacher needing more experiences exploring division or trying to plan a good sequence for her students.

Huinker, D. (1998). Letting fraction algorithms emerge through problem solving. In L. J. Morrow (Ed.), *The teaching and learning of algorithms in school mathematics* (pp. 170–182). Reston, VA: NCTM.

Huinker takes the idea of students inventing algorithms as described for whole numbers in Chapter 12 and applies it to problems involving fractions. With examples of children's work, this article makes a good case for avoiding rules and letting students work with ideas that make sense.

Imm, K. L., Stylianou, D. A., & Chae, N. (2008). Student representations at the center: Promoting classroom equity. *Mathematics Teaching in the Middle School, 13*(8), 458–463.

These authors explain how to use a park context to teach multiplication of fractions. Equity and a culture for learning are at the center of their discussion of the lessons.

Perlwitz, M. D. (2005). Dividing fractions: Reconciling self-generated solutions with algorithmic answers. *Mathematics Teaching in the Middle School, 10*(6), 278–282.

On the surface, this article is about dealing with the remainder in fraction division. The discussion gets at the importance of understanding algorithms, wrestling with the minimal knowledge that many teachers bring to this subject, and the value of classroom discourse.

Online Resources

Diffy
http://nlvm.usu.edu/en/nav/frames_asid_326_g_3_t_1.html

The goal in a Diffy puzzle is to find differences between the numbers on the corners of the square, working to a desired difference in the center. When working with fractions, the difference of two fractions is a fraction that can be written in many different ways and students must recognize equivalent forms.

Fraction Bars
http://nlvm.usu.edu/en/nav/frames_asid_203_g_2_t_1.html

Much like Cuisenaire rods, this applet places bars over a number line on which the step size can be adjusted, providing a flexible model that can be used for all four operations.

Fractions—Adding
http://nlvm.usu.edu/en/nav/frames_asid_106_g_2_t_1.html

Two fractions and an area model for each are given. The user must find a common denominator to rename and add the fractions.

Field Experience Guide Connections

The link sheet in FEG 3.4 is an excellent planning tool and an assessment tool, as it focuses on four representations for a topic such as multiplication of fractions. Both FEG 3.4 and FEG 7.2 could be used to interview students to find out what they know about fraction computation. FEG Expanded Lessons 9.7 and 9.9 are designed to help students understand fraction multiplication and division, respectively. In addition, FEG 10.3 ("Factor Quest"), which targets factors, and FEG 10.4 ("Interference"), which targets multiples, are good activities to use when teaching computation of fractions.

Developing Concepts of Decimals and Percents

From Chapter 17 of *Elementary and Middle School Mathematics: Teaching Developmentally*, 7/e. John A. Van de Walle.
Karen S. Karp. Jennifer M. Bay-Williams. Copyright © 2010 by Pearson Allyn and Bacon. All rights reserved.

Developing Concepts of Decimals and Percents

The U.S. curriculum typically follows the recommendations of the *Curriculum Focal Points* (NCTM, 2006) and introduces decimals in the fourth grade, with most of the computation work on decimals occurring in the fifth grade and repeated later in grades 6 and 7. This fractions-first, decimals-later sequence is arguably the best approach. However, the unfortunate fact is that the topics of fractions and decimals are too often developed separately. Linking the ideas of fractions to decimals can be extremely useful, both from a pedagogical view as well as a practical view. Most of this chapter focuses on that connection.

Big Ideas

1. Decimal numbers are simply another way of writing fractions. Both notations have value. Maximum flexibility is gained by understanding how the two symbol systems are related.

2. The base-ten place-value system extends infinitely in two directions: to tiny values as well as to large values. Between any two place values, the ten-to-one ratio remains the same.

3. The decimal point is a convention that has been developed to indicate the units position. The position to the left of the decimal point is the unit that is being counted as singles or ones.

4. Percents are simply hundredths and as such are a third way of writing both fractions and decimals.

5. Addition and subtraction with decimals are based on the fundamental concept of adding and subtracting the numbers in like position values—a simple extension from whole numbers.

6. Multiplication and division of two numbers will produce the same digits, regardless of the positions of the decimal point. As a result, for most practical purposes, there is no reason to develop new rules for decimal multiplication and division. Rather, the computations can be performed as whole numbers with the decimal placed by way of estimation.

Mathematics Content Connections

The most important connections for decimals are built within this chapter—between decimal numbers and the concepts of fractions.

- **Fraction Concepts:** Both decimal and fraction symbolism represents the same ideas—the rational numbers.

- **Proportional Thinking:** Percents are a part-to-whole ratio and can be extended to proportion concepts.

- **Measurement:** The metric system is modeled after the base-ten system, and all metric measures are expressed in decimals rather than fractions. Conversion from one metric measure to another is quite simple, given an understanding of the decimal system.

- **Real Number System:** Decimal numeration is helpful in characterizing and understanding the density of the rational numbers and also for approximating irrational numbers.

Connecting Fractions and Decimals

In a world where almost everything can be measured, people need to be able to interpret decimals for such varied needs as reading metric measures, calculating distances, or understanding sports statistics such as those at the Olympics where winners and losers are separated by hundredths of a second and in baseball where hitters (and fans) evaluate performances to thousandths of points. Decimals are important in many occupations, ranging from nurses and pharmacists to workers building airplanes where the level of precision impacts safety for the general public. Because children have been shown to have greater difficulty understanding decimals than fractions (Martinie, 2007), conceptual understanding of decimals and their connections to fractions must be carefully developed.

The symbols 3.75 and $3\frac{3}{4}$ represent the same quantity, yet on the surface the two appear quite different. For children especially, the world of fractions and the world of decimals are very distinct. Even adults tend to think of fractions as sets or regions (three-fourths *of* something), whereas we think of decimals as being more like numbers. When we tell children that 0.75 is the same as $\frac{3}{4}$, this can be especially confusing because in decimal fractions, the denominators are hidden. Even though different ways of writing the numbers have been invented, the numbers themselves are not different. A significant goal of instruction in decimal and fraction numeration should be to help students see that both systems represent the same concepts.

There are at least three ways to help students see the connection between fractions and decimals. First, we can use familiar fraction concepts and models to explore rational numbers that are easily represented by decimals: tenths, hundredths, and thousandths. Second, we can help them see how the base-ten system can be extended to include numbers less than 1 as well as large numbers. Third, we can help children use models to make meaningful translations between fractions and decimals. These three components are discussed in turn.

Base-Ten Fractions

Fractions with denominators of 10, 100, 1000, and so on will be referred to in this chapter as *base-ten fractions*. This is simply a convenient label and is not one commonly found in the literature. Fractions such as $\frac{7}{10}$ or $\frac{63}{100}$ are examples of base-ten fractions.

Base-Ten Fraction Models. Most of the common manipulative models for fractions are somewhat limited for the purpose of depicting base-ten fractions. Generally, the familiar fraction models cannot show hundredths or thousandths. It is important to provide models for these fractions using the same conceptual approaches that were used for fractions such as thirds and fourths.

Two very useful region models can be used to model base-ten fractions. First, to model tenths and hundredths, circular disks such as the one shown in Figure 17.1 can be printed on cardstock (see Blackline Master 28). Each disk is marked with 100 equal intervals around the edge and is cut along one radius. Two disks of different colors, slipped together as shown, can be used to model any fraction less than 1. Fractions modeled on this rational number wheel can be read as base-ten fractions by noting the spaces around the edge but are still reminiscent of the traditional circle model.

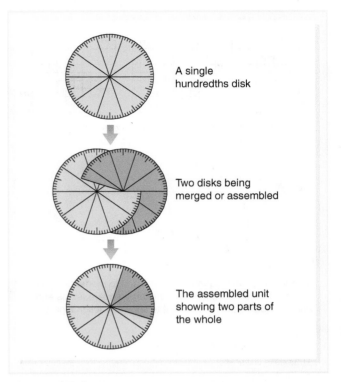

A single hundredths disk

Two disks being merged or assembled

The assembled unit showing two parts of the whole

Figure 17.1 Rational number wheel. For example, turn the wheel to show $\frac{25}{100}$ on the blue plate (also $\frac{1}{4}$ of the circle) (see Blackline Master 28).

However, the most common regional model for base-ten fractions is a 10 × 10 square (see Figure 17.2 and Blackline Master 27). An important variation is to use base-ten place-value strips and squares. As a fraction model, the 10-cm square that was used as the hundreds model for whole numbers is taken as the whole or 1. Each strip is then 1 tenth, and each small square is 1 hundredth. Blackline Master 29 provides a large square that is subdivided into 10,000 tiny squares. When shown on an overhead projector, individual squares or ten-thousandths can easily be identified and shaded in with a pen.

One of the best length models is a meter stick. Each decimeter is one-tenth of the whole stick, each centimeter is one-hundredth, and each millimeter is one-thousandth. Any number-line model broken into 100 subparts is likewise a useful model for hundredths.

Blank number lines are also very useful in helping students compare decimals and think about scale and place value (Martinie & Bay Williams, 2003). Given two or more decimals, students can use the blank number line to position the values, revealing what they know about the size of these decimals using zero, one, other whole numbers, or other decimal values as benchmarks. Again, the use of multiple representations will broaden not only students' understanding but your understanding of their level of performance.

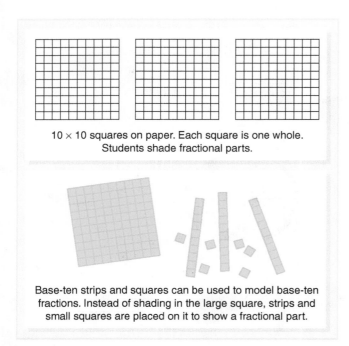

10 × 10 squares on paper. Each square is one whole. Students shade fractional parts.

Base-ten strips and squares can be used to model base-ten fractions. Instead of shading in the large square, strips and small squares are placed on it to show a fractional part.

Figure 17.2 10 × 10 squares model base-ten fractions (see Blackline Master 27).

Many teachers use money as a model for decimals, and to some extent this is helpful. However, for children, money is almost exclusively a two-place system: Numbers like 3.2 or 12.1389 do not relate to money and can cause confusion (Martinie, 2007). Children's initial contact with decimals should be more flexible, and so money is not recommended as a decimal model, at least not at the introductory level. Money is certainly an important *application* of decimal numeration.

Multiple Names and Formats. Early work with base-ten fractions is designed primarily to acquaint students with the models, to help them begin to think of quantities in terms of tenths and hundredths, and to learn to read and write base-ten fractions in different ways.

Have students show a base-ten fraction using any base-ten fraction model. Once a fraction, say, $\frac{65}{100}$, is modeled, the following ideas can be explored:

- Is this fraction more or less than $\frac{1}{2}$? Than $\frac{2}{3}$? Than $\frac{3}{4}$? Some familiarity with base-ten fractions can be developed by comparison with fractions that are easy to think about.
- What are some different ways to say this fraction using tenths and hundredths? ("6 tenths and 5 hundredths," "65 hundredths") Include thousandths when appropriate.

- Show two ways to write this fraction ($\frac{65}{100}$ or $\frac{6}{10} + \frac{5}{100}$).

The last two questions are very important. When base-ten fractions are later written as decimals, they are usually read as a single fraction. That is, 0.65 is read "sixty-five hundredths." But to understand them in terms of place value, the same number must be thought of as 6 tenths and 5 hundredths. A mixed number such as $\frac{513}{100}$ is usually read the same way as a decimal: 5.13 is "five and thirteen-hundredths." Please note that it is accurate to use the word "and," which represents your decimal point. For purposes of place value, it should also be understood as $5 + \frac{1}{10} + \frac{3}{100}$.

The expanded forms will be helpful in translating these fractions to decimals. Given a model or a written or oral fraction, students should be able to give the other two forms of the fraction, including equivalent forms where appropriate.

Extending the Place-Value System

Before considering decimal numerals with students, it is advisable to review some ideas of whole-number place value. One of the most basic of these ideas is the 10-to-1 relationship between the value of any two adjacent positions. In terms of a base-ten model such as strips and squares, 10 of any one piece will make 1 of the next larger, and vice versa.

A Two-Way Relationship. The 10-makes-1 rule continues indefinitely to larger and larger pieces or positional values. If you are using the strip-and-square model, for example, the strip and square shapes alternate in an infinite progression as they get larger and larger. Having established the progression to larger pieces, focus on the idea that each piece to the right in this string gets smaller by one-tenth. The critical question becomes "Is there ever a smallest piece?" In the students' experience, the smallest piece is the centimeter square or unit piece. But couldn't even that piece be divided into 10 small strips? And couldn't these small strips be divided into 10 very small squares, and so on? In the mind's eye, there is no smallest strip or smallest square.

The goal of this discussion is to help students see that a 10-to-1 relationship can extend *infinitely in two directions*. There is no smallest piece and no largest piece. The relationship between adjacent pieces is the same regardless of which two adjacent pieces are being considered. Figure 17.3 illustrates this idea.

The Role of the Decimal Point. An important idea to be realized in this discussion is that there is no built-in reason

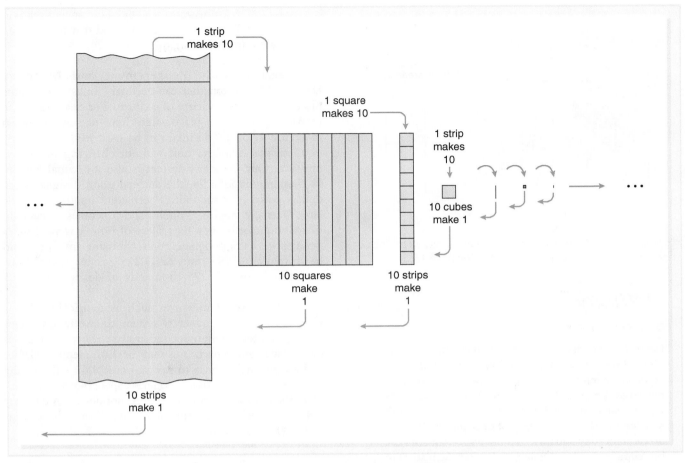

Figure 17.3 Theoretically, the strips and squares extend infinitely in both directions.

why any one position (or base-ten piece) should naturally be chosen to be the unit or ones position. In terms of strips and squares, for example, which piece is the ones piece? The small centimeter square? Why? Why not a larger or a smaller square? Why not a strip? *Any piece could effectively be chosen as the ones piece.*

As shown in Figure 17.4, a given quantity can be written in different ways, depending on the choice of the unit or what piece is used to count the entire collection. The decimal point is placed between two positions with the convention that the position to the left of the decimal is the units or ones position. Thus, the role of the decimal point is *to designate the units position,* and it does so by sitting just to the right of that position.

A fitting caricature for the decimal is shown in Figure 17.5. The "eyes" of the decimal always focus up toward the name of the units or ones. If the "smiling" decimal point were placed between the squares and strips in Figure 17.4, the squares would then be designated as the units, and 16.24 would be the correct written form for the model.

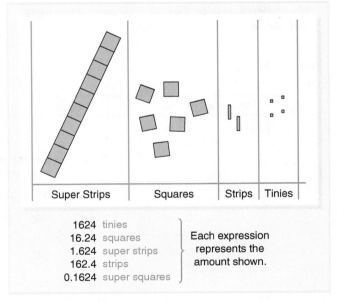

1624	tinies
16.24	squares
1.624	super strips
162.4	strips
0.1624	super squares

Each expression represents the amount shown.

Figure 17.4 The placement of the decimal point indicates which position is the units.

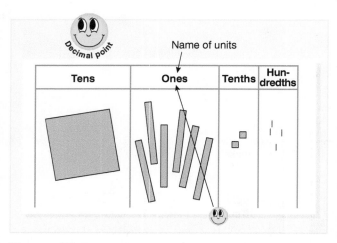

Figure 17.5 The decimal point always "looks up at" the name of the units position. In this case, we have 16.24.

Activity 17.1

The Decimal Names the Unit

Have students display a certain number of base-ten pieces on their desks. For example, put out three squares, seven strips, and four tinies. Refer to the pieces as "squares," "strips," and "tinies," and reach an agreement on names for the theoretical pieces both smaller and larger. To the right of tinies can be "tiny strips" and "tiny squares." To the left of squares can be "super strips" and "super squares." Each student should also have a smiling decimal point. Now ask students to write and say how many squares they have, how many super strips, and so on, as in Figure 17.4. The students position their decimal point accordingly and both write and say the amounts.

Activity 17.1 illustrates vividly the convention that the decimal indicates the named unit and that the unit can change without changing the quantity.

The Decimal with Measurement and Monetary Units. The notion that the decimal "looks at the units place" is useful in a variety of contexts. For example, in the metric system, seven place values have names. As shown in Figure 17.6, the decimal can be used to designate any of these places as the unit without changing the actual measure. Our monetary system is also a decimal system. In the amount $172.95, the decimal point designates the dollars position as the unit. There are 1 hundred (of dollars), 7 tens, 2 singles, 9 dimes, and 5 pennies or cents in this amount of money regardless of how it is written. If pennies were the designated unit, the same amount would be written as 17,295 cents or 17,295.0 cents. It could just as correctly be 0.17295 thousands of dollars or 1729.5 dimes.

In the case of measures such as metric lengths or weights or the U.S. monetary system, the name of the unit is written after the number rather than above the digit as on a place-value chart. You may be 1.62 meters tall, but it does not make sense to say you are "1.62 tall." In the paper, we may read about Congress spending $7.3 billion. Here the units are billions of dollars, not dollars. A city may have a population of 2.4 million people. That is the same as 2,400,000 individuals.

Fraction-Decimal Connection

To connect fractions and decimals, students should make concept-oriented translations—that is, translations based on understanding rather than a rule or algorithm. The purpose of such activities has less to do with the skill of

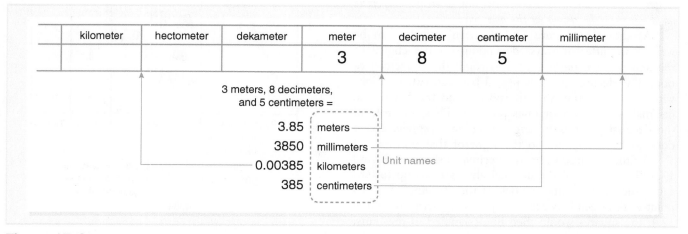

Figure 17.6 In the metric measurement system, each place-value position has a name. The decimal point can be placed to designate which length is the unit length. Again, the decimal point will "look up" at the unit length. The arrows point to the corresponding location of the decimal point.

converting a fraction to a decimal than with construction of the concept that both systems are used to express the same ideas. The place to begin is with base-ten fractions.

Activity 17.2

Base-Ten Fractions to Decimals

For this activity, have students use their place-value strips and squares (Blackline Master 14). Agree that the large square represents one. Have students cover a base-ten fractional amount of the square using their strips and tinies. For example, have them cover $2\frac{35}{100}$ of the square. Whole numbers require additional squares. The task is to decide how to write this fraction as a decimal and demonstrate the connection using their physical models.

For the last activity, a typical (and correct) reason why $2\frac{35}{100}$ is the same as 2.35 is that there are 2 wholes, 3 tenths, and 5 hundredths. It is important to see this physically. The exact same materials that are used to represent $2\frac{35}{100}$ of the square can be rearranged or placed on an imaginary place-value chart with a paper decimal point used to designate the units position as shown in Figure 17.7.

The reverse of this activity is also worthwhile. Give students a decimal number such as 1.68 and have them show it with base-ten pieces. Their task is to write it as a fraction and show it as a fractional part of a square.

Although these translations between decimals and base-ten fractions are rather simple, the main agenda is

for students to learn from the beginning that decimals are simply fractions.

The calculator can also play a significant role in decimal concept development.

Activity 17.3

Calculator Decimal Counting

Recall how to make the calculator "count" by pressing ⊞ 1 ⊟ ⊟ . . . Now have students press ⊞ 0.1 ⊟ ⊟ . . . When the display shows 0.9, stop and discuss what this means and what the display will look like with the next press. Many students will predict 0.10 (thinking that 10 comes after 9). This prediction is even more interesting if, with each press, the students have been accumulating base-ten strips as models for tenths. One more press would mean one more strip, or 10 strips. Why should the calculator not show 0.10? When the tenth press produces a display of 1 (calculators are not usually set to display trailing zeros to the right of the decimal), the discussion should revolve around trading 10 strips for a square. Continue to count to 4 or 5 by tenths. How many presses to get from one whole number to the next? Try counting by 0.01 or by 0.001. These counts illustrate dramatically how small one-hundredth and one-thousandth really are. It requires 10 counts by 0.001 to get to 0.01 and 1000 counts to reach 1.

The fact that the calculator counts 0.8, 0.9, 1, 1.1 instead of 0.8, 0.9, 0.10, 0.11 should give rise to the question "Does this make sense? If so, why?"

Calculators that permit entry of fractions also have a fraction-decimal conversion key. On some calculators a decimal such as 0.25 will convert to the base-ten fraction $\frac{25}{100}$ and allow for either manual or automatic simplification. Graphing calculators can be set so that the conversion is either with or without simplification. The ability of fraction calculators to go back and forth between fractions and decimals makes them a valuable tool as students begin to connect fraction and decimal symbolism.

Developing Decimal Number Sense

So far, the discussion has revolved around the connection of decimals with base-ten fractions. Number sense implies more. It means having intuition about or a friendly understanding of numbers. To this end, it is useful to connect decimals to the fractions with which children are familiar, to be able to compare and order decimals readily, and to approximate decimals with useful familiar numbers.

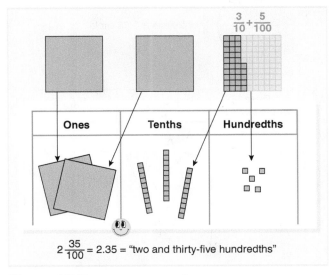

$2\frac{35}{100} = 2.35 = $ "two and thirty-five hundredths"

Figure 17.7 Translation of a base-ten fraction to a decimal.

Familiar Fractions Connected to Decimals

An earlier chapter showed how to help students develop a conceptual familiarity with simple fractions, especially halves, thirds, fourths, fifths, and eighths. We should extend this familiarity to the same concepts expressed as decimals. One way to do this is to have students translate familiar fractions to decimals by means of a base-ten model.

The following two activities have the same purpose—to help students think of decimals in terms of familiar fraction equivalents and to make this connection in a conceptual manner.

Activity 17.4

Friendly Fractions to Decimals

Students are given a "friendly" fraction to convert to a decimal. They first model the fraction using either a 10 × 10 grid or the base-ten strips and squares. With the model as a guide, they then write and draw an explanation for the decimal equivalent. If strips and squares are used, be sure that students draw pictures as part of their explanations.

A good sequence is to start with halves and fifths, then fourths, and possibly eighths. Thirds are best done as a special activity.

Figure 17.8 shows how translations in the last activity might go with a 10 × 10 grid. For fourths, students will often shade a 5 × 5 section (half of a half). The question then becomes how to translate this to decimals. Ask these students how they would cover $\frac{1}{4}$ with strips and squares if they were only permitted to use nine or fewer tinies. The fraction $\frac{3}{8}$ represents a wonderful challenge. A hint might be to find $\frac{1}{4}$ first and then notice that $\frac{1}{8}$ is half of a fourth. Remember that the next smaller pieces are tenths of the little squares. Therefore, a half of a little square is $\frac{5}{1000}$.

Because the circular model carries such a strong mental link to fractions, it is well worth the time to do some fraction-to-decimal conversions with the rational number wheel shown in Figure 17.1 (see Blackline Master 28).

Activity 17.5

Estimate, Then Verify

With the blank side of the wheel facing them, have students adjust the wheel to show a particular friendly fraction, for example, $\frac{3}{4}$. Next they turn the wheel over and record how many hundredths they estimate were in the section (note that the color reverses when the wheel is turned over). Finally, they should make an argument for the correct number of hundredths and the corresponding decimal equivalent.

The estimation component of the last activity adds the visual "feeling" for fractions. In one fifth-grade class that was having difficulty finding a decimal equivalent for their rational number wheel fraction, the teacher cut up some extra disks into tenths and hundredths so that these parts of the fraction could be placed on a chart (see Figure 17.9).

The exploration of modeling $\frac{1}{3}$ as a decimal is a good introduction to the concept of an infinitely repeating decimal.

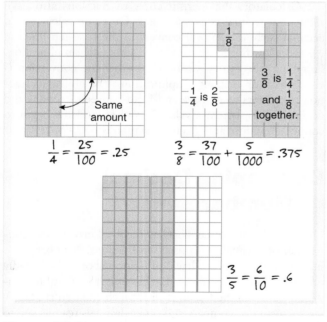

Figure 17.8 Familiar fractions converted to decimals using a 10 × 10 square.

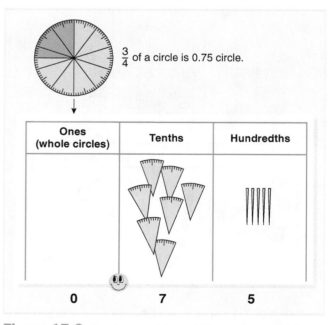

Figure 17.9 Fraction models could be decimal models.

Try to partition the whole 10 × 10 square into 3 parts using strips and little squares. Each part receives 3 strips with 1 strip left over. To divide the leftover strip, each part gets 3 little squares with 1 left over. To divide the little square, each part gets 3 small strips with 1 left over. (Recall that with base-ten pieces, each smaller piece must be $\frac{1}{10}$ of the preceding size piece.) It becomes obvious that this process is never-ending. As a result, $\frac{1}{3}$ is the same as 0.333333 . . . or $0.\overline{3}$. For practical purposes, $\frac{1}{3}$ is about 0.333. Similarly, $\frac{2}{3}$ is a repeating string of sixes, or about 0.667. Later, students will discover that many fractions cannot be represented by a finite decimal.

The number line is another good connecting model. Students are more apt to think of decimals as numbers that appear on the number line than they are to think of fractions in that way. The following activity continues the development of fraction-decimal equivalences.

Activity 17.6

Decimals on a Friendly Fraction Line

Give students five decimal numbers that have friendly fraction equivalents. Keep the numbers between two consecutive whole numbers. For example, use 3.5, 3.125, 3.4, 3.75, and 3.66. Show a number line encompassing the same whole numbers. The subdivisions on the number line should be only fourths, only thirds, or only fifths but without labels. The students' task is to locate each of the decimal numbers on the number line and to provide the fraction equivalent for each.

Results of National Assessment of Educational Progress (NAEP) examinations consistently reveal that students have difficulties with the fraction-decimal relationship. Kouba et al. (1988a) note that students could express proper fractions as decimals but only 40 percent of seventh graders could give a decimal equivalent for a mixed number. In the sixth NAEP, students had difficulty placing decimals on a number line where the subdivisions were fractions (Kouba, Zawojewski, & Strutchens, 1997). In the 2005 NAEP, only 56 percent of eighth graders correctly placed decimal numbers on a number line when the increments were multiples of 0.2—not even in fraction increments. Division of the numerator by the denominator may be a means of converting fractions to decimals, but it contributes nothing to understanding the resulting equivalence. Note that this method has not been and will not be suggested in this chapter.

 A simple yet powerful assessment of decimal understanding has students represent two related decimal numbers, such as 0.6 and 0.06, using each of three or four different representations: a number line (not provided but student drawn), a

10 × 10 grid, money, and base-ten materials (Martinie & Bay-Williams, 2003). For additional information, have students give reasons for their representations. If students have significantly more difficulty with one model than others, this may mean that they have learned how to use certain models but have not necessarily developed true conceptual understanding of decimal fractions. Placement of decimals on a blank number line is perhaps the most interesting—and the most telling—task (see Figure 17.10). ◆

Approximation with a Nice Fraction

In the real world, decimal numbers are rarely those with exact equivalents to nice fractions. What fraction would you say approximates the decimal 0.52? In the sixth NAEP exam, only 51 percent of eighth graders selected $\frac{1}{2}$. The other choices were $\frac{1}{50}$ (29 percent), $\frac{1}{5}$ (11 percent), $\frac{1}{4}$ (6 percent), and $\frac{1}{3}$ (4 percent) (Kouba et al., 1997). Again, a possible explanation for this performance is a reliance on rules. Students need to wrestle with the size of decimal numbers and begin to develop a sense of familiarity with them.

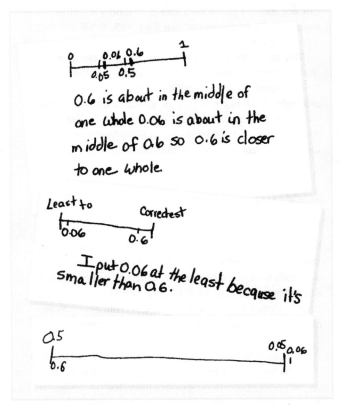

Figure 17.10 Three different sixth-grade students attempt to draw a number line and show the numbers 0.6 and 0.06.

Source: Reprinted with permission from Martinie, S. L., & Bay-Williams, J. (2003). "Investigating Students' Conceptual Understanding of Decimal Fractions Using Multiple Representations." *Mathematics Teaching in the Middle School, 8,* p. 246. Copyright © 2003 by the National Council of Teachers of Mathematics, Inc. www.nctm.org. All rights reserved.

As with fractions, the first benchmarks that should be developed are 0, $\frac{1}{2}$, and 1. For example, is 7.3962 closer to 7 or 8? Why? (Would you accept this response: "Closer to 7 because 3 is less than 5"?) Is it closer to 7 or $7\frac{1}{2}$? Often the 0, $\frac{1}{2}$, or 1 benchmarks are good enough to make sense of a situation. If a closer approximation is required, students should be encouraged to consider the other nice fractions (thirds, fourths, fifths, and eighths). In this example, 7.3962 is close to 7.4, which is $7\frac{2}{5}$. A good number sense with decimals would imply the ability to think quickly of a meaningful fraction that is a close substitute for almost any number.

To develop this type of familiarity with decimals, children do not need new concepts or skills. They do need the opportunity to apply and discuss the related concepts of fractions, place value, and decimals in activities such as the following.

Activity 17.7

Close to a Friendly Fraction

Make a list of about five decimals that are close to but not exactly equal to a nice or friendly fraction equivalent. For example, use 24.8025, 6.59, 0.9003, 124.356, and 7.7.

The students' task is to decide on a decimal number that is close to each of these decimals and that also has a friendly fraction equivalent that they know. For example, 6.59 is close to 6.6, which is $6\frac{3}{5}$. They should write an explanation for their choices. Different students may select different equivalent fractions, providing for a discussion of which is closer.

Activity 17.8

Best Match

On the chalkboard or whiteboard, list a scattered arrangement of five familiar fractions and at least five decimals that are close to the fractions but not exact. Students are to pair each fraction with the decimal that best matches it. The difficulty is determined by how close the various fractions are to one another.

In Activities 17.7 and 17.8, students will have a variety of reasons for their answers. Sharing their thinking with the class provides a valuable opportunity for all to learn. Do not focus on the answers but on the rationales.

 The connections between models and the two symbol systems for rational numbers—fractions and decimals—provide good tasks for a diagnostic interview. Provide students with a number represented in any one of these three ways and have

them provide the other two along with an explanation. Here are a few examples:

- Write the fraction $\frac{5}{8}$ as a decimal. Use a drawing or a physical model (meter stick or 10 × 10 grid) and explain why your decimal equivalent is correct.
- What fraction is also represented by the decimal 2.6? Use words, pictures, and numbers to explain your answer.
- Use both a fraction and a decimal to tell what point might be indicated on this number line. Explain your reasoning.

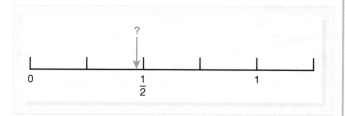

In the last example, it is especially interesting to see which representation students select first—fraction or decimal. Furthermore, do they then translate this number to the other representation or make a second independent estimate? ◆

Ordering Decimal Numbers

Putting a list of decimal numbers in order from least to greatest is a skill closely related to the one just discussed. Consider the following list: 0.36, 0.058, 0.375, and 0.4. The most common error is to select the number with more digits as largest, an incorrect application of whole-number ideas. Another common error is the idea that because digits far to the right represent very small numbers, longer numbers are smaller (Steinle & Stacey, 2004). Both errors reflect a lack of conceptual understanding of how decimal numbers are constructed. The following activities can help promote discussion about the relative sizes of decimal numbers.

Activity 17.9

Line 'Em Up

Prepare a list of four or five decimal numbers that students might have difficulty putting in order. They should all be between the same two consecutive whole numbers. Have students first predict the order of the numbers, from least to greatest. Require students to use a model of their choice to defend their ordering. As students wrestle with representing the numbers with a model (perhaps a number line with 100 subdivisions or the 10,000 grid), they will necessarily confront the idea of which digits contribute the most to the size of a decimal.

In the world outside of classrooms, we almost never have to even think about the order of "ragged" decimals—decimals with different numbers of digits after the decimal point. The real purpose of exercises such as "Line 'Em Up" is not to develop a skill—but rather to create a better understanding of decimal numeration. Tasks such as this will, however, continue to be on standardized tests because they are good assessments of decimal understanding.

Activity 17.10

Close "Nice" Numbers

Write a four-digit decimal on the board—3.0917, for example. Start with the whole numbers: "Is it closer to 3 or 4?" Then go to the tenths: "Is it closer to 3.0 or 3.1?" Repeat with hundredths and thousandths. At each answer, challenge students to defend their choices with the use of a model or other conceptual explanation. A large number line without numerals, shown in Figure 17.11, is useful.

Other Fraction-Decimal Equivalents

Recall that the denominator is a divisor and the numerator is a multiplier. For example, $\frac{3}{4}$, therefore, means the same as $3 \times (1 \div 4)$ or $3 \div 4$. So how would you express $\frac{3}{4}$ on a simple four-function calculator? Simply enter $3 \div 4$. The display will read 0.75.

Too often students think that dividing the denominator into the numerator is simply an algorithm for converting fractions to decimals, and they have no understanding of why this might work. Use the opportunity to help students develop the idea that in general $a/b = a \div b$.

The calculator is an important tool when developing familiarity with decimal concepts. Finding the decimal equivalents with a calculator can produce some interesting patterns and observations. For example, here are some questions to explore:

- Which fractions have decimal equivalents that terminate? Is the answer based on the numerator, the denominator, or both?
- For a given fraction, how can you tell the maximum length of the repeating part of the decimal? Try dividing by 7 and 11 and 13 to reach an answer.
- Explore all of the ninths—$\frac{1}{9}$, $\frac{2}{9}$, $\frac{3}{9}$, . . . $\frac{8}{9}$. Remember that $\frac{1}{3}$ is $\frac{3}{9}$ and $\frac{2}{3}$ is $\frac{6}{9}$. Use only the pattern you discover to predict what $\frac{9}{9}$ should be. But doesn't $\frac{9}{9} = 1$?
- How can you find what fraction produces this repeating decimal: 3.454545 . . . ?

The last question in the list can be generalized for any repeating decimal, illustrating that every repeating decimal is a rational number. It is not at all useful for students to become skillful at this.

 Much of what was discussed in this section is recommended by the *Standards*. "Students in [grades 3 to 5] should use models and other strategies to represent and study decimal numbers. For example, they should count by tenths (one-tenth, two-tenths, three-tenths, . . .) verbally or use a calculator to link and relate whole numbers with decimal numbers. . . . They should also investigate the relationship between fractions and decimals, focusing on equivalence" (p. 150). ◆

Introducing Percents

The term *percent* is simply another name for *hundredths* and as such is a standardized ratio with a denominator of 100. If students can express common fractions and simple decimals as hundredths, the term *percent* can be substituted for the term *hundredth*. Consider the fraction $\frac{3}{4}$. As a fraction expressed in hundredths, it is $\frac{75}{100}$. When $\frac{3}{4}$ is written in decimal form, it is 0.75. Both 0.75 and $\frac{75}{100}$ are read in exactly the same way, "seventy-five hundredths." When used as operators, $\frac{3}{4}$ of something is the same as 0.75

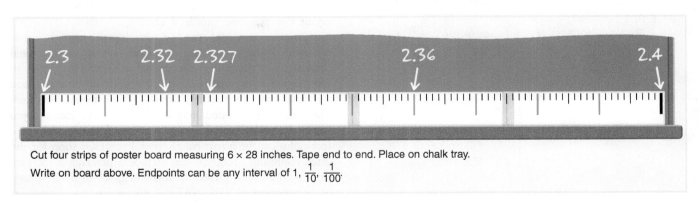

Cut four strips of poster board measuring 6 × 28 inches. Tape end to end. Place on chalk tray.

Write on board above. Endpoints can be any interval of 1, $\frac{1}{10}$, $\frac{1}{100}$.

Figure 17.11 A decimal number line.

or 75 percent of that same thing. Thus, percent is merely a new notation and terminology, not a new concept.

The results of the NAEP tests and numerous other studies have consistently shown that students have difficulty with problems involving percents (Wearne & Kouba, 2000). For example, on the 2005 NAEP, only 37 percent of eighth graders could determine an amount following a given percent of increase. Most are likely to select the answer obtained by adding the percent itself to the original amount. That is, for a 10 percent increase, they would select the answer that was 10 more than the original amount. Only 30 percent of the students could accurately calculate the tip percentage when given the cost of the meal and the amount of the tip left by the diners. A reason for this continual dismal performance is a failure to develop percent concepts meaningfully. In this book we explore percentages twice. Here we will connect them to fractions and decimals.

Models and Terminology

Models provide the main link among fractions, decimals, and percents, as shown in Figure 17.12 (see Blackline Masters 27 and 28). Base-ten fraction models are suitable for fractions, decimals, and percents, since they all represent the same idea. Students should use base-ten models for percents in much the same way as for decimals. The wheel (Figure 17.1) with 100 markings around the edge is now a model for percents as well as a fraction model for hundredths. The same is true of a 10 × 10 square. Each little square inside is 1 percent of the square. Each row or

strip of 10 squares is not only a tenth but also 10 percent of the square.

Zambo (2008) suggests linking fractions to percent using the 10 × 10 blank hundreds chart. By marking one out of every four squares on the chart students can discover the link between $\frac{1}{4}$ and $\frac{25}{100}$ or 25 percent. He goes on to suggest that even more complex representations such as $\frac{1}{8}$ can lead to interesting discussions about the remaining squares left at the end resulting in $12\frac{1}{2}$ out of 100 squares or $12\frac{1}{2}$ percent.

Similarly, the familiar fractions (halves, thirds, fourths, fifths, and eighths) should become familiar in terms of percents as well as decimals. Three-fifths, for example, is 60 percent as well as 0.6. One-third of an amount is frequently expressed as $33\frac{1}{3}$ percent instead of 33.3333 . . . percent. Likewise, $\frac{1}{8}$ of a quantity is $12\frac{1}{2}$ percent or 12.5 percent of the quantity. These ideas should be explored with base-ten models and not as rules about moving decimal points.

One representation that can be used to link percentages with data collection is a percent necklace. Using fishing cord or other sturdy string, link 100 beads and knot them in a tight, circular necklace. Anytime a circle graph is created or observed in class the percent necklace can provide an estimation tool to help think about the percent that falls in any given category. Given any circle graph, place the necklace in a circle so that its center coincides with the center of the circle, rather than trying to align with the outside edge of the circle graph. If the necklace makes a wider concentric circle, the students can use a ruler to extend the lines distinguishing the different categories straight out to meet the necklace. If the circle is larger than the necklace, you will use the actual radial lines marking off the categories. Have students explore the number of beads between any two given lines that represent a wedge of the circle. For example, they might find that 24 beads are in the section of the circle graph that shows how many students like blue as their favorite color. That is an estimate that approximately 24 percent of the students favor blue. Such counting of beads gives students an informal approach to estimating percent, while investigating a meaningful model for thinking about the per one hundred concept.

Percent concepts can be developed through other powerful visual representations that link to proportional thinking. One option is the use of a three-part model to represent the original amount, the decrease/increase, and the final amount (Parker, 2004). Using three rectangles that can be positioned and divided, students can analyze components and consider each piece of the model. The rectangles can be a particularly useful representation for the often confusing problems that include a percentage increase to find an amount greater than the original, as in the previously mentioned 2005 NAEP item, which asked students to calculate how many employees there were at a company

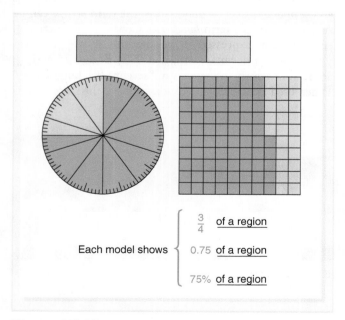

Each model shows:
- $\frac{3}{4}$ of a region
- 0.75 of a region
- 75% of a region

Figure 17.12 Models connect three different notations.

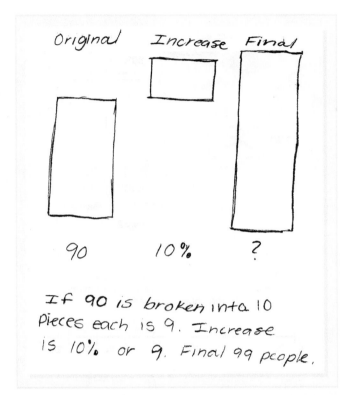

Figure 17.13 A proportional model for reasoning about percent.

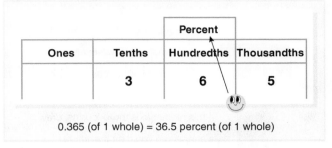

0.365 (of 1 whole) = 36.5 percent (of 1 whole)

Figure 17.14 Hundredths are also known as percents.

whose workforce increased by 10 percent over the previous level of 90. Using Parker's suggested model, you can see in Figure 17.13 how a student used this proportional model to come up with a correct solution. The use of the proportional model to think about percents will be revisited in the next chapter on proportional reasoning.

Another helpful approach to the terminology of percent is through the role of the decimal point. Recall that the decimal identifies the units. When the unit is ones, a number such as 0.659 means a little more than 6 tenths of 1. The word *ones* is understood (6 tenths of 1 *one* or one *whole*). But 0.659 is also 6.59 tenths and 65.9 hundredths and 659 thousandths. The name of the unit must be explicitly identified, or else the unit would change with each position of the decimal. Since *percent* is another name for *hundredths*, when the decimal identifies the hundredths position as the units, the word *percent* can be specified as a synonym for *hundredths*. Thus, 0.659 (of some whole or 1) is 65.9 hundredths or 65.9 percent of that same whole. As illustrated in Figure 17.14, the notion of placing the decimal point *to identify the percent position* is conceptually more meaningful than the apparently arbitrary rule: "To change a decimal to a percent, move the decimal two places to the right." A more conceptually focused idea is to equate hundredths with percent both orally and in notation.

Realistic Percent Problems

Some middle school teachers may talk about "the three percent problems." The sentence "_____ is _____ percent of _____" has three spaces for numbers; for example, "20 is 25 percent of 80." The classic three percent problems come from this sterile expression; two of the numbers are given, and the students are asked to produce the third. Students learn very quickly that you either multiply or divide the two given numbers, and sometimes you have to move a decimal point. But they have no way of determining when to do what, which numbers to divide, or which way to shift the decimal point. As a result, performance on percentage problems is very poor. Furthermore, commonly encountered expressions using percent terminology, such as sales figures, taxes, census data, political information, and trends in economics, are almost never in the "_____ is _____ percent of _____" format. So when asked to solve a realistic percent problem, students are frequently at a loss.

Previously explored exercises with fractions in which one element—part, whole, or fraction—was unknown. Students used models and simple fraction relationships in those exercises, which are actually the same as the three percent problems. Developmentally, then, it makes sense to help students make the connection between the exercises done with fractions and those done with percents. How? Use the same types of models and the same terminology of parts, wholes, and fractions. The only thing that is different is that the word *percent* is used instead of *fraction*. In Figure 17.15, the three-part whole-fraction exercises demonstrate the link between fractions and percents.

Teaching Percents. Though students must have some experience with the noncontextual situations in Figure 17.15, it is important to have them explore percent relationships in real contexts. Find or make up percent problems, and present them in the same way that they appear in newspapers, on television, and in other real contexts. In addition to realistic problems and formats, follow these maxims for your instruction on percents:

- Limit the percents to familiar fractions (halves, thirds, fourths, fifths, and eighths) or easy percents ($\frac{1}{10}$, $\frac{1}{100}$),

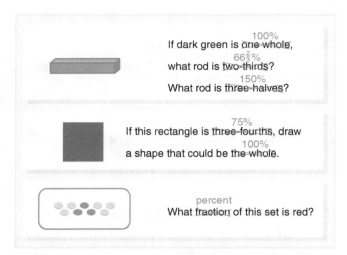

Figure 17.15 Part-whole fraction exercises can be translated into percent exercises.

and use numbers compatible with these fractions. The focus of these exercises is the relationships involved, not complex computational skills.

- Do not suggest any rules or procedures for different types of problems. Do not categorize or label problem types.
- Use the terms *part*, *whole*, and *percent* (or *fraction*). *Fraction* and *percent* are interchangeable. Help students see these percent exercises as the same types of exercises they did with simple fractions.
- Require students to use models or drawings to explain their solutions. It is wiser to assign three problems requiring a drawing and an explanation than to give 15 problems requiring only computation and answers. Remember that the purpose is the exploration of relationships, not computational skill.
- Encourage mental computation.

The following sample problems meet these criteria for familiar fractions and compatible numbers. Try working each problem, identifying each number as a part, a whole, or a fraction. Draw length or area models to explain or work through your thought process. Examples of this informal reasoning are illustrated with additional problems in Figure 17.16.

1. **The PTA reported that 75 percent of the total number of families were represented at the meeting last night. If children from 320 families go to the school, how many were represented at the meeting?**

2. **The baseball team won 80 percent of the 25 games it played this year. How many games were lost?**

3. **In Mrs. Carter's class, 20 students, or $66\frac{2}{3}$ percent, were on the honor roll. How many students are in her class?**

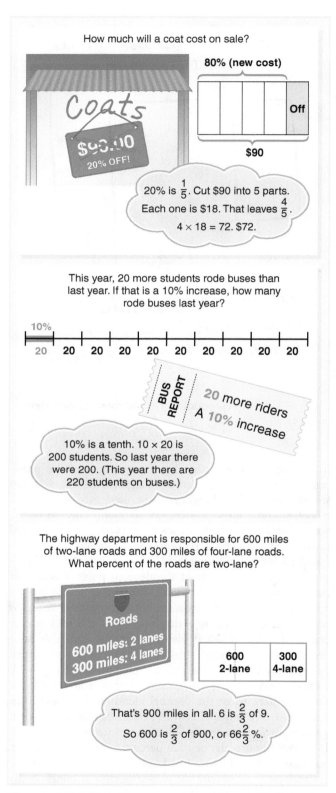

Figure 17.16 Real percent problems with compatible numbers. Simple drawings help with reasoning.

4. Zane bought his new computer at a $12\frac{1}{2}$ percent discount. He paid $700. How many dollars did he save by buying it at a discount?

5. If Nicolas has read 60 of the 180 pages in his library book, what percent of the book has he read so far?

6. The hardware store bought widgets at 80 cents each and sold them for $1 each. What percent did the store mark up the price of each widget?

 Pause and Reflect

Examine the examples in Figure 17.16. Notice how each problem is solved with simple fractions and mental math. Then try each of the six problems just listed. Each can be done easily and mentally using familiar fraction equivalents. Use a model or drawing that you think your students might use.

Realistic percent problems are still the best way to assess a student's understanding of percent. Assign one or two, and have students explain why they think their answer makes sense. You might take a realistic percent problem and substitute fractions for percents (e.g., use $\frac{1}{8}$ instead of 12.5 percent) to see how students handle these problems with fractions compared to percents.

If your focus is on reasons and justifications rather than number of problems correct, you will be able to collect all the assessment information you need. ◆

Estimation

Of course, not all real percent problems have nice numbers. Frequently in real life an approximation or estimate in percent situations is all that is required or is enough to help one think through the situation. Even if a calculator will be used to get an exact answer, an estimate based on an understanding of the relationship can confirm that a correct operation was performed or that the decimal point was positioned correctly.

To help students with estimation in percent situations, two ideas that have already been discussed can be applied. First, when the percent is not a "nice" one, substitute a close percent that is easy to work with. Second, select numbers that are compatible with the percent involved, to make the calculation easy to do mentally. In essence, convert the not-nice percent problem into one that is nice. Here are some examples.

1. The 83,000-seat stadium was 73 percent full. How many people were at the game?

2. The treasurer reported that 68.3 percent of the dues had been collected, for a total of $385. How much

more money could the club expect to collect if all dues are paid?

3. Max McStrike had 217 hits in 842 at-bats. What was his batting average?

 Pause and Reflect

Use nice fractions and compatible numbers to estimate solutions to each of these last three problems. Do this before reading on.

Possible Estimates

1. (Use $\frac{3}{4}$ and 80,000) $\longrightarrow$ about 60,000

2. (Use $\frac{2}{3}$ and $380; will collect $\frac{1}{3}$ more) $\longrightarrow$ about $190

3. ($4 \times 217 > 842$; $\frac{1}{4}$ is 25 percent, or 0.250) $\longrightarrow$ a bit more than 0.250

Here are three more percent problems with two sets of numbers. The first number in the set is a nice number that allows the problem to be worked mentally using fraction equivalents. The second number requires a substitution with an approximation allowing for an estimate as in the last activity.

1. The school enrolls {480, 547} students. Yesterday {$12\frac{1}{2}$ percent, 13 percent} of the students were absent. How many came to school?

2. Mr. Carver sold his lawn mower for {$45, $89}. This was {60 percent, 62 percent} of the price he paid for it new. What did the mower cost when it was new?

3. When the box fell off the shelf {90, 63} of the {720, 500} widgets broke. What percentage was lost in the breakage?

The first problem asks for a part (whole and fraction given), the second asks for a whole (part and fraction given), and the third asks for a fraction (part and whole given).

It is also convenient at times to use simple base-ten equivalents: 1 percent and 10 percent and multiples of these (including halves). For example, we often use 10 percent plus half of that much to compute a 15 percent tip at a restaurant. To find 0.5 percent we can think of half of 1 percent.

There are several rules of thumb for estimating percentages in real-world situations. As students gain full conceptual understanding and flexibility, there are ways to think about percents that are useful as you are shopping or in situations that bring thinking about percents to the forefront. As mentioned previously to figure a tip you can find 10 percent of the amount and then half of that again to make 15 percent. The same approach is used for adding on sales tax. Depending on your amount, you can find 10 percent, take half of that, and then find 1 percent and add or subtract that amount as needed. But you can encourage other approaches as well. First, students should realize that finding percents is a process of multiplication; therefore, finding 50 percent of 16 will generate the same result as finding 16 percent of 50. This is an important estimation tool when you are "on the go." Also, a 30 percent decrease is the same as 70 percent of the original amount, and sometimes, depending on the original amount, using one of those percents is easier to use in mental calculations than the other. Again, these are nothing more than using the full understanding of percent concepts to your advantage.

Computation with Decimals

Certainly, students should develop computational fluency with decimal numbers. In the past, decimal computation was dominated by the following rules: Line up the decimal points (addition and subtraction), count the decimal places (multiplication), and shift the decimal point in the divisor and dividend so that the divisor is a whole number (division). Some textbooks continue to emphasize these rules. The position taken in this book and in some of the standards-based curricula is that specific rules for decimal computation are not really necessary, especially if computation is built on a firm understanding of place value and a connection between decimals and fractions.

> **myeducationlab**
> Go to the Activities and Application section of Chapter 17 of MyEducationLab. Click on Videos and watch the video entitled "**John Van de Walle on Computation with Decimals**" to see him lead activities with teachers that focus on computation with decimals.

 NCTM Standards At the 3–5 level, the *Standards* says that students should "develop and use strategies to estimate computations involving fractions and decimals in situations relevant to students' experience" (p. 148). At the 6–8 level, students are to "select appropriate methods and tools for computing with fractions and decimals from among mental computation, estimation, calculators or computers, and paper and pencil, depending on the situation" (p. 214). ◆

The Role of Estimation

Students should become adept at estimating decimal computations well before they learn to compute with pencil and paper. For many decimal computations, rough estimates can be made easily by rounding the numbers to nice whole numbers or simple base-ten fractions. A minimum goal for your students should be to have the estimate contain the correct number of digits to the left of the decimal—the whole-number part. Start your instruction by selecting problems for which estimates are not terribly difficult.

⏸ ────────────── *Pause and Reflect*

Before going on, try making whole-number estimates of the following computations. Do not spend time with fine adjustments in your estimates.

1. **4.907 + 123.01 + 56.1234**
2. **459.8 − 12.345**
3. **24.67 × 1.84**
4. **514.67 ÷ 3.59**

Your estimates might be in the following ranges:

1. Between 175 and 200
2. More than 400, or about 425 to 450
3. More than 25, closer to 50 (1.84 is more than 1 and close to 2)
4. More than 125, less than 200 (500 ÷ 4 = 125 and 600 ÷ 3 = 200)

In these examples, an understanding of decimal numeration and some simple whole-number estimation skills can produce rough estimates. When estimating, focus on the meanings of the numbers and the operations and not on counting decimal places. However, students who are taught to focus on the pencil-and-paper rules for decimal computation do not even consider the actual values of the numbers, much less estimate.

Therefore, a good *place* to begin decimal computation is with estimation. Not only is it a highly practical skill, but it also helps children look at answers in terms of a reasonable range and can form a check on calculator computation.

A good *time* to begin computation with decimals is as soon as a conceptual background in decimal numeration has been developed. An emphasis on estimation is very important, even for students in the seventh and eighth grades who have been exposed to and have used rules for decimal computation, especially for multiplication and division. Many students who are totally reliant on rules for decimals make mistakes without being aware, as they are not using number sense.

Addition and Subtraction

Consider this problem:

Jessica and MacKenna each timed her own quarter-mile run with a stopwatch. Jessica says that she ran the quarter in 74.5 seconds. MacKenna was more accurate. She reported her run as 81.34 seconds. How many seconds faster did Jessica run than MacKenna?

Students who understand decimal numeration should first of all be able to tell approximately what the difference is—close to 7 seconds. With an estimate as a beginning, students should then be challenged to figure out the exact difference. The estimate will help them avoid the common error of lining up the 5 under the 4. A variety of student strategies are possible. For example, students might note that 74.5 and 7 is 81.5 and then figure out how much extra that is. Others may count on from 74.5 by adding 0.5 and then 6 more seconds to get to 81 seconds and then add on the remaining 0.34 second. These and other strategies will eventually confront the difference between the 0.5 and 0.34. Students can resolve this issue by returning to their understanding of place value. Similar story problems for addition and subtraction, some involving different numbers of decimal places, will help develop students' understanding of these two operations. Always require an estimate prior to computation.

After students have had several opportunities to solve addition and subtraction story problems, the following activity is reasonable.

Activity 17.11

Exact Sums and Differences

Give students a sum involving different numbers of decimal places. For example: 73.46 + 6.2 + 0.582. The first task is to make an estimate and explain how the estimate was made. The second task is to compute the exact answer and explain how that was done (no calculators). In the third and final task students devise a method for adding and subtracting decimal numbers that they can use with any two numbers.

When students have completed these three tasks, have students share their strategies for computation and test them on a new computation that you provide. The same task can be repeated for subtraction.

The earlier estimation practice will focus students' attention on the meanings of the numbers. Remember, students can also think about rewriting decimals as fractions with the same denominator to make connections. It is reasonable to expect that students will develop an algorithm that is essentially the same as aligning the decimal points.

 If students have difficulty with Activity 17.11, it is an indication that they have a weak understanding of decimal concepts and the role of the decimal point. This is true even for students who get a correct sum by using a rule they learned in an earlier grade but who have difficulty with their explanations. Rather than focus on how to add or subtract decimals, return or shift your focus to decimal concepts as discussed earlier in the chapter. ◆

Multiplication

Estimation should play a significant role in developing an algorithm for multiplication. As a beginning point, consider this problem:

The farmer fills each jug with 3.7 liters of cider. If you buy 4 jugs, how many liters of cider is that?

Begin with an estimate. Is it more than 12 liters? What is the most it could be? Could it be 16 liters? Once an estimate of the result is decided on, let students use their own methods for determining an exact answer. Many will use repeated addition: 3.7 + 3.7 + 3.7 + 3.7. Others may begin by multiplying 3 × 4 and then adding up 0.7 four times. Eventually, students will agree on the exact result of 14.8 liters. Explore other problems involving whole-number multipliers. Multipliers such as 3.5 or 8.25 that involve nice fractional parts—here, one-half and one-fourth—are also reasonable.

As a next step, have students compare a decimal product with one involving the same digits but no decimal. For example, how are 23.4 × 6.5 and 234 × 65 alike? Interestingly, both products have exactly the same digits: 15210. (The zero may be missing from the decimal product.) Using a calculator, have students explore other products that are alike except for the location of the decimals involved. The digits in the answer are always alike. After seeing how the digits remain the same for these related products, do the following activity.

Activity 17.12

Where Does the Decimal Go?: Multiplication

Have students compute the following product: 24 × 63. Using only the result of this computation and estimation, have them give the exact answer to each of the following:

0.24 × 6.3   24 × 0.63   2.4 × 63   0.24 × 0.63

For each computation they should write a rationale for how they made the placement of the decimal point in each answer. They can check their results with a calculator. Any errors must be acknowledged and the rationale that produced the error adjusted.

⏸ ———————— *Pause and Reflect*

The product of 24 × 63 is 1512. Use this information to give the answer to each of the products in the previous activity. Do *not* count decimal places. Remember your fractional equivalents.

The method of placing the decimal point in a product by way of estimation is more difficult as the product gets smaller. For example, knowing that 54 × 83 is 4482 does not make it easy to place the decimal in the product 0.0054 × 0.00083. Even the product 0.054 × 0.83 is hard. A reasonable algorithm for multiplication is: *Ignore the decimal points, and do the computation as if all numbers were whole numbers. When finished, place the decimal by estimation.* Even if students have already learned the traditional algorithm, they need to know the conceptual rationale centered on place value and the powers of ten for "counting" and shifting the decimal places. By focusing on rote applications of rules, students lose out on approaches that emphasize opportunities to understand the meaning and effects of operations and are more prone to misapply procedures (Martinie & Bay-Williams, 2003).

 Questions such as the following keep the focus on number sense and provide useful information about your students' understanding.

1. Consider these two computations: $3\frac{1}{2} \times 2\frac{1}{4}$ and 2.276 × 3.18. Without doing the calculations, which product do you think is larger? Provide a reason for your answer that can be understood by someone else in this class.

2. How much larger is 0.76 × 5 than 0.75 × 5? How can you tell without doing the computation (Kulm, 1994)?

Student discussions and explanations as they work on these or similar questions can provide insights into their decimal and fraction number sense and the connections between the two representations. ◆

Division

Division can be approached in a manner exactly parallel to multiplication. In fact, the best approach to a division estimate generally comes from thinking about multiplication rather than division. Consider the following problem:

The trip to Washington was 282.5 miles. It took exactly $4\frac{1}{2}$ hours or 4.5 hours to drive. What was the average miles per hour?

To make an estimate of this quotient, think about what times 4 or 5 is close to 280. You might think 60 × 4.5 = 240 + 30 = 270. So maybe about 61 or 62 miles per hour.

Here is a second example without context. Make an estimate of 45.7 ÷ 1.83. Think only of what times $1\frac{8}{10}$ is close to 45.

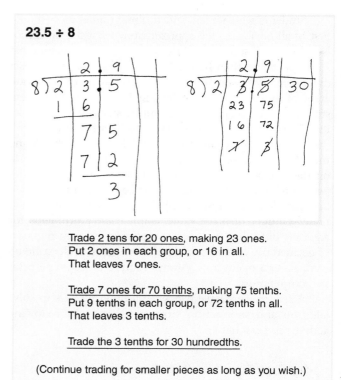

23.5 ÷ 8

Trade 2 tens for 20 ones, making 23 ones.
Put 2 ones in each group, or 16 in all.
That leaves 7 ones.

Trade 7 ones for 70 tenths, making 75 tenths.
Put 9 tenths in each group, or 72 tenths in all.
That leaves 3 tenths.

Trade the 3 tenths for 30 hundredths.

(Continue trading for smaller pieces as long as you wish.)

Figure 17.17 Extension of the division algorithm.

Pause and Reflect

Will the answer be more or less than 45? Why? Will it be more or less than 20? Now think about 1.8 being close to 2. What times 2 is close to 46? Use this to produce an estimate.

Since 1.83 is close to 2, the estimate is near 22. And since 1.83 is less than 2 the answer must be greater than 22—say 25 or 26. (The actual answer is 24.972677.)

Okay, so estimation can produce a reasonable result, but you may still require a pencil-and-paper algorithm to produce the digits the way it was done for multiplication. Figure 17.17 shows division by a whole number and how that can be carried out to as many places as you wish. (The explicit-trade method is shown on the right.) It is not necessary to move the decimal point up into the quotient. Leave that to estimation.

Activity 17.13

Where Does the Decimal Go?: Division

Provide a quotient such as 146 ÷ 7 = 20857 correct to five digits but without the decimal point. The task is to use only this information and estimation to give a fairly precise answer to each of the following:

$146 \div 0.7 \quad 1.46 \div 7 \quad 14.6 \div 0.7 \quad 1460 \div 70$

For each computation students should write a rationale for their answers and then check their results with a calculator. Any errors should be acknowledged, and the rationale that produced the error adjusted.

A reasonable algorithm for division is parallel to that for multiplication: *Ignore the decimal points, and do the computation as if all numbers were whole numbers. When finished, place the decimal by estimation.* This is reasonable for divisors greater than 1 or close to a familiar value (e.g., .1, .5, .01). If students have a method for dividing by 45, they can divide by 0.45 and 4.5.

Reflections

Writing to Learn

1. Describe three different base-ten models for fractions and decimals, and use each to illustrate how base-ten fractions can easily be represented.
2. How can we help students think about very small place values such as thousandths and millionths in the same way we get students to think about very large place values such as millions and billions?
3. Use an example involving base-ten pieces to explain the role of the decimal point in identifying the units position. Relate this idea to changing units of measurement as in money or metric measures.
4. For addition and subtraction of decimals, the line-up-the-decimals rule can be reasonably developed through practice with estimation. Explain.
5. Give an example explaining how, in most problems, multiplication and division with decimals can be replaced with estimation and whole-number methods.

For Discussion and Exploration

1. One way to order a series of decimal numbers is to annex zeros to each number so that all numbers have the same number of decimal places. For example, rewrite

0.34		0.3400
0.3004	as	0.3004
0.059		0.0590

Now ignore the decimal points and any leading zeros, and order the resulting whole numbers. Discuss the merits of teaching this approach to children. If taught this procedure, what would students learn about decimal numeration? How will you ensure that this process is not just a "rule without reason"?

Resources

Literature Connections

In the daily paper and weekly magazines, you will find decimal and percent situations with endless real-world connections. One issue with percents in news stories is the frequent omission of the base amount or the whole on which the percent is determined. "March sales of video games were reported to be up 3.6 percent." Does that mean an increase over February or over March of the previous year? Increase and decrease by percents are interesting to project over several years. If the consumer price index rises 3 percent a year, how much will a $100 basket of groceries cost by the time your students are 21 years old?

The Phantom Tollbooth *Juster, 1961*

References to mathematical ideas abound throughout this book about Milo's adventures in Digitopolis, where everything is number-oriented. There, Milo meets a boy who is only half of a boy, appearing in the illustration to be the left half of a boy cut top to bottom. As it turns out, the boy is actually 0.58 since he is a member of the average family: a mother, father, and 2.58 children. The boy is the 0.58. One advantage, he explains, is that he is the only one who can drive the 0.3 of a car—the average family owning 1.3 cars. This section of the tale involves a great discussion of averages that come out in decimal numbers.

An obvious extension of the story is to explore averages of things that are interesting to the students (average number of siblings, average arm span, etc.) and see where these odd decimal fractions come from. In the case of measures of length, for example, an average length can be a real length even if no one has it. But an average number of something like pets can be very humorous.

This same book can be used to develop mathematical concepts such as time (when Milo visits the Doldrums), data collection and analysis through percents (How do students in the class spend their day?), measurement with distances to Digitopolis given in various measures on a chart, and humorous discussions and in some cases misunderstandings of such concepts as infinity and proportional thinking. This book is a gem for use with intermediate and middle grade students.

Piece = Part = Portion: Fraction = Decimal = Percent *Gifford & Thaler, 2008*

Illustrated with vivid photos, this is a beginning look at how fractions relate to corresponding decimals and percents. Written by an elementary classroom teacher, the links between the concepts are drawn through common representations, such as one sneaker representing $\frac{1}{2}$ a pair of shoes, 0.50 in decimal form or 50 percent. Real-world links such as one-seventh of a week and one-eleventh of a soccer team will connect with students. Note that some decimals and percents are rounded. The book is available in English and Spanish.

Recommended Readings

Articles

Irwin, K. C. (2001). Using everyday knowledge of decimals to enhance understanding. *Journal for Research in Mathematics Education, 32*(4), 399–420.
Irwin's article describes her work with 16 children, ages 11 and 12. The students worked in eight pairs, half of whom solved problems given in contexts. The other four pairs solved the same problems but without contexts. The article is enlightening on a number of fronts, particularly the transcriptions that clearly indicate the students' misconceptions of decimal numeration.

Martinie, S. L., & Bay-Williams, J. (2003). Investigating students' conceptual understanding of decimal fractions using multiple representations. *Mathematics Teaching in the Middle School, 8*(5), 244–247.
This article describes the results of 43 sixth-grade students who were asked to represent 0.6 and 0.06 with four different representations: a number line, a 10 × 10 grid, money, and base-ten materials. The results indicate that students may appear to understand decimals with one model but not with another. The authors make an argument for using multiple models in teaching decimals.

Books

Albert, L., & McAdam, J. (2007). Making sense of decimal fraction algorithms using base-ten blocks. In W. Gary Martin, Marilyn Strutchens, and Portia Elliott (Eds.), *The learning of mathematics: Sixty-ninth yearbook of the National Council of Teachers of Mathematics* (pp. 303–315). Reston, VA: NCTM.
This chapter emphasizes the critical need for precise mathematical language in the development of algorithms for multiplying decimal fractions. A classroom example details how teachers can use place-value knowledge and arrays of base-ten blocks to build students' conceptual understanding of decimals. Since the article is about prospective teachers' learning of this material, it is easy to relate to the challenges and connections readers may be experiencing.

Online Resources

Base Blocks—Decimals
http://nlvm.usu.edu/en/nav/frames_asid_264_g_3_t_1.html
Base-ten blocks can be placed on a place-value chart. The number of decimal places can be selected, thus designating any of the four blocks as the unit. Addition and subtraction problems can be created or can be generated randomly.

Circle 3
http://nlvm.usu.edu/en/nav/frames_asid_187_g_3_t_1.html
This game challenges students to use logic as they combine decimals to add to 3. Not as easy as it sounds.

Concentration
http://illuminations.nctm.org/ActivityDetail.aspx?ID=73
This is an engaging matching game using representations of percents, fractions, and a regional model.

Fractions Bar Applet
www.arcytech.org/java/fractions/fractions.html
This applet develops the relationships among fractions, decimals, and percents. Bars for one whole are displayed and can be partitioned according to selected fraction, decimal, or percent values and then labeled in any of these representations. This makes equivalencies easy to explore.

Fraction Model—Version 3
http://illuminations.nctm.org/tools/tool_detail.aspx?id=45
The equivalence of fraction, decimal, and percent representations in a circle, set, or rectangle model is demonstrated.

Percentages
http://nlvm.usu.edu/en/nav/frames_asid_160_g_3_t_1.html?open=activities
The user enters any two of the values—whole, part, and percent—and clicks on Compute. Although the computer does the work, the applet nicely models percent problems.

Railroad Repair
http://pbskids.org/cyberchase/games/decimals/decimals
.html

This fun activity has students repairing a railroad by choosing and combining different sized decimal pieces of railroad tracks to help get Cybertrain back to the station.

Sock
www.interactivestuff.org/sums4fun/sock.html

Click on directional arrows to guide the sphere into pushing the green cubes into holes that contain the decimals that will make the target number.

Field Experience Guide Connections

Expanded Lesson 9.8 is an engaging lesson with the goal of helping students be able to fluently convert common fractions to their decimal equivalencies. In Expanded Lesson 9.10 ("How Close Is Close?") students shade 10×10 grids to explore density of fractions and decimals, thus learning that for any two decimals, another decimal can be found between them.

Proportional Reasoning

From Chapter 18 of *Elementary and Middle School Mathematics: Teaching Developmentally*, 7/e. John A. Van de Walle.
Karen S. Karp. Jennifer M. Bay-Williams. Copyright © 2010 by Pearson Allyn and Bacon. All rights reserved.

Proportional Reasoning

Proportional reasoning has been referred to as the capstone of the elementary curriculum and the cornerstone of algebra and beyond (Lesh, Post, & Behr, 1987). It begins with the ability to understand multiplicative relationships, distinguishing them from relationships that are additive. The development of proportional reasoning is one of the most important goals of the 5–8 curriculum.

Proportional reasoning goes well beyond the notion of setting up a proportion to solve a problem—it is a way of reasoning about multiplicative situations. In fact, proportional reasoning, like equivalence, is considered a unifying theme in mathematics. You will see this evidence in the many content connections listed on this page.

Big Ideas

1. A ratio is a multiplicative comparison of two quantities or measures. A key developmental milestone is the ability of a student to begin to think of a ratio as a distinct entity, different from the two measures that made it up.

2. Ratios and proportions involve multiplicative rather than additive comparisons. Equal ratios result from multiplication or division, not from addition or subtraction.

3. Proportional thinking is developed through activities involving comparing and determining the equivalence of ratios and solving proportions in a wide variety of problem-based contexts and situations without recourse to rules or formulas.

Mathematics Content Connections

Proportional reasoning is indeed the cornerstone of a wide variety of essential topics in the middle and high school curriculum.

- **Algebra:** Much of algebra concerns a study of change and, hence, rates of change (ratios) are particularly important. In this chapter you will see that the graphs of equivalent ratios are straight lines passing through the origin. The slope of the line is the unit ratio.

- **Fractions:** Equivalent fractions are found through a multiplicative process; numerators and denominators are multiplied or divided by the same number. Equivalent ratios can be found in the same manner. In fact, part-whole relationships (fractions) are an example of ratio. Fractions are also one of the principal methods of representing ratios.

- **Percents:** Percents are a way of describing an amount as if it were out of 100. This is a part-whole ratio. For example a 65 percent approval rating means the ratio of those approving to those asked is 65 to 100.

- **Geometry:** When two figures are the same shape but different sizes (i.e., similar), they constitute a visual example of a proportion. The ratios of linear measures in one figure will be equal to the corresponding ratios in the other.

- **Data Graphs:** A relative frequency histogram shows the frequencies of different related events compared to all outcomes (visual part-to-whole ratios). A box-and-whisker plot shows the relative distribution of data along a number line and can be used to compare distributions of populations of very different sizes.

- **Probability:** A probability is a ratio that compares the number of outcomes in an event to the total possible outcomes. Proportional reasoning helps students understand these ratios, especially in comparing large and small sample sizes.

Ratios

Regardless of how the objectives are stated in your curriculum concerning the ability to solve proportions or percent problems, the ultimate goal for your students should be focused on the development of proportional reasoning, not a collection of skills. To this end it is useful to have a good idea of what constitutes a ratio and a proportion and in what contexts these mathematical ideas appear. With this information we can then examine what it means to reason proportionally and begin to work toward helping students achieve that goal.

According to *Curriculum Focal Points* (NCTM, 2006), ratios and rates are a focus in sixth grade, developed by looking at pairs of rows (or columns) on the multiplication table and in drawings. In seventh grade ratios are extended to understanding and applying proportional reasoning—for example, investigating contexts such as interest, taxes, and tips as well as connecting to work with similar figures, graphing, and slope. That is not to say that proportional reasoning doesn't begin until middle school. Understanding one-to-one correspondence, place value, fraction concepts, and multiplicative reasoning are among topics that involve early proportional reasoning (Seeley & Schieleck, 2007).

Types of Ratios

A *ratio* is a number that relates two quantities or measures within a given situation in a multiplicative relationship (in contrast to a difference or additive relationship). A ratio can be applied to another situation where the relative amounts of the quantities or measures are the same as in the first situation (Smith, 2002). Ratios appear in a variety of different contexts. Part of proportional reasoning is the ability to recognize ratios in these various settings. To the student just beginning to develop an understanding of ratio, different settings or contexts may well seem like different ideas even though they are essentially the same from a mathematical viewpoint.

Research on Chinese and U.S. teachers shows that Chinese teachers spend more time making sense of the subtle differences among fractions, ratios, and division, whereas U.S. teachers connect ratios quickly to percents without discussion of these interrelated concepts (Cai and Wang, 2006). Table 18.1 offers comparisons among fractions, ratios, and division similar to those used in Chinese lessons as prompts for students to discuss the relationships among these ideas.

Part-to-Whole Ratios. Ratios can express comparisons of a part to a whole, for example, the ratio of the number of girls in a class to the number of students in the class. Because fractions are also part-whole ratios, it follows that every fraction is also a ratio. In the same way, percentages are ratios, and in fact, percentages are sometimes used to express ratios. Probabilities are ratios of a part of the sample space to the whole sample space.

Part-to-Part Ratios. A ratio can also relate one part of a whole to another part of the same whole. For example, the number of girls in the class can be compared to the number of boys. The ratio of the length to the width of a rectangle is a part-to-part relationship. Although the probability of an event is a part-to-whole ratio, the *odds* of an event happening is a ratio of the number of ways an event can happen to the number of ways it cannot happen—a part-to-part ratio.

Rates as Ratios. Both part-to-whole and part-to-part ratios compare two measures of the same type of thing. A ratio can also be a *rate*. A rate is a comparison of the measures of two different things or quantities; the measuring unit is different for each value.

For example, if 4 similar boats carry 36 passengers, then the comparison of 4 boats to 36 passengers is a ratio. Boats and passengers are different types of things. The rate would be the passengers per boat: $\frac{p}{b} = \frac{36}{4} = \frac{9}{1}$. The ratio of passengers to boats is 36:4, which can also be written as $\frac{36}{4}$ or 36 to 4. The rate is 9 passengers per boat. Similarly, all rates of speed are ratios that compare distance to time, such as driving at 55 miles per hour or jogging at 9 minutes per mile.

Miles per gallon, square yards of wall coverage per gallon of paint, passengers per busload, and roses per bouquet are all rates. Relationships between two units of measure are also rates or ratios, for example, inches per foot, milliliters per liter, and centimeters per inch.

Examples of Ratio. In geometry, the ratios of corresponding parts of similar geometric figures are always the same. The diagonal of a square is always $\sqrt{2}$ times a side; that is, the ratio of the diagonal of a square to its side

Table 18.1

Comparison of Fractions, Ratios, and Division				
Concept	First Value	Symbol	Second Value	Result
Ratio	First term	: Colon	Second term	Value of ratio
Fraction	Numerator	— Fraction line	Denominator	Value of fraction
Division	Dividend	÷ Division sign	Divisor	Quotient

Source: Adapted from Cai and Wang, 2006.

is $\sqrt{2}$. The value π (pi) is the ratio of the circumference of a circle to the diameter. The trigonometric functions can be developed from ratios of sides of right triangles.

The slope of a line or of a roof is a ratio of rise for each unit of horizontal distance or run. Slope is an extremely important ratio in algebra. Not only does it describe the steepness of a line, but also it tells us the rate of change of one variable in terms of another.

In nature, the ratio known as the *golden ratio* is found in many spirals, from nautilus shells to the swirls of a pinecone or a pineapple. Artists and architects have used the same ratio in creating shapes that are naturally pleasing to the eye.

Recall that a ratio is a number that expresses a multiplicative relationship that can be applied to a second situation where the relative quantities or measures are the same as in the first situation.

Proportional Reasoning

Proportional reasoning is difficult to define in a simple sentence or two. It is not something that you either can or cannot do. It is both a qualitative and quantitative process. According to Lamon (1999), the following are a few of the characteristics of proportional thinkers:

- Proportional thinkers have a sense of covariation. That is, they understand relationships in which two quantities vary together and are able to see how the variation in one coincides with the variation in another.
- Proportional thinkers recognize proportional relationships as distinct from nonproportional relationships in real-world contexts.
- Proportional thinkers develop a wide variety of strategies for solving proportions or comparing ratios, most of which are based on informal strategies rather than prescribed algorithms.
- Proportional thinkers understand ratios as distinct entities representing a relationship different from the quantities they compare.

It is estimated that more than half of the adult population cannot be viewed as proportional thinkers (Lamon, 1999). That means that we do not acquire the habits and skills of proportional reasoning simply by getting older. On the other hand, Lamon's research and that of others indicate that instruction that focuses on reasoning (rather than a formula) can have an effect on a student's ability to reason proportionally, which begins early with multiplicative reasoning. Chinese students begin their formal exploration of ratio and proportion in the elementary grades (Cai & Sun, 2002, 2006). In the United States, these concepts are typically taught in grades 6 to 9. However, merely focusing on the procedure of finding the missing value in a proportion encourages students to apply rules without thinking and,

thus, the ability to reason proportionally often does not develop.

Such rote work is particularly troubling in the area of proportional reasoning, which is at the core of so many important concepts students will encounter during and after middle school, including "similarity, relative growth and size, dilations, scaling, pi, constant rate of change, slope, speed, rates, percent, trigonometric ratios, probability, relative frequency, density, and direct and inverse variations" (Heinz & Sterba-Boatwright, 2008, p. 528). Wow!

Considerable research has been conducted to determine how children reason in various proportionality tasks and to determine if developmental or instructional factors are related to proportional reasoning (for example, see Bright, Joyner, & Wallis, 2003; Karplus, Pulos, & Stage, 1983; Lamon, 1993, 2002; Lo & Watanabe, 1997; Noelting, 1980; and Post, Behr, & Lesh, 1988).

The research provides direction for how to help children develop proportional thought processes. These ideas are summarized in the following list:

1. Provide ratio and proportion tasks in a wide range of contexts, including situations involving measurements, prices, geometric and other visual contexts, and rates of all sorts.
2. Encourage discussion and experimentation in predicting and comparing ratios. Help children distinguish between proportional and nonproportional comparisons by providing examples of each and discussing the differences.
3. Help children relate proportional reasoning to existing processes. The concept of unit fractions is very similar to unit rates. Research indicates that the use of a unit rate for comparing ratios and solving proportions is the most common approach among middle school students even when cross-product methods have been taught. (This approach is explained later.)
4. Recognize that symbolic or mechanical methods, such as the cross-product algorithm, for solving proportions do not develop proportional reasoning and should not be introduced until students have had many experiences with intuitive and conceptual methods.

In 1989, the *Curriculum Standards* noted that proportional reasoning "was of such great importance that it merits whatever time and effort must be expended to assure its careful development" (NCTM, 1989, p. 82). The emphasis on proportional reasoning is similarly reflected in *Principles and Standards*, where emphasis is on the need for an integrative approach, one that involves "percent, similarity, scaling,

myeducationlab

Go to the Activities and Application section of Chapter 18 of MyEducationLab. Click on Videos and watch the video entitled "**John Van de Walle on Proportional Reasoning**" to see him talk with teachers about proportional reasoning.

linear equations, slope, relative frequency histograms, and probability" (NCTM, 2000, p. 212). ◆

Additive Versus Multiplicative Situations

Consider the following problem adapted from the book *Adding It Up* (National Research Council, 2001).

Two weeks ago, two flowers were measured at 8 inches and 12 inches, respectively. Today they are 11 inches and 15 inches tall. Did the 8-inch or 12-inch flower grow more?

❚❚ ——————————— *Pause and Reflect*

Before reading further, find and defend two different answers to this problem.

One answer is that they both grew the same amount—3 inches. This correct response is based on additive reasoning. That is, a single quantity was added to each measure to result in the two new measures. A second way to look at the problem is to compare the amount of growth to the original height of the flower. The first flower grew $\frac{3}{8}$ of its height while the second grew $\frac{3}{12}$. Based on this multiplicative view ($\frac{3}{8}$ *times as much* more), the first flower grew more. This is a proportional view of this change situation. Here, both the additive reasoning and multiplicative reasoning produce valid, albeit different, answers. Discussions should focus on the comparison and, thus, highlight the distinction between additive and multiplicative comparisons. An ability to understand the difference between these situations is an indication of proportional reasoning.

 To further help you understand the complexities of proportional reasoning, consider the five-item assessment shown in Figure 18.1, devised to examine students' appropriate use of additive or multiplicative reasoning (Bright, Joyner, & Wallis, 2003). Notice the way each item addresses the possibility of using additive versus multiplicative reasoning. This instrument could easily be used in the classroom as a preassessment, as a series of good classroom tasks to then be discussed, or as a summative assessment to see how well students have acquired an understanding of multiplicative comparisons. In item 1, you might want to explain that the 200 percent setting doubles each dimension of the photo. ◆

❚❚ ——————————— *Pause and Reflect*

Answer the questions in Figure 18.1. Discuss your answers with your colleagues. Which item is not a proportional situation? What is the difference between items 2 and 4?

For each problem, circle the correct answer.

1. Mrs. Allen took a 3-inch by 5-inch photo of the Cape Hatteras Lighthouse and made an enlargement on a photocopier using the 200% option. Which is "more square," the original photo or the enlargement?
   a. The original photo is "more square."
   b. The enlargement is "more square."
   c. The photo and the enlargement are equally square.
   d. There is not enough information to determine which is "more square."

2. The Science Club has four separate rectangular plots for experiments with plants:

1 foot by 4 feet	7 feet by 10 feet
17 feet by 20 feet	27 feet by 30 feet

   Which rectangular plot is most square?
   a. 1 foot by 4 feet
   b. 7 feet by 10 feet
   c. 17 feet by 20 feet
   d. 27 feet by 30 feet

3. Sue and Julie were running equally fast around a track. Sue started first. When Sue had run 9 laps, Julie had run 3 laps. When Julie completed 15 laps, how many laps had Sue run?
   a. 45 laps
   b. 24 laps
   c. 21 laps
   d. 6 laps

4. At the midway point of the basketball season, you must recommend the best free-throw shooter for the all-star game. Here are the statistics for four players:

Novak: 8 of 11 shots	Peterson: 22 of 29 shots
Williams: 15 of 19 shots	Reynolds: 33 of 41 shots

   Which player is the best free-throw shooter?
   a. Novak   b. Peterson   c. Williams   d. Reynolds

5. Write your answer to this problem.

   A farmer has three fields. One is 185 feet by 245 feet, one is 75 feet by 114 feet, and one is 455 feet by 508 feet. If you were flying over these fields, which one would seem most square? Which one would seem least square? Explain your answers.

Figure 18.1 Five items to assess proportional reasoning.
Source: Reprinted with permission from Bright, G. W., Joyner, J. J., & Wallis, C. (2003). "Assessing Proportional Thinking." *Mathematics Teaching in the Middle School, 9*(3), p. 167. Copyright © 2003 by the National Council of Teachers of Mathematics, Inc. www.nctm.org. All rights reserved.

Notice that the items involving rectangles (1, 2, and 5) cannot be answered correctly using additive reasoning, as could the flower-growth problem discussed previously. For a group of 132 eighth- and ninth-grade students, item

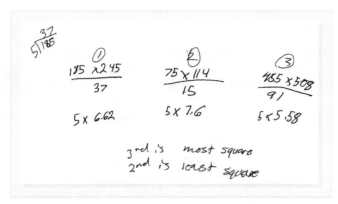

Figure 18.2 Jacob noticed that each length was divisible by 5; therefore, he simplified each ratio to have a side of 5 and then compared the widths.

2 was the easiest (67 percent correct). The percentage correct on the other three multiple-choice items ranged only from 45 percent to 59 percent correct. The open-response item, number 5, proved quite difficult (37 percent correct for most square, 28 percent correct for least square). Over 52 percent of the students selected the 75 × 114 rectangle as the most square, and 45 percent selected the 185 × 245 rectangle as the least square.

Item 5 was given to an eighth grader, who first solved it incorrectly, using an additive strategy (subtracting the sides). When asked if a very large rectangle, 1,000,000 by 1,000,050 would look less square, he replied, "No—oh, this is a proportional situation." He then solved it using a novel strategy (see Figure 18.2).

Identifying Multiplicative Relationships

As noted earlier, students may confuse additive situations for multiplicative situations. Making explicit the type of relationships that exist between two values can greatly support students' understanding of ratios and proportions. Using the multiplication chart, as recommended in *Curriculum Focal Points* (NCTM, 2006), is one way to nurture this understanding. Consider the following sample problem suggested by Cai and Sun in their discussion of how teachers in Chinese classrooms introduce the concept of ratio (2002, p. 196):

> Miller Middle School has 16 sixth-grade students, and 12 of them say that they are basketball fans. The remaining students are not basketball fans.

Students are asked to describe whatever relationships they can between students who are basketball fans and those who are not. Once it is determined that there are four nonfans, there are now several different possibilities including the following:

- There are eight more fans than nonfans.
- There are three times as many fans as nonfans.
- For every three students who like basketball, there is one who does not.

Of these, the first is an additive relationship—focusing on the difference between the two numbers. The other two are variations of the multiplicative relationship, each expressing the 3-to-1 ratio of fans to nonfans in a slightly different way. A discussion helps to contrast the multiplicative relationship with the additive one.

In the following activities, two ratios are compared. As with the earlier flower-growing problem, the choices can be made using either additive or multiplicative reasoning, providing your class with a helpful distinction between the two types of relationships without your attempt to define ratio for them.

Activity 18.1

Which Has More?

Provide students with two or three situations similar to those in Figure 18.3. Whether students work individually or in groups, a follow-up class discussion is imperative. This discussion can provide you with insights into how students are thinking and can also provide opportunities for students to help others see the situations from different perspectives.

Do not prompt students by telling them to look for a multiplicative relationship, but wait to see what sort of answers the students provide.

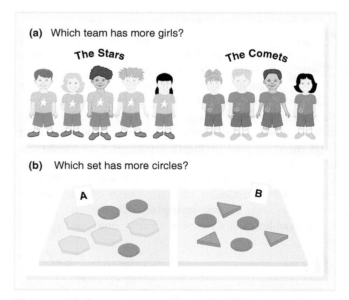

Figure 18.3 Two pictorial situations that can be interpreted with either additive or multiplicative comparisons.

The situations in Figure 18.3 can be interpreted either additively or multiplicatively. The ambiguity is the key: If students recognize and understand the difference between the additive and multiplicative approaches, this is a beginning to being able to reason proportionally. As with the flower problem, both interpretations are correct. You are looking for an awareness that there is a different way of looking at the situation. If at first they do not voluntarily suggest another way, ask a different question: for example, "Amy says it is the second group. Can you explain why she made that choice?" or "Which class team has a larger proportion of girls?"

Return for a moment to item 3 in Figure 18.1. This item has been used in other studies showing that students try to solve this as a proportion problem when it is strictly an additive situation. The two runners will end up six laps apart, which is how they began. Watson and Shaughnessy (2004) note that often the way that we word problems is a dead giveaway that a proportion is involved. Students also recognize the current unit of study is proportional reasoning and then set up proportions even when it is not appropriate, as in item 3. Students have learned how to arrange four quantities in a proportion, but they aren't paying attention to whether there is a multiplicative relationship between the numbers. They are focused on the structure of the proportion, not the concept of the proportion (Heinz & Boatwright, 2008).

The next problem is similar to the flower problem discussed earlier, allowing an additive or multiplicative interpretation.

Equivalent Ratios

In selection activities, a ratio is presented, and students select an equivalent ratio from others presented. The focus should be on an intuitive rationale for why the pairs selected are in the same ratio. Sometimes numeric values will play a part to help students develop numeric methods to explain their reasoning. In later activities, students will be asked to construct an equivalent ratio without choices being provided.

It is extremely useful in these activities to include pairs of ratios that are not proportional but have a common difference. For example, $\frac{5}{8}$ and $\frac{9}{12}$ are not equivalent ratios, but the corresponding differences are the same: $8 - 5 = 12 - 9$. Students who focus on this additive relationship are not seeing the multiplicative relationship of proportionality. Using contexts in comparing ratios helps students articulate their multiplicative or proportional thinking. Activity 18.3 uses sides of a rectangle as the context (linking to the important concepts of similarity and scale drawings).

Activity 18.2

Weight Loss

Show students the data in the following chart:

Week	Max	Moe	Minnie
0	210	158	113
2	202	154	108
4	196	150	105

Max, Moe, and Minnie are each on a diet and have recorded their weight at the start of their diet and at two-week intervals. After four weeks, which person is the most successful dieter?

The task is to make three different arguments—each favoring a different dieter.

Activity 18.3

Look-Alike Rectangles

Provide groups of students with a copy of Blackline Masters 30 and 31 shown in Figure 18.4 and have them cut out the ten rectangles. Three of the rectangles (A, I, and D) have sides in the ratio of 3 to 4. Rectangles C, F, and H have sides in the ratio of 5 to 8. J, E, and G have sides in the ratio of 1 to 3. Rectangle B is a square, so its sides are in the ratio of 1 to 1.

The task is to group the rectangles into three sets of three that "look alike" with one "oddball." If your students know the word *similar* from geometry, you can use that instead of "look alike." To explain what "look alike" means, draw three rectangles on the

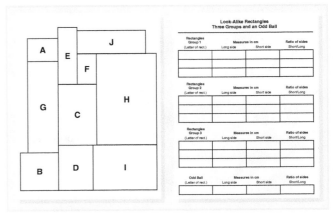

Figure 18.4 Blackline Masters 30 and 31 for use with Activity 18.3.

The way that the task in "Weight Loss" is presented, the students are forewarned that there are differing arguments and the results will assure a good discussion. (The argument for Moe is that he is the most steady in his loss.)

board with two that are similar and one that is clearly dissimilar to the other two, as in the following example. Have students use their language to explain why rectangles 1 and 3 are alike.

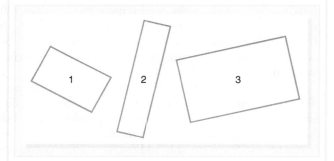

When students have decided on their groupings, stop and discuss the reasons they classified the rectangles as they did. Be prepared for some students to try to match sides or look for rectangles that have the same amount of difference between them. Next have the students measure and record the sides of each rectangle to the nearest half-centimeter. They should then calculate the ratios of the short to long sides for each. Blackline Master 31 can be used to record the data. Discuss these results and ask students to offer explanations of how the ratios and groupings are related. If the groups are formed of proportional (similar) rectangles, the ratios within each group will all be the same.

From a geometric standpoint, "Look-Alike Rectangles" is an activity concerning similarity. The two concepts—proportionality and similarity—are closely connected.

Another characteristic of proportional rectangles can be observed by stacking like rectangles aligned at one corner, as in Figure 18.5. Place a straightedge across the diagonals, and you will see that opposite corners also line up. If the rectangles are placed on a coordinate axis with the common corner at the origin, the slope of the line joining the corners is the ratio of the sides. Here is a connection between proportional reasoning and algebra.

Activity 18.4

Different Objects, Same Ratios

Prepare cards with distinctly different objects, as shown in Figure 18.6. Given one card, students are to select a card on which the ratio of the two types of objects is the same. This task moves students toward a numeric approach rather than a visual one and introduces the notion of ratios as rates. In this context, it makes the most sense to find the boxes per truck as the rate (rather than trucks per box). Finding the rate (amount for 1 unit) for pairs of quantities facilitates comparisons (like the unit prices provided in grocery stores to allow you to compare different products).

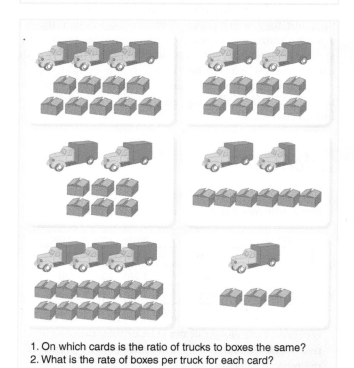

1. On which cards is the ratio of trucks to boxes the same?
2. What is the rate of boxes per truck for each card?

Figure 18.6 Ratio cards for exploring ratios and rates.

Differerent Ratios

An understanding of proportional situations includes being able to compare two ratios as well as to identify equivalent ratios. The following activity has been used in various studies of proportional reasoning.

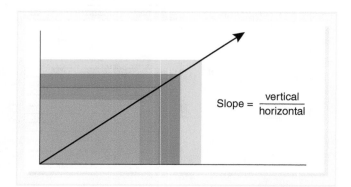

$$\text{Slope} = \frac{\text{vertical}}{\text{horizontal}}$$

Figure 18.5 The slope of a line through a stack of proportional rectangles is equal to the ratio of the two sides.

Activity 18.5

Lemonade Recipes

Show students a picture of two lemonade pitchers as in Figure 18.7. The pitchers each have the same amount of lemonade. The little squares indicate the recipes used in each pitcher. A yellow square is a cup of lemonade concentrate and the blue square is a cup of water. Ask which pitcher will have the stronger lemonade flavor or whether they will both taste the same. Ask them to justify their answers.

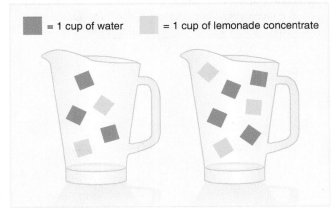

■ = 1 cup of water   ■ = 1 cup of lemonade concentrate

Figure 18.7 A comparing ratios problem: Which pitcher will have the stronger lemon flavor, or will they be the same?

❚❚ ——————— *Pause and Reflect*

Solve the lemonade problem and write down your reasoning. Is there more than one way to justify the answer?

The task in "Lemonade Recipes" is challenging for many students. It is interesting because of how many ways there are to make the comparison. A common method is to figure out how much water goes with each cup of lemonade mix. As we will see later, this is using a unit rate: cups of water per cup of lemonade mix ($1\frac{1}{2}$ vs. $1\frac{1}{3}$). Other approaches use fractions instead of unit rates and attempt to compare the fractions: lemonade mix compared to water ($\frac{2}{3}$ vs. $\frac{3}{4}$) or the reverse, and also lemonade mix as a fraction of the total ($\frac{2}{5}$ vs. $\frac{3}{7}$). This can also be done with water as a fraction of the total. Some students may also use percentages instead of fractions, creating the same arguments. Another way to justify is to use multiples of one or both of the pitchers until either the water or the lemonade mix is equal in both.

One interesting argument is that the pitchers will taste the same: If the lemonade mix and water are matched up in

> **myeducationlab**
>
> Go to the Building Teaching Skills and Dispositions section of Chapter 18 of MyEducationLab. Click on Expanded Lessons to download the Expanded Lesson for **"Lemonade Recipes"** and complete the related activities.

each pitcher, then there will be one cup of water left in each recipe. Although incorrect (can you tell why?), your class will likely have a spirited discussion of these ideas.

The lemonade task can be adjusted for difficulty. As given, the two mixtures are reasonably close and there are no simple relationships between the two pitchers. If the solutions are 3 to 6 and 4 to 8 (equal flavors), the task is much simpler. For a 2-to-5 recipe versus a 4-to-9 recipe, it is easy to double the first and compare it to the second. When a 3-to-6 recipe is compared to a 2-to-5 recipe, the unit rates are perhaps more obvious (1 to 2 vs. 1 to $2\frac{1}{2}$).

The following problem also is adapted from the research literature.

Two camps of Scouts are having pizza parties. The Bear Camp ordered enough so that every 3 campers will have 2 pizzas. The leader of the Raccoons ordered enough so that there would be 3 pizzas for every 5 campers. Did the Bear campers or the Raccoon campers have more pizza to eat?

Figure 18.8 shows two different reasoning strategies. When the pizzas are sliced up into fractional parts as in Figure 18.8(a), the approach is to look for a unit rate—pizzas per camper. A sharing approach has been used for each ratio. But notice that this problem does not say that the camps have only 3 and 5 campers, respectively. Any multiples of 2 to 3 and 3 to 5 can be used to make the appropriate comparison, the same as making multiple pitchers of lemonade. This is the approach used in Figure 18.8(b). Three "clones" of the 2-to-3 ratio and two clones of the 3-to-5 ratio are made so that the number of campers getting a like number of pizzas can be compared. From a vantage of fractions, this

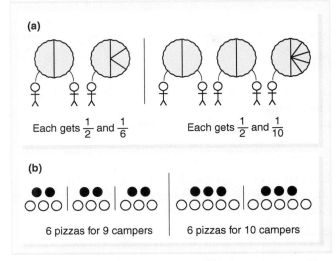

(a) Each gets $\frac{1}{2}$ and $\frac{1}{6}$ Each gets $\frac{1}{2}$ and $\frac{1}{10}$

(b) 6 pizzas for 9 campers   6 pizzas for 10 campers

Figure 18.8 Two reasoning methods for comparing two ratios.

Connected Mathematics

Grade 7, *Comparing and Scaling*
Investigation 3: Comparing and Using Ratios

Context

This investigation occurs in the second week of the unit on ratio and proportions. In earlier activities, students explored ratios and percents to compare survey data from large populations with similar data gathered from their own class. Students used fractions, decimals, and percents to express ratios, and they compared ratios using their own strategies.

Task Description

In the juice problem shown (2.1: Mixing Juice), students apply proportional reasoning to figure out which recipe is the most orangey and which is the least orangey. Students are to apply their knowledge of ratios to reason to a solution. Students have solved this task in a variety of ways, including:

1. Make equal amounts of each recipe to compare (e.g., make 120 cups of each).

2. Make the cups of concentrate the same and look at how much water goes with each (e.g., for 30 cups of concentrate, how much water is needed for each recipe?).

3. Find part-to-whole fractions, find common denominators, and compare.

4. Find part-to-whole fractions, convert to percents, and compare.

5. Draw pictures to show how much water per cup of concentrate. For example, for Mix D:

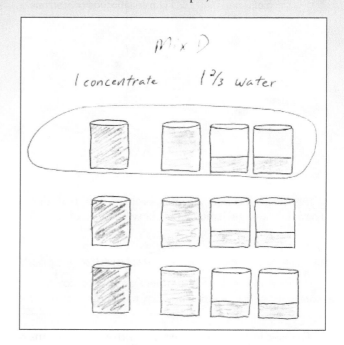

is like getting common numerators. Because there are more campers in the Raccoon ratio (larger denominator), there is less pizza for each camper.

Ratio Tables

Ratio tables or charts that show how two variable quantities are related are often good ways to organize information. Consider the following table:

Acres	5	10	15	20	25		
Pine trees	75	150	225				

If the task is to find the number of trees for 65 acres of land or the number of acres needed for 750 trees, students can proceed by using addition. That is, they can add 5s along the top row until they reach 65. This is a recursive pattern, or repeated addition strategy. The pattern that connects acres to pine trees ($\times 15$) is the generative pattern and the multiplicative relationship between the values. The equation for this situation is $y = 15x$, a proportional situation.

Ratio tables may not always be in organized lists where a pattern can be found. In fact, ratio tables can be used when only one ratio is known and you are trying to find a

The context of this problem, a familiar one, allows students to apply their own creative and clever strategies to solve a proportional situation without instructions on *how* to solve the problem.

The full unit contains six investigations, each with numerous real contexts. Scaling, the use of unit rates, and percentages are suggested techniques for solving the proportional situations.

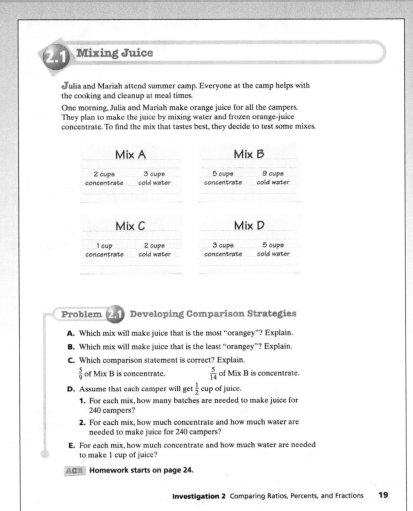

specific equivalent ratio. Then the ratio table can be used as a strategy for solving a proportion. The following activity provides examples and Figure 18.9 gives illustrations of this use of a ratio table.

Activity 18.6
Using Ratio Tables

Build a ratio table and use it to answer the question. Tasks are adapted from Lamon (1999, p. 183).

- **A person who weighs 160 pounds on Earth will weigh 416 pounds on the planet Jupiter. How much will a person weigh on Jupiter who weighs 120 pounds on earth?**
- **At the local college, five out of every eight seniors live in apartments. How many of the 30 senior math majors are likely to live in an apartment?**
- **The tax on a purchase of $20 is $1.12. How much tax will there be on a purchase of $45.50?**
- **When in Australia you can exchange $4.50 in U.S. dollars for $6 Australian. How much is $17.50 Australian in U.S. dollars?**

The tasks in this activity are typical "solve the proportion" tasks. One ratio and part of a second are given

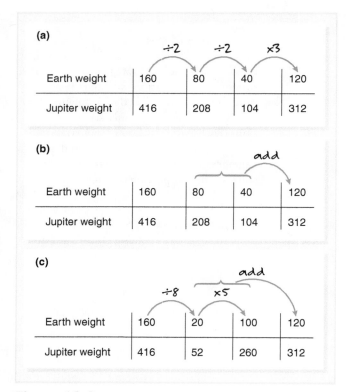

Figure 18.9 160 pounds on Earth is 416 pounds on Jupiter. If something weighs 120 pounds on Earth, how many pounds would it weigh on Jupiter? Three solutions using ratio tables.

	Pounds	Cost	Notes
A	1	4.25	Given
B	10	42.50	A × 10
C	2	8.50	A × 2
D	0.1	0.425	A ÷ 10
E	12.1	51.425	B + C + D
F	0.01	0.0425	D ÷ 10
G	0.03	0.1275	F × 3
H	12.13	51.5525	E + G

Figure 18.10 A more structured ratio table. The Notes column shows what was done in each step. The task is to find the cost of 12.13 pounds.

Cheese is $4.25 per pound. How much will 12.13 pounds cost?

with the task being to find the fourth number. However, tasks such as these should come long before any formal approach is suggested. Further note that in no case is it easy to simply add or subtract to get to the desired entry. Rather, the student should use a ratio table to find equivalent ratios that lead to a desired result. Figure 18.9 shows three different ways to solve the Jupiter weight task using ratio tables.

The format of these ratio tables is not at all important. Some students may not use a table format at all and simply draw arrows and explain in words how they got from one ratio to another. You may find value in a more structured format.

Pause and Reflect

Use a ratio table strategy to solve the last three problems from Activity 18.6. Describe any advantages this approach has over a cross-product algorithm?

The following problem and the table in Figure 18.10 are taken from Lamon (1999, p. 233). Notice that the numbers are not "nice" at all.

The format in Figure 18.10 allows for easier tracing of what was done at each step. The format is just that—a format. It is not the same as an algorithm. For any problem there are likely to be several different reasonable ratio tables. In applying this technique, students are using multiplicative relationships to transform a given ratio into an equivalent ratio. As Lamon points out, the process is not at all random. Students should mentally devise a plan for getting from one number to another.

The tasks suggested in Activity 18.6 have quite reasonable numbers. However, as you can see from the cheese example, it is quite possible to use this technique with almost any numbers. By using easy multiples and divisors, often the arithmetic can be done mentally.

 It should be clear to students why the same factor must be used on both entries in a ratio table. For example, in row B of Figure 18.10, both the 1 and 4.25 are multiplied by 10. In row G, both parts are multiplied by 3. Each pair of entries comprises a ratio. An equivalent ratio is found by multiplying both parts by the same number. ◆

Proportional Reasoning Across the Curriculum

As noted at the start of this chapter, proportional reasoning is essential to many concepts in the curriculum. Here are some brief examples in algebra, measurement and geometry, statistics, and number.

Algebra

Graphing ratios provides a powerful connection to algebra. As discussed earlier in this chapter, proportional situations are linear situations. In fact, ratios are a special case of linear situations that will always go through the origin, since they are multiplicative relationships. The ratio or rate is the slope of the graph.

Any ratio table provides data that can be graphed. Make each axis correspond to one of the quantities in the table. This idea is developed in the next activity.

Activity 18.7

Rectangle Ratios—Revisited

Have students make a graph of the data from a collection of equal ratios that they have scaled or discussed. The graph in Figure 18.11 is based on the ratios of two sides of similar rectangles. If only a few ratios have actually been plotted, the graph can be drawn carefully and then used to determine other equivalent ratios. In the rectangle example, students can draw rectangles with sides determined by the graphs and compare them to the original rectangles. A unit ratio can be found by locating the point on the line at $x = 1$ or at $y = 1$. Ask students to find the rate each way. Ask students to see if they can find a rectangle that has a noninteger side (e.g., $4\frac{1}{2}$ units). Ask students how, if they know the short side, they could find the long side (and vice versa).

Graphs provide another way of thinking about proportions, and they connect proportional thought to algebraic interpretations. All graphs of equivalent ratios fall along straight lines that pass through the origin. If the equation of one of these lines is written in the form $y = mx$, the slope m is always one of the equivalent ratios. Note that the slope of any line through the origin is the ratio of the y-coordinate at any point with the x-coordinate of the same point.

Measurement and Geometry

In these activities, students make measurements or construct physical or visual models of equivalent ratios in order to provide a tangible example of a proportion as well as look at numeric relationships.

Activity 18.8

Different Units, Equal Ratios

Cut strips of adding machine tape all the same length, and give one strip to each group in your class. Each group is to measure the strip using a different non-standard unit. Possible units include different Cuisenaire rods, a piece of chalk, a pencil, or the edge of a book or index card. When every group has measured the strip, ask for the measure of one of the groups, and display the unit of measure. Next, hold up the unit of measure used by another group, and have the class compare it with the first unit. See if the class can estimate the measurement that the second group found. The ratio of the measuring units should be the inverse of the measurements made with those units. For example, if two units are in a ratio of 2 to 3, the respective measures will be in a ratio of 3 to 2. Examine measurements made with other units. Finally, present a unit that no group has used, and see if the class can predict the measurement when made with that unit.

Activity 18.8 can be extended by providing each group with an identical set of four strips of quite different lengths. Good lengths might be 20, 50, 80, and 120 cm. As before, each group is given a different unit to measure the strips.

This time, have each group enter data into a common spreadsheet. (Alternatively, share group data so that all groups can enter data on their own spreadsheets.) Figure 18.12 shows what a spreadsheet might look like for three

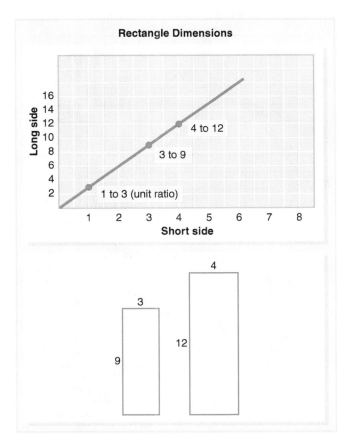

Figure 18.11 Graphs show ratios of sides in similar rectangles.

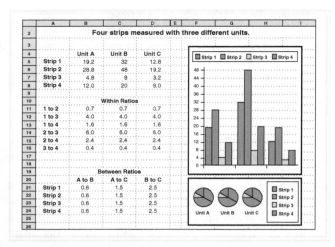

Figure 18.12 A spreadsheet can be used to record data, create tables of interesting ratios, and produce bar and circle graphs.

Source: Screen reprinted with permission from Apple Computer, Inc.

groups. A template can be prepared ahead of time, or students can create their own spreadsheets. Almost all spreadsheets will offer a variety of graphing options. In this activity, bar graphs show the actual measurements for each group and circle graphs show each measure in ratio to the sum of the measures (i.e., a percentage of total measures.)

Once the graphs are completed, there are numerous opportunities to observe and explore multiplicative relationships within and between ratios. The bar graphs, though different in size, all look "alike." Since the circle graphs illustrate the ratios rather than the actual measurements, they will be identical or nearly so. Within ratios (for a set of strips) and between ratios (one unit to another) are easily calculated with the spreadsheet. (Within and between ratios are discussed later in the chapter.)

Continue the exploration by introducing a new strip. If you know its measure with any one of the units, what will its measure be with the other units? Similarly, if a new unit of measure is introduced, how can the measures of the strips be determined? Can this be done by comparing the new unit with an old one? If a known strip is measured with the new unit, can all other measures and ratios be determined?

The task just described may take several days to complete with students, but the time is well spent, as students are able to solidify the different multiplicative relationships through numeric and graphic representations.

Scale Drawings

The connection between proportional reasoning and the geometric concept of similarity is very important. Similar figures provide a visual representation of proportions, and proportional thinking enhances the understanding of similarity. Discussion of the similar figures should focus on the ratios between and within the figures. The next activity is aimed at this connection.

Activity 18.9

Scale Drawings

On grid or dot paper (see Blackline Masters 34–37), have students draw a simple shape using straight lines with vertices on the dots. After one shape is complete, have them draw a larger or smaller shape that looks similar to the first. This can be done on a grid of the same size or a different size, as shown in Figure 18.13. First compare ratios within (see the first problem in Figure 18.13). Then compare ratios between the figures (see the second problem in Figure 18.13).

Corresponding sides from one figure to the next should all be in the same ratio. The ratio of two sides within one figure should be the same as the ratio of the corresponding two sides in another figure.

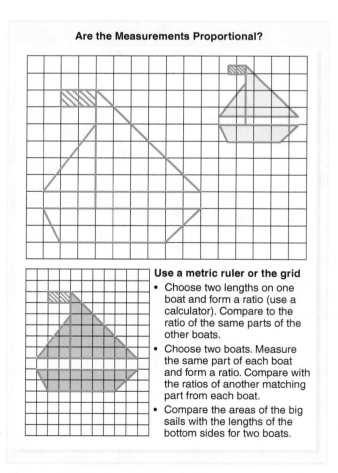

Figure 18.13 Comparing similar figures drawn on grids.

Part three of Activity 18.9 involves area as well as length. Comparisons of corresponding lengths, areas, and volumes in proportional figures lead to some interesting patterns. If two figures are proportional (similar), any two linear dimensions you measure will be in the same ratio on each, say, 1 to k (the variable k is often used with proportions, whereas m is used with equations to describe slope—both refer to the rate or ratio between two values). That means if a similar figure is twice the length of the original figure, then each corresponding side is in a ratio of original to new figure of 1:2. To find the length of a new side, you multiply by 2, which is the value of k in this case.

Imagine you have a square that is 3 by 3 and you create a new square that is 6 by 6. The ratio between the lengths is 1:2. What is the ratio between the two areas? Why is it 1:4? Try the same concept for volume of a cube—what is the relationship of the original to the new volume? Why? Returning to the sailboat in Figure 18.13, what would you conjecture is the ratio between the areas of the two sailboats? Measure and test your hypothesis.

As a means of contrasting proportional situations with additive ones, try starting with a figure on a grid or a building made with blocks and adding two units to every dimension in the figure. The result will be larger but will be a similar shape. Try this with a simple rectangle that is 1 cm by 15 cm. The new rectangle is twice as "thick" (2 cm) but only a bit longer. It will not appear to be the same shape as the original.

 Dynamic geometry software such as *GeoGebra* (a free download from www.geogebra.org/cms) or *The Geometer's Sketchpad* (Key Curriculum Press) offers a very effective method of exploring the idea of ratio. In Figure 18.14, two lengths are drawn on a grid using the "snap-to-grid" option. The lengths are measured, and two ratios are computed. As the length of either line is changed, the measures and ratios are updated instantly. A screen similar to this could be used to discuss ratios of lengths as well as inverse ratios with your full class. In this example, notice that the second pair of lines has the same difference but that the ratios are not the same. A similar drawing could be prepared for the overhead on a transparency of a centimeter dot grid if software is not available.

You can also explore similar figures and corresponding measures. Using the Dilate feature, a figure can be drawn and then dilated (reduced or enlarged proportionally) according to any scale factor of your choosing. The ratios of beginning and ending measures (lengths and areas) can then be compared to the scale factor. All of the computations can be done within the software program. ◆

More interesting situations to consider for scale drawings are shown in the following list:

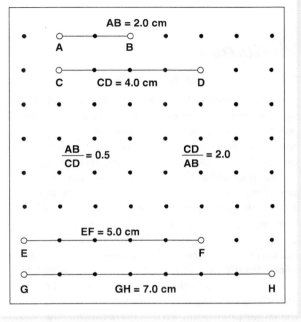

Figure 18.14 Dynamic geometry software or just a centimeter grid can be used to discuss ratios of two lengths.
Source: From *The Geometer's Sketchpad*, Key Curriculum Press, 1150 65th Street, Emeryville, CA 94608, 1-800-995-MATH, www.keypress.com. Reprinted by permission.

- If you wanted to make a scale model of the solar system and use a Ping-Pong ball for the earth, how far away should the sun be? How large a ball would you need?
- What scale should be used to draw a scale map of your city (or some interesting region) so that it will nicely fit onto a standard piece of poster board?
- Use the scale on a map to estimate the distance and travel time between two points of interest.
- Roll a toy car down a ramp, timing the trip with a stopwatch. How fast was the car traveling in miles per hour? If the speed is proportional to the size of the car, how fast would this have been for a real car?
- Your little sister wants a table and chair for her doll. Her doll is 14 inches tall. How big should you make the table?
- Determine the various distances that a ten-speed bike travels in one turn of the pedals. You will need to count the sprocket teeth on the front and back gears.

Statistics

Have you ever wondered how scientists estimate wildlife counts such as the number of bass in a lake or the number of monarch butterflies that migrate each year to Mexico? One method often used is a capture-recapture technique modeled in the next activity.

Activity 18.10

Capture-Recapture

Prepare a shoebox full of some uniform small object such as centicubes or plastic chips. You could also use a larger box filled with Styrofoam packing "peanuts." If the box is your lake and the objects are the fish you want to count, how can you estimate the number without actually counting them? Remember, if they were fish, you couldn't even see them! Have a student reach into the box and "capture" a representative sample of the "fish." For a large box, you may want to capture more than a handful. "Tag" each fish by marking it in some way—marking pen or sticky dot. Count and record the number tagged and then return them to the box. The assumption of the scientist is that tagged animals will mix uniformly with the larger population, so mix them thoroughly. Next, have five to ten students make a recapture of fish from the box. Each counts the total captured and the number in the capture that are tagged. Accumulate these data.

Now the task is to use all of the information to estimate the number of fish in the lake. The recapture data provide an estimated ratio of tagged to untagged fish. The number tagged to the total population should be in the same ratio. After solving the proportion, have students count the actual items in the box to see how close their estimate is.

For a more detailed description of the "Capture-Recapture" activity, see the NCTM Addenda Series book *Understanding Rational Numbers and Proportions* (Curcio & Bezuk, 1994).

Number: Fractions and Percent

Percent has traditionally been included as a topic with ratio and proportion because percent is one form of ratio, a part-to-whole ratio. In an earlier chapter, it was shown that percent problems can be connected to fraction concepts. Here the same part-to-whole fraction concept of percent will be extended to ratio and proportion concepts. Ideally, all of these ideas (fractions, decimals, ratio, proportion, and percent) should be conceptually integrated. The better that students connect these ideas, the more flexible and useful their reasoning and problem-solving skills will be.

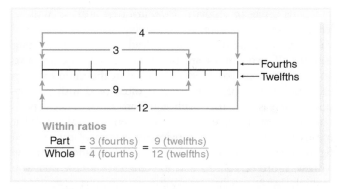

Figure 18.15 Equivalent fractions as proportions.

Equivalent Fractions. First consider how equivalent fractions can be interpreted as a proportion using the same simple models already used. In Figure 18.15, a line segment is partitioned in two different ways: in fourths on one side and in twelfths on the other. In the previous examples, proportions were established based on two amounts of apples, two different distances or runs, and two different sizes of drawings. Here only one thing is measured—the part of a whole—but it is measured or partitioned two ways: in fourths and in twelfths.

A simple line segment drawing similar to the one in Figure 18.15 could be drawn to set up a proportion to solve any equivalent-fraction problem, even ones that do not result in whole-number numerators or denominators. An example is shown in Figure 18.16.

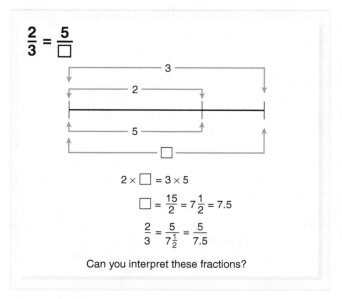

Figure 18.16 Solving equivalent-fraction problems as equivalent ratios using cross-products.

Percents. All percent problems are exactly the same as the equivalent-fraction examples. They involve a part and a whole measured in some unit and the same part and whole measured in hundredths—that is, in percents. A simple line segment drawing can be used for each of the three types of percent problems. Let the measures on one side of the line correspond to the numbers or measures in the problem. On the opposite side of the line, indicate the corresponding values in terms of percents. Label the segments of the line rather than endpoints. Examples of each type of problem are shown in Figure 18.17.

Notice how flexible this simple line model is for every type of percent problem. It allows modeling of not only part-whole scenarios but also increase-decrease situations and those in which there is a comparison between two distinct quantities. One of each of these is included in Figure 18.17. Another advantage of the line model is that it does not restrict students from thinking about percents greater than 100 as does a circle graph or a 10 × 10 grid (Parker, 2004).

Proportions

The activities to this point have been designed to lead students to an intuitive concept of ratio and proportion to help in the development of proportional reasoning.

One practical value of proportional reasoning is to use observed proportions to find unknown values. Knowledge of one ratio can often be used to find a value in the other. Comparison pricing, using scales on maps, and solving percentage problems are just a few everyday instances where solving proportions is required. Students need to learn to set up proportions symbolically and to solve them.

NCTM Standards "Attention to developing flexibility in working with rational numbers contributes to students' understanding of, and facility with, proportionality. Facility with proportionality involves much more than setting two ratios equal and solving for a missing term. It involves recognizing quantities that are related proportionally and using numbers, tables, graphs, and equations to think about the quantities and their relationship" (p. 217). ◆

A *proportion* is a statement of equality between two ratios. If 4 boats carry 36 passengers, then 2 boats of the same size will carry 18 passengers, 3 boats will carry 27 passengers, and 20 boats will carry 180 passengers. Here the ratio of 4 to 36 can be applied to each of these situations even though the measures are different in each case.

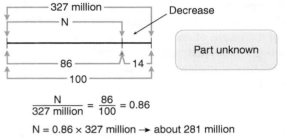

In 1960, U.S. railroads carried 327 million passengers. Over the next 20 years, there was a 14 percent decrease in passengers. How many passengers rode the railroads in 1980?

$$\frac{N}{327 \text{ million}} = \frac{86}{100} = 0.86$$

N = 0.86 × 327 million → about 281 million

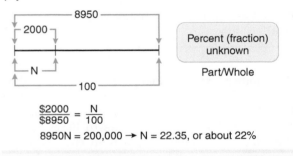

Sylvia's new boat cost $8950. She made a down payment of $2000. What percent of the sales price was Sylvia's down payment?

$$\frac{\$2000}{\$8950} = \frac{N}{100}$$

8950N = 200,000 → N = 22.35, or about 22%

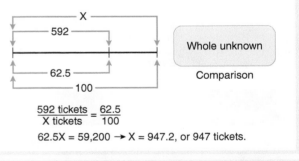

The seventh- and eighth-grade classes at Robious Middle School had a contest to see which class would sell more raffle tickets at the school festival. The eighth grade sold 592 tickets. However, this turned out to be only 62.5 percent of the number of tickets sold by the seventh grade. How many tickets did the seventh grade sell?

$$\frac{592 \text{ tickets}}{X \text{ tickets}} = \frac{62.5}{100}$$

62.5X = 59,200 → X = 947.2, or 947 tickets.

Figure 18.17 Percentage problems solved by setting up a proportion using a simple line-segment model.

Within and Between Ratios

When examining two ratios, it is useful to think of them as being either *within* ratios or *between* ratios. A ratio of two measures in the same setting is a *within* ratio. For example, in the case of similar rectangles, the ratio of length to width for any one rectangle is a within ratio, that is, it is "within" the context of that rectangle. For all similar rectangles, corresponding within ratios will be equal.

A *between* ratio is a ratio of two corresponding measures in different situations. In the case of similar rectangles, the ratio of the length of one rectangle to the length of another is a between ratio; that is, it is "between" the two rectangles. For two similar rectangles, all of the between ratios will be equal.

⏸ ———————————— *Pause and Reflect*

Consider three rectangles *A*, *B*, and *C*. *A* measures 2 × 6, *B* measures 3 × 9, and *C* measures 8 × 24. Find the within ratio for each rectangle. This should convince you that the rectangles are similar. Now examine the between ratios for *A* and *B* and for *A* and *C*. Why are these ratios different?

As another example Figure 18.6 (p. 354) shows six pictures of trucks and boxes. The within ratios are trucks to boxes (within one picture). The between ratios are from trucks to trucks and boxes to boxes.

The drawing in Figure 18.18 is an effective way of looking at two ratios and determining if a ratio is between or within. A drawing similar to this will be very helpful to students in setting up proportions, especially students who struggle with abstract representatives. Pick any two equivalent truck and box pictures and place the numbers in this figure.

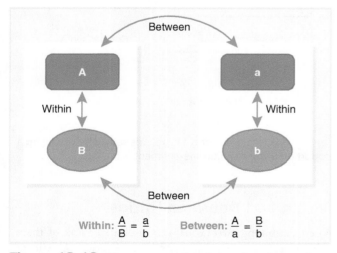

Figure 18.18 Given a proportional situation, the two between ratios and the two within ratios will be equivalent.

Reasoning Approaches

Traditional textbooks show students how to set up an equation of two ratios involving an unknown, "cross-multiply," and solve for the unknown. This can be a very mechanical approach and can lead to confusion and error. Although you may wish eventually to cover the cross-product algorithm, it is well worth the time for students to find ways to solve proportions using their own ideas. If you have been exploring proportions and discussing between and within relationships, students will have a good foundation on which to build their own approaches.

To illustrate some intuitive approaches for solving typical proportion tasks, consider the following:

Tammy bought 3 widgets for $2.40. At the same price, how much would 10 widgets cost?

Tammy bought 4 widgets for $3.75. How much would a dozen widgets cost?

⏸ ———————————— *Pause and Reflect*

Before reading further, solve these two problems using an approach other than the cross-product algorithm.

In the first situation, it is perhaps easiest to determine the cost of one widget—the unit rate or unit price. This can be found by dividing the price of three widgets by 3. Multiplying this unit rate of $0.80 per widget by 10 will produce the answer. This approach is referred to as a *unit-rate* method of solving proportions. Notice that the unit rate is a within ratio.

In the second problem, a unit-rate approach could be used, but the division does not appear to be easy. Since 12 is a multiple of 4, it is easier to notice that the cost of a dozen is 3 times the cost of 4. This is called a *scale factor* method. It could have been used on the first problem but would have been awkward. The scale factor between 3 and 10 is $3\frac{1}{3}$. Multiplying $2.40 by $3\frac{1}{3}$ will produce the correct answer. (When you multiply entries in a ratio table, you are using a scale factor.) Although the scale factor method is a useful way to think about proportions, it is most frequently used when the numbers are compatible. Students should be given problems in which the numbers lend themselves to both approaches so that they will explore both methods. The scale factor is a between ratio.

Try using the unit-rate method or scale factors to solve the next two problems. You can set up the proportions using the format in Figure 18.18.

At the Office Super Store, you can buy plain #2 pencils, 4 for 59 cents. The store also sells the same pencils in a large box of 5 dozen pencils for $7.79. How much do you save by buying the large box?

The price of a box of 2 dozen candy bars is $4.80. Bridget wants to buy 5 candy bars. What will she have to pay?

To solve the pencil problem, you might notice that the between ratio of pencils to pencils is 4 to 60, or 1 to 15. If you multiply the 59 cents by 15, the factor of change, you will get the price of the box of 60 if the pencils were sold at the same price. In the candy problem, the within ratio of 24 to $4.80 is easy to use to get the unit rate of 20 cents per candy bar.

It is important to follow these tasks with problems that have more difficult numbers, asking students to still apply the same strategies to reason to an answer. For example, try to apply both strategies to the next problem.

Brian can run 5 km in 18.4 minutes. If he keeps on running at the same speed, how far can he run in 23 minutes?

Cross-Product Approach

"The central challenge of developing students' capacity to think with ratios (to reason proportionally) is to teach ideas and restrain the quick path to computation" (Smith, 2002, p. 15).

The methods just described come close to being well-defined algorithms, though they are a bit more flexible than cross-product methods. The reality is that the computations involved are exactly the same as in cross-multiplication. Sixth- and seventh-grade students rarely use cross-multiplication to solve proportion problems, even when that method has been taught (Smith, 2002). A possible reason is that, although the method is relatively efficient, it does not appear on the surface to look like the earlier conceptual approaches. If teaching cross-products, connect the unit-rate and/or scale factor approaches to this procedure.

Draw a Simple Model. Given a ratio word problem, the greatest difficulty students have is setting up a correct proportion or equation of two ratios, one of which includes the missing value. "Which fractions do I make? Where does the x go?"

Rather than drill and drill in the hope that they will somehow eventually get it, show students how to sketch a simple picture that will help them determine what parts are related. In Figure 18.19, a simple model is drawn

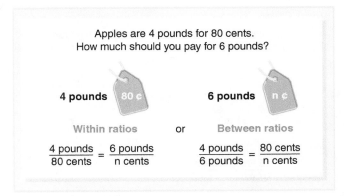

Figure 18.19 A simple drawing helps to establish correct proportion equations.

for a typical rate or price problem. The two equations in the figure come from setting up within and between ratios.

Solve the Proportion. Examine the left (within) ratios. Find out what to multiply the left fraction by to get the right. You may see that this is a scale factor of 1.5, or you can divide to find the scale (6 ÷ 4). Then multiply 80 cents by the same scale factor to get $1.20.

$$\frac{6}{4} \times 80$$

Looking at the same left equation in Figure 18.19, we could also determine the unit price or the price for 1 pound by dividing the 80 cents by 4 and then multiplying this result by 6 to determine the price of 6 pounds:

$$\frac{80}{4} \times 6$$

Now look what happens if we cross-multiply in the original equation:

$$4n = 6 \times 80$$
$$n = \frac{6 \times 80}{4}$$

This equation can be solved by dividing the 6 by 4 and multiplying by 80 or dividing 80 by 4 and multiplying by 6. These are exactly the two devices we employed in the other two approaches (scale factor and unit rate). If you cross-multiply the between ratios, you get exactly the same result. Furthermore, you get the same result if you had written the two ratios inverted, that is, with the reciprocals of each fraction. Try it!

So if you want to develop a cross-product algorithm, it is not unreasonable to do problems like these while encouraging students to use their own methods. If the cross-product approach is understood and presented as one strategy, and not necessarily the only approach or the best approach, students will be more likely to continue to reason and chose the strategy that makes sense given the context and the numbers involved in the problem.

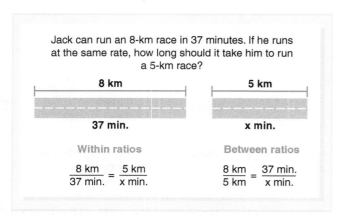

Figure 18.20 Line segments can be used to model both time and distance.

Providing visual cues to set up proportions is a very effective way to support a wide range of learners. In Figure 18.20 the visual of the road is used to help students consider the quantities involved and set up ratios appropriately. Notice how the visual is much like the ratio table and much like the picture in Figure 18.19. Different students will find different strategies more logical—encourage students to select a strategy that makes sense to them.

Reflections

Writing to Learn

1. Describe the idea of a ratio in your own words. Explain how your idea fits with each of the following statements:
   a. A fraction is a ratio.
   b. Ratios can compare things that are not at all alike.
   c. Ratios can compare two parts of the same whole.
   d. Rates such as prices or speeds are ratios.
2. Describe a situation in which the comparison involved could be interpreted both in an additive sense as well as multiplicatively. Why might you want to explore a situation such as this early on in your discussion of ratio and proportion?
3. What can you say about the graph of a collection of equivalent ratios?
4. Make up a realistic proportional situation that can be solved mentally by a scale factor approach and another that can be solved mentally by a unit-rate approach.
5. Consider this problem: If 50 gallons of fuel oil cost $56.95, how much can be purchased for $100? Draw a sketch to illustrate the proportion, and set up the equation in two different ways. One equation should equate within ratios and the other between ratios.

6. Make up a realistic percentage problem and set up a line-segment model to represent it. Then write a proportion.

For Discussion and Exploration

1. Proportional reasoning is a unifying theme in mathematics. For each of the content strands (number, algebra, measurement, geometry, and data analysis and probability) think about content that involves proportional reasoning and explain the connections among all of these ideas.
2. You've learned about how the three percent problems were developed around the theme of which element was missing—the part, the whole, or the fraction that related the two. In this chapter, percent is related to proportions, an equality of two ratios with one of these ratios a comparison to 100. How are these two approaches alike? How are they different? Explain how 100 percent could, in some problems, be a part rather than a whole.

Resources

Literature Connections

Literature brings an exciting dimension to the exploration of proportional reasoning. Many books and stories discuss comparative sizes, concepts of scale as in maps, giants and min-

iature people who are proportional to regular people, comparative rates, especially rates of speed, and so on. For example, Beckman, Thompson, and Austin (2004) explore the popular *Harry Potter* stories, *The Lord of the Rings*, and *The*

Perfect Storm for exciting contexts for proportional reasoning activities.

If You Hopped Like a Frog *Schwartz, 1999*

David Schwartz, the author of *How Much Is a Million?* and *If You Made a Million*, uses proportional reasoning to determine what it would be like if we had the skills or dimensions of familiar animals. "If you hopped like a frog, you could jump from home plate to first base in one mighty leap." This short picture book contains 12 more fascinating comparisons. At the end of the book, Schwartz provides some factual data on which the proportions are based. Students can figure out how strong or tall they would be if they were one of the featured animals.

Holes *Sachar, 2000*

A popular book and movie, this novel tells the story of boys in a "camp" digging holes every day, which provides an opportunity to look at daily rates of dirt removal. Pugalee et al. (2008) describe an excellent activity with this book that not only involves proportional reasoning, but also measurement and algebra.

Literature with Large and/or Small People

There is a plethora of literature involving very little or very big people (or animals). With any of these books, body parts can be compared as a way to explore within and between ratios. The following list of some great literature can lead to wonderful lessons on proportional reasoning:

Alice's Adventures in Wonderland *Carroll, 1865/1982*

In this classic, Alice becomes very small and very tall, opening doors to many ratio and proportion investigations.

The Borrowers *Norton, 1953*

A classic tale of little folk living in the walls of a house. Furnishings are created from odds and ends of the full-sized human world.

Gulliver's Travels *Swift, 1726, amended 1735/1999*

Yet another classic story. In this case Gulliver first visits the Lilliputians, where he is 12 times their size, and then goes to Brobdingnag, where he is $\frac{1}{10}$ the size of the inhabitants.

Jim and the Beanstalk *Briggs, 1970*

What happened to the giant after Jack? Jim comes along. Jim wants to help the poor, pessimistic giant. This heartwarming story is great for multiplicative or proportional reasoning across grades K–8.

Kate and the Beanstalk *Osborne, 2000*

This version of *Jack and the Beanstalk* includes a giantess. The giantess falls to earth and Kate finds out the castle belongs to her family.

"One Inch Tall" in *Where the Sidewalk Ends* *Silverstein, 1973*

Shel Silverstein is a hit with all ages. This poems asks what it would be like if you were one inch tall.

Swamp Angel *Isaacs, 1999*

A swamp angel named Angelica is born very tiny but grows into a giant. Students can explore birth height to current height or compare Angelica's measurements to their own.

Recommended Readings

Articles

Langrall, C. W., & Swafford, J. (2000). Three balloons for two dollars. *Mathematics Teaching in the Middle School, 6*(4), 254–261.
The authors describe and give examples of four levels of proportional reasoning using examples from the classroom. A good article on a difficult topic.

Lo, J., Watanabe, T., & Cai, J. (2004). Developing ratio concepts: An Asian perspective. *Mathematics Teaching in the Middle School, 9*(7), 362–367.
These well-known researchers discuss the way that the concepts of ratio and proportion are developed in Asian countries. They share a sequence of activities adapted from textbooks used in China, Taiwan, and Japan. The series of examples will certainly be useful in your classroom.

Books

Lamon, S. J. (1999). *Teaching fractions and ratios for understanding: Essential content knowledge and instructional strategies for teachers.* Mahwah, NJ: Lawrence Erlbaum.
Lamon is one of the most prolific researchers and writers on the subject of fractions, ratios, and proportional reasoning. This book is full of specific practical examples of activities and is freely illustrated with children's work. Many of the ideas found in this chapter are adapted from this book and other works by Lamon.

Litwiller, B. (Ed.). (2002). *Making sense of fractions, ratios, and proportions: 2002 yearbook.* Reston, VA: NCTM.
Eleven of the 26 short chapters in this NCTM yearbook discuss explicitly the issue of multiplicative relationships and/or proportional reasoning. The remaining chapters are on various aspects of fraction concepts and fraction computation, many illustrating the connection with proportional thinking. Accompanying the yearbook is a book of Classroom Activities *complete with Blackline Masters.*

Online Resources

Fibonacci Sequence
http://nlvm.usu.edu/en/nav/frames_asid_315_g_3_t_1
.html

The applet simply computes successive terms of the Fibonacci sequence and shows in both fraction and decimal forms the ratio of successive terms of the sequence. This ratio converges to the *golden ratio*. For what may be the most information assembled anywhere on the Fibonacci sequence, go to www.mcs.surrey.ac.uk/Personal/R.Knott/Fibonacci.

Fish Simulation Applet I
http://mathforum.org/escotpow/puzzles/fish/applet
.html

A collection of two colors of fish is to be placed into three ponds to create specified ratios within each pond. Students should find out if there is more than one solution and then make up similar problems for their classmates.

Learning about Length, Area, Volume, Surface Area of Similar Objects (e-Example 6.3)
http://standards.nctm.org/document/eexamples

A two-part exploration complete with extensive teacher notes. The applets compare two rectangles or two prisms showing ratios of measures in both numeric and graphical form.

Understanding Ratios of Inscribed Figures (e-Example 7.3)
http://standards.nctm.org/document/eexamples

A nice geometry/measurement link to ratio. The user explores the ratio of figures inscribed in polygons formed by joining midpoints of sides. These points can also be adjusted. The supporting lesson and activity suggestions are quite good.

Ameba (The Math Forum's Teacher Exchange)
http://mathforum.org/te/exchange/hosted/ameba

In this game, students select a total number of pellets to eat that is equal to the target ratio given at the top of the board, then return to the start/finish location.

The Futures Channel
www.thefutureschannel.com

This site provides lessons and includes video clips. Two related to proportional reasoning are "How Tall?," which engages students in finding the heights of people and objects using proportional thinking, and "Snow," which explores the ratio of inches of snowfall to liquid water.

Field Experience Guide Connections

Because ratios and proportions are important to many topics in the curriculum, they are the topic for many of the field experiences in Part I of the *Field Experience Guide*. For example, any of the proportional reasoning tasks in this chapter (including the assessment in Figure 18.1) can be used for FEG 7.2. FEG 3.5 ("Create a Web of Ideas") can be done by you to prepare for a lesson, or by students to see if they connect ideas of ratio, fraction, division, and rate. This chapter includes many literature links; see Field Experience 2.6 for designing (and teaching) a lesson using children's literature. In Part II, FEG Expanded Lesson 9.11 provides interesting problem-solving contexts to explore proportional situations. FEG Activity 10.7 helps students connect representations for ratios.

Developing Measurement Concepts

easurement is one of the most useful mathematics content strands as it is an important component in everything from occupational tasks to life skills for the mathematically literate citizen. From gigabytes that measure amounts of information to font size on computers, from miles per gallon to recipes for a meal, people are surrounded daily with measurement concepts that apply to a variety of real-world situations. However, measurement is not an easy topic for students to understand. Data from both international studies (TIMSS) and from NAEP consistently indicate that students are weaker in the area of measurement than any other topic in the curriculum (Thompson & Preston, 2004). Although learning both the metric and the customary measurement systems may be a contributing factor, the poor performance is more likely a function of how the subject is taught—too much reliance on pictures and worksheets rather than hands-on experiences and a focus on skills with less attention to the concepts of measurement.

In this chapter you will learn how to help students develop a conceptual understanding of the measurement process and the tools of measurement. You will also learn about nonstandard and standard units of measurement, estimation in measurement including the use of benchmarks, and the development of measurement formulas.

Big Ideas

1. Measurement involves a comparison of an attribute of an item or situation with a unit that has the same attribute. Lengths are compared to units of length, areas to units of area, time to units of time, and so on.

2. Meaningful measurement and estimation of measurements depend on a personal familiarity with the unit of measure being used.

3. Estimation of measures and the development of benchmarks for frequently used units of measure help students increase their familiarity with units, preventing errors and aiding in the meaningful use of measurement.

4. Measurement instruments are devices that replace the need for actual measurement units. It is important to understand how measurement instruments work.

5. Area and volume formulas provide a method of measuring these attributes by using only measures of length.

6. Area, perimeter, and volume are related. For example, as the shapes of regions or three-dimensional objects change while maintaining the same areas or volumes, there is a predictable effect on the perimeters and surface areas.

Mathematics Content Connections

In order to provide more time for students to engage in meaningful measurement activities, measurement should be integrated across the mathematics curriculum as well as the science curriculum.

- **Number:** Early measurement activities are a very meaningful context for counting. Measurement of important objects in the familiar environment connects ideas of number to the real world, enhancing number sense.

- **Place Value:** Multiples of ten are profitably used by young children in counting nonstandard measures. The metric system of measurement is built on the base-ten system of numeration.

- **Algebra:** Measurement formulas are themselves functions. Measurement provides data from which generalizations and functional relationships can be derived.

- **Fractions:** The need for increased precision leads to fractional parts of units.

- **Proportional Reasoning:** The use of benchmarks in estimating measures promotes multiplicative thinking. Measures are used in scale drawings. Proportions are used to find unknown measures of similar figures.

- **Geometry:** The development and understanding of perimeter, area, and volume formulas require an understanding of the shapes and relationships involved. Measures help to describe shapes, and angular measures play a significant role in the properties of shapes.

- **Data:** Statistics and graphs are used to describe our world and help us answer questions about it. Often this description is in terms of measures.

The Meaning and Process of Measuring

Suppose that you asked your students to measure an empty bucket. The first thing they would need to know is *what* about the bucket is to be measured. They might measure the height, depth, diameter (distance across), or circumference (distance around). All of these are length measures. The surface area of the side could be determined. A bucket also has volume (or capacity) and weight. Each of these aspects that can be measured is an *attribute* of the bucket.

Once students determine the attribute to be measured, they need to choose a unit that has the attribute being measured. Length is measured with units that have length, volume with units that have volume, and so on.

Technically, a *measurement* is a number that indicates a comparison between the attribute of the object (or situation, or event) being measured and the same attribute of a given unit of measure. We commonly use small units of measure to determine a numeric relationship (the measurement) between what is measured and the unit. For example, to measure a length, the comparison can be done by lining up copies of the unit directly against the length being measured. To measure weight, which is a pull of gravity or a force, the weight of the object might first be applied to a spring. Then the comparison is made by finding out how many units of weight produce the same effect on the spring. In either case, the number of units is the measure of the object.

For most of the attributes that are measured in schools, we can say that *to measure* means that the attribute being measured is "filled" or "covered" or "matched" with a unit of measure with the same attribute (as illustrated in Figure 19.1).

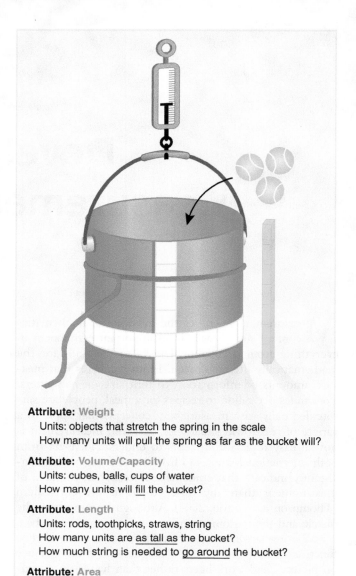

Attribute: Weight
Units: objects that <u>stretch</u> the spring in the scale
How many units will pull the spring as far as the bucket will?

Attribute: Volume/Capacity
Units: cubes, balls, cups of water
How many units will <u>fill</u> the bucket?

Attribute: Length
Units: rods, toothpicks, straws, string
How many units are <u>as tall as</u> the bucket?
How much string is needed to <u>go around</u> the bucket?

Attribute: Area
Units: index cards, squares of paper, tiles
How many cards will <u>cover</u> the surface of the bucket?

Figure 19.1 Measuring different attributes of a bucket.

In summary, to measure something, one must perform three steps:

1. Decide on the attribute to be measured.
2. Select a unit that has that attribute.
3. Compare the units, by filling, covering, matching, or using some other method, with the attribute of the object being measured. The number of units required to match the object is the measure.

Standard measuring instruments such as rulers, scales, protractors, and clocks are devices that make the filling, covering, or matching process easier.

Concepts and Skills

If a typical group of first graders attempt to measure the length of their classroom by laying strips 1 meter long end to end the strips sometimes overlap, and the line can weave in a snakelike fashion. Do they understand the concept of length as an attribute of the classroom? Do they understand that each 1-meter strip has this attribute of length? Do they understand that their task is to fill or match smaller units of length into the length of the classroom? What they most likely understand is that they are supposed to be making a line of strips stretching from wall to wall (and from their vantage point, they are doing quite well). They are performing this task procedurally without conceptual understanding. The skill of measuring with a unit must be explicitly linked to the concept of measuring as a process of comparing attributes, using measuring units and using measuring instruments. A sequence of experiences for measurement instruction is summarized in Table 19.1 and the following discus-

myeducationlab

Go to the Building Teaching Skills and Dispositions section of Chapter 19 of MyEducationLab. Click on Videos and watch the video entitled "**Measurement Lesson**" to see students learn how to measure perimeter.

Table 19.1

Measurement Instruction—A Sequence of Experiences
Step One—Making Comparisons *Goal:* Students will understand the attribute to be measured. *Type of Activity:* Make comparisons based on the attribute. For example, longer/shorter, heavier/lighter. Use direct comparisons whenever possible. *Notes:* When it is clear that the attribute is understood, there is no further need for comparison activities.
Step Two—Using Models of Measuring Units *Goal:* Students will understand how filling, covering, matching, or making other comparisons of an attribute with measuring units produces a number called a *measure*. *Type of Activity:* Use physical models of measuring units to fill, cover, match, or make the desired comparison of the attribute with the unit. *Notes:* Begin with nonstandard units. Progress to the direct use of standard units when appropriate and certainly before using formulas or measuring tools.
Step Three—Using Measuring Instruments *Goal:* Students will use common measuring tools with understanding and flexibility. *Type of Activity:* Make measuring instruments and use them in comparison with the actual unit models to see how the measurement tool is performing the same function as the individual units. Be certain to make direct comparisons between the student-made tools and the standard tools. *Notes:* Student-made tools are usually best made with nonstandard units. Without a careful comparison with the standard tools, much of the value in making the tools can be lost.

sion suggests the types of activities that will develop these skills.

Making Comparisons. The first and most critical goal is for students to understand the attribute they are going to measure. When students compare objects on the basis of some measurable attribute, that attribute becomes the focus of the activity. For example, is the capacity of one box more than, less than, or about the same as the capacity of another? No measurement is required, but some manner of comparing one volume to the other must be devised. The attribute of "capacity" (how much a container can hold) is inescapable.

Many attributes can be compared directly, such as placing one length directly in line with another. In the case of volume or capacity, some indirect method is probably required, such as filling one box with beans and then pouring the beans into the other box. Using a string to compare the height of a wastebasket to the distance around is another example of an indirect comparison. The string is the intermediary, as it is impossible to compare these two lengths directly.

Constructing or making something that is the same in terms of a measurable attribute is another type of comparison activity—for example, "Cut the straw to be about as long as this piece of chalk" or "Draw a rectangle that is about the same size (has the same area) as this triangle."

Using Physical Models of Measuring Units. The second goal is for students to understand what units of measure are appropriate for the particular attribute in question and how these units are used to produce a measurement. Regardless of grade level, you cannot make assumptions that students have an understanding of measuring units. For most attributes that are measured in elementary schools, it is possible to have physical models of the units of measure. Time and temperature are exceptions. (Many other attributes not commonly measured in school also do not have physical units of measure. Light intensity, speed, loudness, viscosity, and radioactivity are just a few examples.) Unit models can be found for both nonstandard (sometimes referred to as informal) units and standard units. For length, for example, drinking straws (nonstandard) or tagboard strips 1 foot long (standard) might be used as units.

The most easily understood use of unit models is actually to use as many copies of the unit as are needed to fill or match the attribute measured. To measure the area of the desktop with an index card as your unit, you can literally cover the entire desk with index cards. Somewhat more difficult, especially for younger children, is to use a single copy of the unit with an iteration process. That would mean the same desktop area can be measured with a single index card by repeatedly moving it from position to position and keeping track of which areas the card has covered.

It is useful to measure the same object with different-sized units. Results should be estimated in advance and discussed afterward. This will help students understand that the unit used is important. The fact that smaller units produce larger numeric measures, and vice versa, is hard for young children to understand. This inverse relationship can only be mentally constructed by predicting, then experimenting, and finally reflecting on measurements with varying-sized units.

Using Measuring Instruments. Understanding the devices we use for measuring is the third goal. In the 2003 National Assessment of Educational Progress (Blume, Galindo, & Walcott, 2007), only 20 percent of fourth-grade students could give the correct measure of an object not aligned with the end of a ruler, as in Figure 19.2. These results point to the difference between using a measuring device and understanding how it works. Students also experienced difficulty when the increments on a measuring device were not one unit.

If students actually make simple measuring instruments using unit models with which they are familiar, it is more likely that they will understand how an instrument measures. A ruler is a good example. If students line up individual physical units along a strip of tagboard and mark them off, they can see that it is the *spaces* on rulers and not the hash marks or numbers that are important. It is essential that students discuss how measurement with individual units compares with measurement using an instrument. Without this comparison and discussion, students may not understand that these two methods are essentially the same.

A discussion of student-made measuring instruments for various attributes is provided in the text and on the Web. Of course, children should also use standard, ready-made instruments such as rulers and scales and should compare the use of these devices with the use of the models they constructed.

Nonstandard Units and Standard Units: Reasons for Using Each

It is common in primary grades to use nonstandard units to measure length and sometimes area. Unfortunately, measurement activities in the upper grades, where other attributes are measured, often do not begin with nonstandard units. The use of nonstandard units for beginning measurement activities is beneficial at all grade levels for the following reasons:

- Nonstandard units make it easier to focus directly on the attribute being measured. For example, in a discussion of how to measure the area of an irregular shape, units such as lima beans, square tiles, or circular counters may be suggested. Each unit covers area and each will give a different result. The discussion should then focus on what it means to measure area.
- The use of nonstandard units can avoid conflicting objectives in the same beginning lesson. Is your lesson about what it means to measure area or about understanding square centimeters?
- Nonstandard units provide a good rationale for using standard units. A discussion of the need for a standard unit can have more meaning after groups in your class have measured the same objects with their own units and arrived at different and sometimes confusing answers.
- Using nonstandard units can be motivating.

The use of standard units is also important in your measurement program at any grade level for these reasons:

- Knowledge of standard units is an essential objective of a measurement program. Students must not only develop a familiarity with standard units but must also learn appropriate relationships between them.
- Once a measuring concept is fairly well developed, standard units can be effectively introduced. If there is no good instructional reason for nonstandard units, use standard units to increase students' experience and familiarity with the unit.

The amount of time that should be spent using nonstandard unit models varies with the age of the children and the attributes being measured. Pre-K–grade 1 children need a lot of experience with a variety of nonstandard units of length, weight, and capacity. Conversely, the benefits of nonstandard measuring units may last only a day or two for measurements of angles at the middle school level. When nonstandard units have served their purpose, move on.

The Role of Estimation and Approximation

Always have students estimate a measurement before they make it. This is true with both nonstandard and standard units. There are at least four good reasons for including estimation in measurement activities:

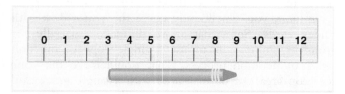

Figure 19.2 "How long is this crayon?"

- Estimation helps students focus on the attribute being measured and the measuring process. Think how you would estimate the area of the front of this book using standard playing cards as the unit. To do so, you have to think about what area is and how the units might be placed on the book cover.
- Estimation provides intrinsic motivation to measurement activities. It is interesting to see how close you can come in your estimate.
- When standard units are used, estimation helps develop familiarity with the unit. If you estimate the height of the door in meters before measuring, you have to think about the size of a meter.
- The use of a benchmark to make an estimate promotes multiplicative reasoning. The width of the building is about one-fourth of the length of a football field—perhaps 25 yards.

In all measuring activities, emphasize the use of approximate language. The desk is *about* 15 orange rods long. The chair is *a little less than* 4 straws high. The use of approximate language is very useful for younger children because many measurements do not result in whole numbers. Older children will begin to search for smaller units or will use fractional units to try to measure exactly. Here is an opportunity to develop the idea that all measurements include some error. First acknowledge that each smaller unit or subdivision produces a greater degree of *precision*. For example, a length measure can never be more than one-half unit in error. And yet, since there is mathematically no "smallest unit," there is always some error involved.

NCTM Standards The Measurement Standard in *Principles and Standards* for grades 3–5 states that "students should understand that measurements are approximations and understand how differences in units affect precision" (NCTM, 2000, p. 398). In grades 6–8, NCTM states that "middle school students should select and apply techniques and tools to accurately find length, area, volume, and angle measure to appropriate levels of precision" (p. 300). ◆

Length

Length is usually the first attribute students learn to measure. Be aware, however, that length measurement is not immediately understood by young children. Likewise, upper elementary and middle school students may have challenges with the concept of length as they attempt to investigate problems that include perimeter and circumference.

Comparison Activities

At the pre-K–kindergarten level, children should begin with direct comparisons of two or more lengths.

Activity 19.1

Longer, Shorter, Same

Make several sorting-by-length learning stations at which students sort objects as longer, shorter, or about the same as a specified object. The reference object can be changed to produce different sorts. A similar task involves putting objects in order from shortest to longest.

Activity 19.2

Length (or Unit) Hunt

Give pairs of students a strip of tagboard, a stick, a length of rope, or some other object with an obvious length dimension. The task on one day might be to find five things in the room that are shorter than, longer than, or about the same length as their target unit. They can draw pictures or write the names of the things they find.

   By making the target length a standard unit (e.g., a meter stick or a 1-meter length of rope), the activity can be repeated to provide familiarity with important standard units.

It is important to compare lengths that are not in straight lines. One way to do this is by using string or rope. Students can wrap string around objects in a search for things that are, for example, as long around as the distance from the floor to their belly button or as long as the distance around one's head or waist. Body measures are always fun.

Indirect comparisons are used in the "Crooked Paths" activity that follows.

Activity 19.3

Crooked Paths

Make some crooked or curvy paths on the floor (or outside) with masking tape or chalk. The task is to determine which path is longest, next longest, and so on. The students should suggest ways to measure the crooked paths so that they can be compared easily. If you wish to offer a hint, provide pairs of students with a long piece of rope. The task is easier if the rope is longer than the crooked paths. Have students explain how they solved the problem.

Units of Length

Students can use a variety of nonstandard units to begin measuring length—for example:

- *Giant footprints:* Make about 20 copies of a large footprint about $1\frac{1}{2}$ to 2 feet long on poster board and cut them out.
- *Measuring ropes:* Cut cotton clothesline into lengths of 1 m. These can measure the perimeter and the circumference of objects such as the teacher's desk, a tree trunk, or the class pumpkin.
- *Plastic straws:* Drinking straws provide large quantities of a useful unit. Straws are easily cut into smaller units or linked together with a long string. The string of straws is an excellent bridge to a ruler or measuring tape.
- *Short units:* Toothpicks, connecting cubes, wooden cubes, and paper clips are all useful nonstandard units for measuring shorter lengths. Cuisenaire rods are a good choice for a set of units because they come in ten different lengths, are readily placed end to end, and can easily be related to each other. They are also metric (cms) and thus make an excellent bridge to a ruler.

The temptation is to carefully explain to students how to use these units to measure and then send them off to practice measuring. This approach will shift students' attention to the procedure (following your instruction) and away from developing an understanding of measurement using units. In the following activity students are provided with a measuring task but are required to develop their own approach.

Activity 19.4

How Long Is the Teacher?

Explain that you have just received an important request from the principal. She needs to know exactly how tall each teacher in the building is. The students are to decide how to measure the teachers and write a note to the principal explaining how tall their teacher is and detailing the process that they used. If you wish to give a hint, have students make marks at your feet and head and draw a straight line between these marks.

Explain that the principal says they can use any ONE of several nonstandard units to measure with (provide choices). For each choice of unit, supply enough units to more than cover your length. Put students in pairs and allow them to select one unit with which to measure.

The value of the last activity will come from the discussion. Good questions include "How did you get your measurement?" "Did students who measured with the same

unit get the same answers? Why not?" "How could the principal make a line that was just as long as the teacher?" In your discussion, focus on the value of lining units up carefully, end to end. Discuss what happens if you overlap units, have a gap in the units, or don't stay in a straight line.

The following activity adds an estimation component.

Activity 19.5

Estimate and Measure

Make lists of items in the room to measure (see Figure 19.3). For younger children, run a piece of masking tape along the dimension of objects to be measured. On the list, designate the units to be used. Do not forget to include curves or other distances that are not straight lines. Include estimates before the measures. Remember that young children have probably had limited experiences with estimating distances.

For students beginning to learn about estimation, add the following component to the "Estimate and Measure" activity: Have students make a row or chain of exactly ten units to use in helping them with their estimates. They

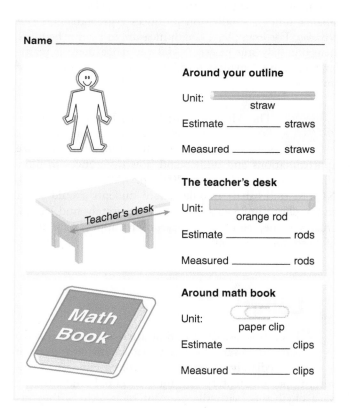

Figure 19.3 Example recording sheet for measuring with nonstandard length units.

first lay ten units against the object and then make their estimate.

It is a challenge to explain to students that larger units will produce a smaller measure and vice versa. Instead, engage students in an activity like the following where this issue is a focus.

Activity 19.6

Changing Units

Have students measure a length with a specified unit. Then provide them with a different unit that is either twice as long or half as long as the original unit. Their task is to predict the measure of the same length using the new unit. Students should write down their estimations and explanations of how they were made. Stop and have a discussion about their estimations and then have them make the actual measurement. Cuisenaire rods are excellent for this activity. Older students can be challenged with units that are more difficult multiples of the original unit.

In "Changing Units," you are looking first for the basic idea that when the unit is longer the measure is smaller and vice versa. This is a good activity to do just before you discuss unit conversion with standard units. For example, if the doorway is 80 inches high, how many feet is that? Changing measurement units is an excellent proportional reasoning task for middle school students.

 Observation and discussion during activities such as those just described provide evidence of how well your students understand length measurement. Additional tasks that can be used as assessments in a diagnostic interview format are:

- Provide a box with assorted units of different sizes (i.e., Cuisenaire rods). Have the students use the materials in the box to measure a given length. Observe whether students understand that all units must be of equal lengths. If different units are used, ask how the students would describe their measurement.
- Ask students to draw a line or mark off a distance of a prescribed number of units. Observe whether the students know to align the units in a straight line without overlaps or gaps.
- Have students measure two different objects. Then ask how much longer is the longer object. Observe whether students can use the measurements to answer or whether a third measurement must be made of the difference.
- Provide a length of string and tell students that the string is 6 units long. Ask how could they use the

string to make a length of 3 units. Ask how could they make a length of 9 units? In this task, you are looking to see if students can mentally subdivide the given length (string) based on an understanding of its measure. That is, can students visualize that 6 units are matched to the string length and half of these are 3 units? ◆

Fractional Parts of Units. Children are sometimes perplexed when their measurements do not result in a whole number. One suggestion you might make to younger students is to use a smaller unit to fill in the remaining gap, as in Figure 19.4. Another idea is to suggest that fractions be used. In the metric system, units are rarely mixed, and fractional units are expressed in decimal form (e.g., 3.2 m). In the customary system a measurement of 4 feet 3 inches is sometimes reported as 51 inches or as $4\frac{1}{4}$ feet. The use of fractional units can help students understand subdivision marks on a ruler. The children's book *Inchworm and a Half* provides a nice way to introduce the idea of fractional units (see the literature section at the end of the chapter).

Width = 5 orange and 4 red rods

Figure 19.4 Using two units to measure length.

Making and Using Rulers

The jump from measuring with nonstandard units to using standard rulers is challenging. One of the best methods of helping students understand rulers is to have them make their own rulers out of actual units.

Activity 19.7

Make Your Own Ruler

Precut narrow strips of construction paper 5 cm long and about 2 cm wide. Use two different colors. Discuss how the strips could be used to measure by laying them end to end. Provide long strips of tagboard

about 3 cm wide. **Without explicit guided direction, have students make their own ruler by gluing the units onto the tagboard. Have a list of a few things to measure. Students use their new rulers to measure the items on the list. Discuss the results.** It is possible that there will be discrepancies due to rulers that were not made properly or to a failure to understand how a ruler works.

The same activity can be done using larger nonstandard units such as tracings of students' footprints glued onto strips of adding machine tape. Older children can use a standard unit (centimeter, inch, foot) to make marks on the strips and color in the spaces with alternating colors.

This activity makes the construction of a ruler a problem-based experience. By not overguiding students in how to make their rulers, you will get formative assessment information concerning students' understanding of the measurement process. At the conclusion of this process, all students should have correctly made a ruler. The multiple copies of units on the student-made rulers (rather than markings and numbers) maximize the connection between the spaces on the ruler and the actual units. Students should use their rulers to measure lengths that are longer than their rulers and discuss how that can be done. Another important challenge is to find more than one way to measure a length with a ruler. Do you have to begin at the end? What if you begin at another unit in the center?

Students should eventually put numbers on their handmade rulers, as shown in Figure 19.5. For young children, numbers can be written in the center of each unit to make it clear that the numbers are a way of precounting the units. When numbers are written in the standard way, at the ends of the units, the ruler becomes a number line. This format is more sophisticated and should be carefully discussed with children.

Much of the value of student-made rulers can be lost if you do not transfer this knowledge to standard rulers. Give children a standard ruler, and discuss how it is like and how it differs from the ones they have made. What are the units? Could you make a ruler with paper units the same as this? What do the numbers mean? What are the other marks for? Where do the units begin?

 Research indicates that when students see standard rulers with the numbers on the hash marks, they often believe that the numbers are counting the marks rather than indicating the units or spaces between the marks. This is an incorrect understanding of rulers that can lead to wrong answers when using them. As an assessment, provide students a ruler with hash marks but no numbers. Have students use the ruler to measure an item that is shorter than the ruler. A correct understanding of rulers is indicated if students count spaces between the hash marks.

Another good assessment of ruler understanding is to have students measure with a "broken" ruler, one with the first two units broken off. Some students will say that it is impossible to measure with such a ruler because there is no starting point. Those who understand rulers will be able to match and count the units meaningfully in their measures. (See Barrett, Jones, Thornton, & Dickson, 2003, for a complete discussion of student development of length measurement, including the use of rulers.)

Observing how children use a ruler to measure an object that is longer than the ruler is also informative. Children who simply read the last mark on the ruler may struggle because they do not understand how a ruler is a representation of a continuous row of units. ◆

Area

Area is the two-dimensional space inside a region. As with other attributes, students must first understand the attribute of area before measuring. Data from the 2003 NAEP suggest that fourth- and eighth-grade students have an incomplete understanding of area (Blume, Galindo, & Walcott, 2007).

Comparison Activities

One of the purposes of comparison activities with areas is to help students distinguish between size (or area) and shape, length, and other dimensions. A long, skinny rectangle may have less area than a triangle with shorter sides.

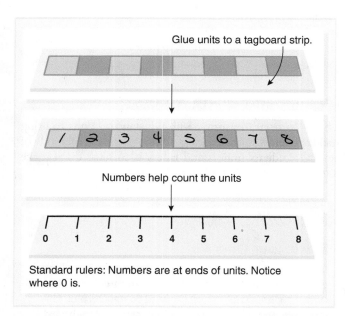

Glue units to a tagboard strip.

Numbers help count the units

Standard rulers: Numbers are at ends of units. Notice where 0 is.

Figure 19.5 Give meaning to numbers on rulers.

Investigations
in Number, Data, and Space

Grade 3, *Perimeter, Angles, and Area*

Context

The perimeter activity continues the development of ideas about linear measurement. At the point of this lesson, it is assumed that students understand the need for standard units and can use tools that measure length in both the metric and customary systems. Students are able to recognize that perimeter is the measure around the outside edges of a two-dimensional shape.

Task

In this investigation, students select real-world objects and measure the perimeter or rim (Hint for students: the word rim is in pe**rim**eter). Key in this process will be the choices the students make, such as whether the object they choose has a perimeter that is regular, like the top of a desk, or more challenging, like the top of a waste paper basket. They also need to choose the tool that will be best for measuring, given yardsticks or metersticks, or adding machine tape or string. At first, students are asked as a group to suggest an object. Then one student traces with a finger the perimeter that will be measured. All students are asked to include this object in the exploration that follows. In this way, students will be able to compare the results of at least one common item, providing a basis for discussing any measurement errors. Students can be asked to include an estimate of the perimeter on their chart prior to actually measuring. During the "after" period of the lesson, students should discuss how they measured objects that were larger than the tool they were using and how they

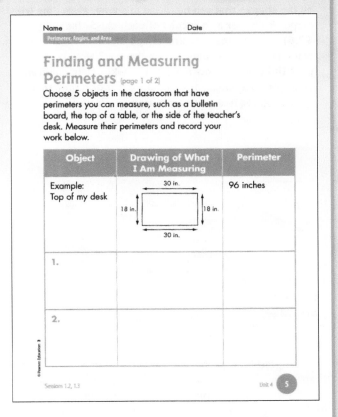

Source: *Investigations in Number, Data, and Space: Grade 3— Perimeter, Angles, and Area*, p. 35. Copyright © 2008 by Pearson Education, Inc., or its affiliate(s). Used by permission. All rights reserved.

knew when to use a "flexible" measuring tool such as the string or adding machine tape.

This is an especially difficult concept for young children to understand. In addition, many 8- or 9-year-olds do not understand that rearranging areas into different shapes does not affect the amount of area.

Direct comparison of two areas is nearly always impossible except when the shapes involved have some common dimension or property. For example, two rectangles with the same width can be compared directly, as can any two circles. Comparison of these special shapes, however, fails to deal with the attribute of area. Instead, activities in which one area is rearranged are suggested. Cutting a shape into

two parts and reassembling it in a different shape can show that the before and after shapes have the same area, even though they are different shapes. This idea is not at all obvious to children in the K–2 grade range.

Activity 19.8

Two-Piece Shapes

Cut a large number of rectangles of the same area, about 3 inches by 5 inches. Each pair of students will

need six rectangles. Have students fold and cut the rectangles on the diagonal, making two identical triangles. Next, have them rearrange the triangles into different shapes, including the original rectangle. The rule is that only sides of the same length can be matched up and must be matched exactly. Have each group find all the shapes that can be made this way, gluing the triangles on paper as a record of each shape (see Figure 19.6). Discuss the area and shape of the different results. Is one shape bigger than the rest? How is it bigger? Did one take more paper to make? Help children conclude that although each figure is a different shape, all the figures have the same *area*.

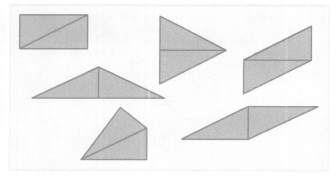

Figure 19.6 Different shapes, same area.

Tangrams, a very old and popular set of puzzle shapes, can be used for the same purpose. The standard set of seven tangram pieces is cut from a square, as shown in Figure 19.7. The two small triangles can be used to

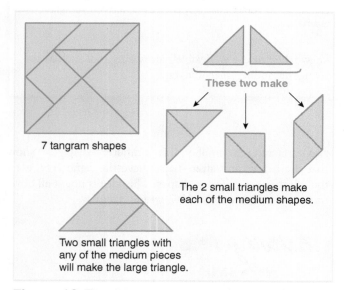

7 tangram shapes

These two make

The 2 small triangles make each of the medium shapes.

Two small triangles with any of the medium pieces will make the large triangle.

Figure 19.7 Tangrams provide an opportunity to investigate area concepts (see Blackline Master 51).

make the parallelogram, the square, and the medium triangle. This permits a similar discussion about the pieces having the same size (area) but different shapes (Seymour, 1971). (Tangram pieces can be found in Blackline Master 51.)

Activity 19.9

Tangram Areas

Draw the outline of several shapes made with tangram pieces, as in Figure 19.8. Let students use tangrams to decide which shapes are the same size, which are larger, and which are smaller. Shapes can be duplicated on paper, and children can work in groups. Let students explain how they came to their conclusions. Use the animal shapes from *Grandfather Tang's Story* (Tompert, 1997) for additional investigations.

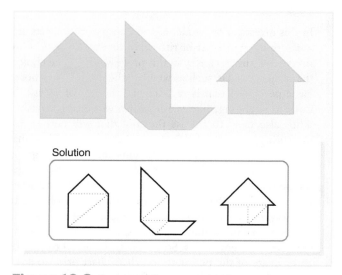

Solution

Figure 19.8 Compare shapes made of tangram pieces.

Pause and Reflect

You might pause here, get a set of tangrams, and make the area comparisons suggested in Figure 19.8.

Units of Area

Although squares are the most common units of area, any tile that conveniently fills up a plane region can be used. Even filling a region with uniform circles or lima beans provides a useful idea of what it means to measure area. Here are some suggestions for area units that are easy to gather or make in large quantities.

- Round plastic chips, pennies, or lima beans can be used. It is not necessary at a beginning stage that the area units fit with no gaps.
- Color tiles (1-inch plastic squares).
- Squares cut from cardboard. Large squares (about 20 cm on a side) work well for large areas. Smaller units should be about 5 to 10 cm on a side.
- Sheets of newspaper make excellent units for very large areas.

Children can use units to measure surfaces in the room such as desktops, bulletin boards, or books. Large regions can be outlined with masking tape on the floor. Small regions can be duplicated on paper so that students can work at their desks. Odd shapes and curved surfaces provide more challenge and interest. The surface of a watermelon or of the side of the wastebasket provide useful challenges.

In area measurements, there may be lots of units that only partially fit. You may wish to begin with shapes in which the units fit by building a shape with units, and drawing the outline. According to *Curriculum Focal Points* (NCTM, 2006), in fourth grade, students should begin to wrestle with partial units and mentally put together two or more partial units to count as one. Figure 19.9 shows one possible measurement exercise.

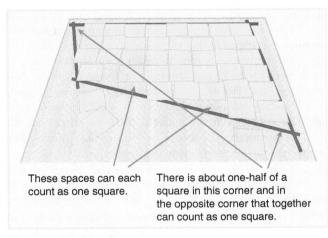

These spaces can each count as one square.

There is about one-half of a square in this corner and in the opposite corner that together can count as one square.

Figure 19.9 Measuring the area of a large shape drawn with tape on the floor. Units are pieces of tagboard all cut to squares of the same size.

The following activity is a good starting point to see what ideas your students bring to their understanding of units of area.

Activity 19.10

Fill and Compare

Draw two rectangles and a blob shape on a sheet of paper. Make it so that the three areas are not the same but with no area that is clearly largest or small-est. The students' task is to first make an estimate about which is the smallest and the largest of the three shapes. After recording their estimate, they should use a filler of their choice to decide. Students should explain in writing what they found out.

Your objective in the beginning is to develop the idea that area is measured by covering. Do not introduce formulas. Groups are very likely to come up with different measures for the same region. Discuss these differences with the children and point to the difficulties involved in making estimates around the edges. Avoid the idea that there is a "right" answer.

By fourth grade, students should begin to relate the concept of multiplication using arrays to the area of rectangles. The following comparison activity is a good step in that direction.

Activity 19.11

Rectangle Comparison—Square Units

Students are given a pair of rectangles that are either the same or very close in area. They are also given a model or drawing of a single square unit and a ruler that measures the appropriate unit. The students are not permitted to cut out the rectangles. They may draw on them if they wish. The task is to use their rulers to determine, in any way that they can, which rectangle is larger or whether they are the same. They should use words, pictures, and numbers to explain their conclusions. Some suggested pairs are as follows:

4×10 and 5×8

5×10 and 7×7

4×6 and 5×5

The goal of this activity is not necessarily to develop an area formula but to apply students' developing concepts of multiplication to the area of rectangles. Not all students will use a multiplicative approach. In order to count a single row of squares along one edge, and then multiply by the length of the other edge, the first row must be thought of as a unit that is then replicated to fill in the rectangle (Outhred & Mitchelmore, 2004). Many students will attempt to draw in all the squares. However, some may use their rulers to determine the number of squares that will fit along each side and, from that, use multiplication to determine the total area (see Figure 19.10). By having students share their strategies, more students can be exposed to the use of multiplication in this context.

Grids. Grids of various types can be thought of as "area rulers." A grid of squares for area does exactly what a ruler

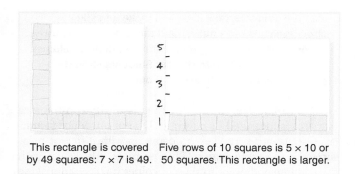

This rectangle is covered by 49 squares: 7 × 7 is 49. Five rows of 10 squares is 5 × 10 or 50 squares. This rectangle is larger.

Figure 19.10 Some students use multiplication to tell the total number of square units.

does for length. It lays out the units for you. Square grids to make transparencies are available in Blackline Masters 34–36. Have students place the grid over a region to be measured and count the units inside. An alternative method is to trace around a region on a paper grid.

The Relationship Between Area and Perimeter

Area and perimeter (the distance around a region) are continually a source of confusion for students. Perhaps it is because both involve regions to be measured or because students are taught formulas for both concepts at about the same time and tend to get formulas confused. Whatever the reason, expect that students even in the fifth and sixth grades will confuse these two ideas. An interesting approach to alleviating this confusion is to contrast the two ideas as in the next activities.

Activity 19.12

Fixed Perimeters

Give students a loop of nonstretching string that is exactly 24 centimeters in circumference. The task is to decide what different-sized rectangles can be made with a perimeter of 24 cm. Students may want to use a 1-cm grid to place their strings on. Each different rectangle can be recorded on grid paper with the area noted inside the figure.

An alternative to the string loop is to simply use grid paper and ask students to find rectangles with perimeters of 24 cm.

Activity 19.13

Fixed Areas

Provide students with centimeter grid paper. The task is to see how many rectangles can be made

with an area of 36—that is, to make filled-in rectangles, not just borders. Each new rectangle should be recorded by sketching the outline and the dimensions on grid paper. For each rectangle, students should determine and record the perimeter inside the figure. (See the "Fixed Areas" lesson on pp. 74–75.)

Pause and Reflect

Before reading further, think about the two previous activities. For "Fixed Areas," will all of the perimeters be the same? If not, what can you say about the shapes with longer or shorter perimeters? For "Fixed Perimeters," will the areas remain the same? Why or why not?

As students complete Activities 19.12 and 19.13 in small groups, have them keep track of the areas and perimeters by writing them on the rectangles (area = 12 cm²). Then they should cut out all the figures, keeping the fixed perimeters in one pile and the fixed areas in another. Labeling either two charts or locations on the board with "Perimeter" and "Area," the teams should come up and place their figures (left to right) from smallest perimeter to largest perimeter on the Perimeter Chart and from smallest area to largest area on the Area Chart. Students are asked to state what they observe, make conjectures, and see if any conclusions can be drawn. They are often surprised to find out that two or more rectangles having the same areas do not necessarily have the same perimeters. Similarly two shapes with the same perimeters do not always have the same areas. And, of course, this fact is not restricted to rectangles.

Students will notice that there is a relationship that is fairly interesting. When the area is fixed, the shape with the smallest perimeter is a square or "square-like." For a fixed perimeter, the rectangle with the largest area is the same. If you allowed for any shapes whatsoever, the shape with the smallest perimeter and a fixed area is a circle. That is, assuming the areas are the same, the "fatter" a shape, the smaller its perimeter and the skinnier a shape, the larger its perimeter. (A corresponding result is true in three dimensions. Replace perimeter with surface area and area with volume.)

Volume and Capacity

Volume and *capacity* are both terms for measures of the "size" of three-dimensional regions. The term *capacity* is generally used to refer to the amount that a container will hold. Standard units of capacity include quarts and gallons or liters and milliliters. The term *volume* can be used to refer to the capacity of a container but is also used for the size of solid objects. Standard units of volume are expressed in terms of length units, such as cubic inches or cubic centimeters.

Comparison Activities

Comparing the volumes of solid objects is very difficult. For children at the primary level, it is appropriate to focus on capacity. A simple method of comparing capacity is to fill one container with something and then pour this amount into the comparison container. By third grade most students will understand the concept of "holds more" with reference to containers. The concept of volume for solid objects may not be as readily understood.

In pre-K settings, young children should have lots of experiences directly comparing the capacities of different containers. Collect a large assortment of cans, small boxes, and plastic containers. Gather as many different shapes as possible. Also gather some plastic scoops. Cut a plastic 2-liter bottle in half, and use the top portion as a funnel. Rice or dried beans are good fillers to use. Sand and water are both possible, particularly if there is a water table available.

Activity 19.14

Capacity Sort

Provide a collection of labeled containers, with one marked as the "target." The students' task is to sort the collection into those that hold more than, less than, or about the same amount as the target container. Provide a recording sheet on which each container is listed and a place to circle "holds more," "holds less," and "holds about the same." List the choices twice for each container. The first choice is to record an estimation made by observation. The second is to record "what was found." Provide a filler (such as beans or rice), scoops, and funnels. Avoid explicit directions, but later discuss students' ideas for solving the task.

Do not expect students to be able to accurately predict which of two containers holds more. Even adults have difficulty making this judgment. Try the following task yourself as well as with students. Take two sheets of construction paper. Make a tube shape (cylinder) by taping the two long edges together. Make a shorter, fatter cylinder from the other sheet by taping the short edges together. When placed upright, which cylinder holds more, or do they have the same capacity?

Before doing this with your class, survey them to see how many select which option. Most groups split roughly in thirds: short and fat, tall and skinny, or same capacity. Use a filler such as Styrofoam packing peanuts or lima beans. Place the skinny cylinder inside the fat one. Fill the inside tube and then lift it up, allowing the filler to empty into the fat cylinder.

The apparent volumes of solid objects are sometimes misleading, and a method of comparison is also difficult. To compare volumes of solids such as a ball and an apple, some method of displacement must be used. Provide students with two or three containers that will each hold the objects to be compared and a filler such as rice or beans. With this equipment some students may be able to devise their own comparison method. One approach is to first fill a container completely and then pour it into an empty holding container. Next, place an object in the first container and fill it again to the top, using filler from the holding container. The volume of filler remaining is equal to the volume of the object. Mark the level of the leftover filler in the holding container before repeating the experiment with other objects. By comparing the level of the leftover filler for two or more objects, the volumes of the objects can be compared.

The following activity is a three-dimensional version of Activity 19.13, "Fixed Areas." Here the volume is fixed and students look for changes in surface area.

Activity 19.15

Fixed Volume: Comparing Prisms

Give each pair of students a supply of centimeter cubes or wooden cubes. Their task is, for a fixed number of cubes, to build different rectangular prisms and record the surface area for each prism formed. A good number of cubes to suggest is 64, since a minimal surface area will occur with a 4 × 4 × 4 cube. With 64 cubes a lot of prisms can be made. However, if you are short of cubes, other good choices are 24 or 36 cubes. Using the tables students construct, they should observe any patterns that occur. In particular, what happens to the surface area as the prism becomes less like a tall, skinny box and more like a cube?

The goal here is for students to realize that volume does not dictate surface area and to recognize the pattern between surface area and volume is similar to the one found between area and perimeter. Namely, prisms that are more cubelike have less surface area than prisms with the same volume that are long and narrow.

Once students have developed formulas for computing area and volume, they can continue to explore the relationships between surface area and volume without actually building the prisms.

Units of Volume and Capacity

Two types of units can be used to measure volume and capacity: solid units and containers. Solid units are objects like wooden cubes or old tennis balls that can be used to fill the container being measured. The other type of unit model is a small container that is filled and poured repeatedly into the container being measured. The following are a few examples of units that you might want to collect:

- Plastic caps and liquid medicine cups.
- Plastic jars and containers of almost any size.
- Wooden cubic blocks or blocks of any shape (as long as you have a lot of the same size).
- Styrofoam packing peanuts (which still produce conceptual measures of volume despite not packing perfectly).

The following activity is similar to Activity 19.11, "Rectangle Comparison—Square Units."

Activity 19.16

Box Comparison—Cubic Units

Provide students with a pair of small boxes that you have folded up from poster board (see Figure 19.11). Use unit dimensions that match the blocks that you have for units. Students are given two boxes, exactly one block, and an appropriate ruler. (If you use 2-cm cubes, make a ruler with the unit equal to 2 centimeters.) The students' task is to decide which box has the greater volume or if they have the same volume.

Here are some suggested box dimensions ($L \times W \times H$):

$6 \times 3 \times 4$ $5 \times 4 \times 4$ $3 \times 9 \times 3$ $6 \times 6 \times 2$ $5 \times 5 \times 3$

Students should use words, drawings, and numbers to explain their conclusions.

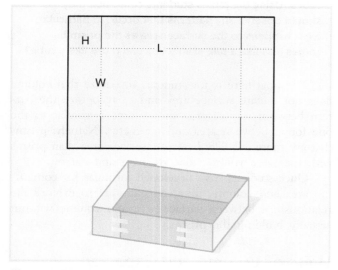

Figure 19.11 Make small boxes by starting with a rectangle and drawing a square on each corner as shown. Cut on the solid lines and fold the box up, wrapping the corner squares to the outside and tape them to the sides as shown.

A useful hint in the last activity is to first figure out how many cubes will fit on the bottom of the box. Some students, although certainly not all, will discover a multiplicative rule for the volume. The boxes can be filled with cubes to confirm conclusions. No formulas should be used unless students can explain them. The development of a formula is not necessarily the goal of this activity.

Using Measuring Cups. Instruments for measuring capacity are generally used for small amounts of liquids or pourable materials such as rice or water. These tools are commonly found in kitchens and laboratories. Students should use measuring cups to explore recipes for food products as well as to create papier-mâché for art or Oobleck for science experiments (Google "making Oobleck" for recipes). The *Better Homes and Gardens New Junior Cookbook* (2004) is a great place to start for student-friendly recipes and multiple measuring experiences with units of capacity.

Weight and Mass

Weight is a measure of the pull or force of gravity on an object. *Mass* is the amount of matter in an object and a measure of the force needed to accelerate it. On the moon, where gravity is much less than on earth, an object has a smaller weight but the identical mass as on earth. For practical purposes, on the earth, the measures of mass and weight will be about the same. In this discussion, the terms *weight* and *mass* will be used interchangeably.

Comparison Activities

The most conceptual way to compare the weights of two objects is to hold one in each hand, extend your arms, and experience the relative downward pull on each—effectively communicating to a pre-K–1 child what "heavier" or "weighs more" means. This personal experience can then be transferred to one of two basic types of scales—balances and spring scales.

When children place the objects in the two pans of a balance, the pan that goes down can be understood to hold the heavier object. Even a relatively simple balance will detect small differences. If two objects are placed one at a time in a spring scale, the heavier object pulls the pan down farther. Both balances and spring scales have real value in the classroom. (Technically, spring scales measure weight and balance scales measure mass. Why?)

With either scale, estimating, sorting, and ordering tasks are possible with very young children. For older children, comparison activities for weight are not necessary. (Why?)

Units of Weight or Mass

Any collection of uniform objects with the same mass can serve as weight units. For very light objects, large paper clips, wooden blocks, or plastic cubes work well. Large metal washers found in hardware stores are effective for weighing slightly heavier objects. You will need to rely on standard weights to weigh things as heavy as a kilogram or more.

Weight cannot be measured directly. Either a two-pan balance or a spring scale must be used. In a balance scale, place an object in one pan and weights in the other until the two pans balance. In a spring scale, first place the object in and mark the position of the pan on a piece of paper taped behind the pan. Remove the object and place just enough weights in the pan to pull it down to the same level. Discuss how equal weights will pull the spring or rubber band with the same force.

While the concept of heavier and lighter is learned rather early, the notion of units of weight or mass is a bit more challenging. At any grade level, even a brief experience with informal unit weights is good preparation for standard units and scales.

Time

Time is a bit different from the other attributes that are commonly measured in school because it cannot be seen or felt and because it is more difficult for students to comprehend units of time or how they are matched against a given time period or duration.

Duration

Time can be thought of as the duration of an event from its beginning to its end. As with other attributes, for students to adequately understand the attribute of time, they should make comparisons of events that have different durations. If two events begin at the same time, the shorter duration will end first and the other last longer. For example, which top spins longer? However, this form of comparison focuses on the ending of the duration rather than the duration itself. In order to think of time as something that can be measured, it is helpful to compare two events that do not start at the same time. This requires that some form of measurement of time be used from the beginning.

An informal unit of time might be the duration of a pendulum swing made with a tennis ball suspended on a long string from the ceiling. The long string produces a slow swing and, thus, keeps the counting manageable. The steady drip of a water faucet into an empty container is another option. The level of the water is marked at the end of the period. When the marked container is emptied and used to time a second duration, the two markings can be compared. One advantage of the water drip method is that there are no units to count. Simple tasks that address duration include the following:

- Stacking ten blocks one at a time and then removing them one at a time
- Printing the alphabet
- Walking slowly around a designated path
- Making a bar of 15 connecting cubes

Only one student does each task, so that there is no competition or racing.

Students also need to learn about seconds, minutes, and hours and to develop some concept of how long these units are. You can help by making a conscious effort to note the duration of short and long events during the day. Timing small events of $\frac{1}{2}$ minute to 2 minutes is fun and useful. TV shows and commercials are a good standard. Have students time familiar events in their daily lives: brushing teeth, eating dinner, riding to school, spending time doing homework.

Activity 19.17

Be Ready for the Bell

Give students a recording sheet with a set of clock faces (see Blackline Master 33). Secretly set a timer to go off at the hour, half hour, or minute. When the bell rings, students should look up and record the time on the clock face and in numerals. This highly engaging activity motivates students to not only think about telling time, but to consider the relationship between the analog clock reading and digital recording. Elapsed time can also be explored by discussing the time between timer rings.

Clock Reading

The common instrument for measuring time is the clock. However, learning to tell time has little to do with time measurement and more to do with the skills of learning to read a dial-type instrument. Clock reading can be a difficult skill to teach.

Some Challenges. Starting in first grade, children are usually taught first to read clocks to the hour, then the half and quarter hours, and finally to 5- and 1-minute intervals in the grades that follow. In the early stages of this sequence, children are shown clocks set exactly to the hour or half hour. Thus, many children who can read a clock at 7:00 or 2:30 are initially challenged by 6:58 or 2:33.

Digital clocks permit students to read times easily but do not relate times very well. To know that a digital reading of 7:58 is nearly 8 o'clock, the child must know that there are 60 minutes in an hour, that 58 is close to 60, and that 2 minutes is not a very long time. These concepts have not been developed by most first-grade and many second-grade children. The analog clock (with hands) shows "close to" times visually without the need for understanding big numbers or even how many minutes in an hour.

Suggested Approach. The following suggestions can help students understand and read analog clocks.

1. Begin with a one-handed clock. A clock with only an hour hand can be read with reasonable accuracy. Use lots of approximate language: "It's about 7 o'clock." "It's a little past 9 o'clock." "It's halfway between 2 o'clock and 3 o'clock" (see Figure 19.12).

2. Discuss what happens to the big hand as the little hand goes from one hour to the next. When the big hand is at 12, the hour hand is pointing exactly to a number. If the hour hand is about halfway between numbers, about where would the minute hand be? If the hour hand is a little past or before an hour (10 to 15 minutes), about where would the minute hand be?

3. Use two real clocks, one with only an hour hand and one with two hands. (Break off the minute hand from an old clock.) Cover the two-handed clock. Periodically during the day, direct attention to the one-handed clock. Discuss the time in approximate language. Have students predict where the minute hand should be. Uncover the other clock and check.

4. Teach time after the hour in 5-minute intervals. After step 3 has begun, count by fives going around the clock. Instead of predicting that the minute hand is pointing at the 4, encourage students to say it is about 20 minutes after the hour. As skills develop, suggest that students always look first at the little or hour hand to learn approximately what time it is and then focus on the minute hand for precision.

5. Predict the reading on a digital clock when shown an analog clock, and vice versa; set an analog clock when shown a digital clock. This can be done with both one-handed and two-handed clocks.

As students learn more about two-digit numbers, the time after the hours can also be related to the time left before the hour. This is helpful not only for telling time but for number sense as well. Note that in the sequence

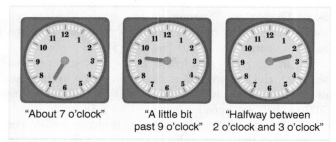

Figure 19.12 Approximate time with one-handed clocks.

suggested, time after the hour is stressed almost exclusively. Time before or till the hour can come later.

The following activity can be used to help students in the second grade and beyond, even if the earlier sequence of one-handed clocks has not been followed.

Activity 19.18

One-Handed Clocks

Prepare a page of clock faces (see Blackline Master 33). On each clock draw an hour hand. Include placements that are approximately a quarter past the hour, a quarter until the hour, half past the hour, and some that are close to but not on the hour. For each clock face, the students' task is to write the digital time and draw a minute hand on the clock where they think it would be.

 "One-Handed Clocks" is a good assessment of students' clock reading. If students in the third grade or above are having difficulty reading clocks, working with a one-handed clock as suggested earlier will offer a different approach. ◆

Elapsed Time

Determining elapsed time is a skill required by most state curricula starting in about grade 3. It is also a skill that can be challenging for students, especially when the period of time includes noon or midnight. Students must know how many minutes are in an hour. On the 2003 NAEP assessment, only 26 percent of fourth graders and 55 percent of eighth-grade students could solve a problem involving the conversion of one measure of time to another (Blume, Galindo, & Walcott, 2007). If given the digital time or the time after the hour, students must be able to tell how many minutes to the next hour. This should certainly be a mental process of counting on for multiples of 5 minutes. Avoid having students use pencil and paper to subtract 25 from 60.

Figuring the time from, say, 8:15 A.M. to 11:45 A.M. is a multistep task regardless of how it is done. Keeping track of the intermediate steps is difficult, as is deciding what to do first. In this case you could count hours from 8:15 to 11:15 and add on 30 minutes. But then what do you do if the endpoints are 8:45 and 11:15? To propose a singular method or algorithm is not helpful.

Next is the issue of A.M. and P.M. The problem is due less to the fact that students don't understand what happens on the clock at noon and midnight as it is that they now have trouble counting the intervals.

In the discussion so far, we have only addressed one form of the problem. There is also the task of

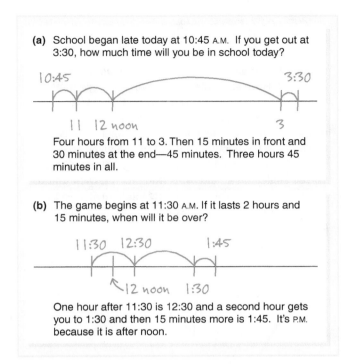

(a) School began late today at 10:45 A.M. If you get out at 3:30, how much time will you be in school today?

Four hours from 11 to 3. Then 15 minutes in front and 30 minutes at the end—45 minutes. Three hours 45 minutes in all.

(b) The game begins at 11:30 A.M. If it lasts 2 hours and 15 minutes, when will it be over?

One hour after 11:30 is 12:30 and a second hour gets you to 1:30 and then 15 minutes more is 1:45. It's P.M. because it is after noon.

Figure 19.13 A sketch of an empty time line can be useful in solving elapsed time problems.

finding the end time given the start time and elapsed time, or finding the start time given the end time and the elapsed time. In keeping with the spirit of problem solving and the use of models, consider the following.

As a general model for all of these elapsed time problems, suggest that students sketch an empty time line. Examples are shown in Figure 19.13. It is important not to be overly prescriptive in telling students how to use the time line since there are various alternatives (Dixon, 2008). For example, in Figure 19.13, a student might count by full hours from 10:45 (11:45, 12:45, 1:45, 2:45, 3:45) and then subtract 15 minutes.

Money

Here is a list of the money ideas and skills typically required in the primary grades:

- Coin recognition
- Values of coins
- Using the values of coins
- Counting sets of coins (including comparing two sets)
- Equivalent collections of coins (same amounts, different coins)
- Selecting coins for a given amount
- Making change

These ideas and skills will be discussed in the following sections.

Coin Recognition and Values

The names of our coins are conventions of our social system. Students learn these names the same way that they learn the names of physical objects in their daily environment—through exposure and repetition.

The value of each coin is also a convention that students must simply be told. For these values to make sense, students must have an understanding of 5, 10, and 25. More than that, they need to be able to think of these quantities without seeing countable objects. Nowhere else do we say, "this is 5," while pointing to a single item. A child whose number concepts remain tied to counts of objects will be challenged to understand the values of coins. Coin value lessons should focus on purchase power—a dime can *buy the same thing* that 10 pennies can buy.

Counting Sets of Coins

To name the total value of a group of coins is the same as mentally adding their values except that there are no numerals visible. Ironically, most state standards require coin counting before they require students to mentally do the symbolic sum. Yet, second-grade students can be asked to do the mental math required in counting a collection of coins. Even though it is actually mental computation, the numbers are fortunately restricted to multiples of 5 and 10 with some 1s added at the end. The next activity is a preparation for counting money.

Activity **19.19**

Money Skip Counts

Explain to students that they will start skip-counting by one number and at your signal they will shift to a count by a different number. Begin with only two different amounts, say, 25 and 10. Write these numbers on the board. Point to the larger number (25), and have students begin to skip-count. After three or more counts, raise your hand to indicate a pause in the counting. Then lower your hand and point to the smaller number (10). Children continue the skip count from where they left off but now count by 10s. Use any two of these numbers: 100, 50, 25, 10, 5, 1. Always start with the larger. Later, try three numbers, still in descending order.

Remember that working with coins requires not only adding up the values but also first mentally giving each coin a value and then ordering the coins.

When discussing solutions to situations involving counting of coins, be sure to value any approach that works. However, pay special attention to those students who begin with the larger values and those who put nice combinations together utilizing thinking with 10s.

Making Change

Because adding on to find a difference is such a valuable skill—much easier than using the usual subtraction algorithm—it makes sense to give students a lot of experience with adding on to find differences before asking them to make change. As students become more skillful at adding on, they can see the process of making change as an extension of a skill already acquired.

This sequence of suggested activities is not a surefire solution to the difficulties students experience with money. It is designed to build on prerequisite number and place-value skills and concepts without or before using coins.

Angles

Angle measurement can be a challenge for two reasons: The attribute of angle size is often misunderstood, and protractors are introduced and used without understanding how they work.

Comparison Activities

The attribute of angle size might be called the "spread of the angle's rays." Angles are composed of two rays that are infinite in length with a common vertex. The only difference in their size is how widely or narrowly the two rays are spread apart.

To help children conceptualize the attribute of the spread of the rays, two angles can be directly compared by tracing one and placing it over the other. Be sure to have students compare angles with sides of different lengths. A wide angle with short sides may seem smaller than a narrow angle with long sides. This is a common misconception among students (Munier, Devichi, & Merle, 2008). As soon as students can tell the difference between a large angle and a small one, regardless of the length of the sides, you can move on to measuring angles.

Units of Angular Measure

A unit for measuring an angle must be an angle (see Blackline Master 32). Nothing else has the same attribute of spread that we want to measure. (Contrary to what many people think, you do not need to use degrees to measure angles.)

Activity 19.20

A Unit Angle

Give each student an index card or a small piece of tagboard. Have students draw a narrow angle on the tagboard (or use the wedges in Blackline Master 32) using a straightedge and then cut it out. The resulting wedge can then be used as a unit of angular measure by counting the number that will fit in a given angle as shown in Figure 19.14. Pass out a worksheet with assorted angles on it, and have students use their unit to measure them. Because students made their own unit angles, the results will differ and can be discussed in terms of unit size.

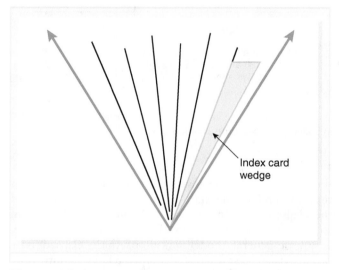

Index card wedge

Figure 19.14 Using a small wedge cut from an index card as a unit angle, this angle measures about $7\frac{1}{2}$ wedges. Accuracy of measurement with these nonstandard angles is less important than the idea of how an angle is used to measure the size of another angle.

Activity 19.20 illustrates that measuring an angle is the same as measuring length or area; unit angles are used to fill or cover the spread of an angle just as unit lengths fill or cover a length. Once this concept is well understood, you can move on to the use of measuring instruments.

Using Protractors and Angle Rulers

The protractor is one of the most poorly understood measuring instruments. Part of the difficulty arises because the units (degrees) are so small. It would be physically impossible for students to cut out and use a single degree to measure an angle accurately. In addition, the numbers that appear on most protractors run clockwise and counterclockwise along the edge, making the scale hard to interpret without a strong conceptual foundation.

Students can make nonstandard waxed-paper protractors (see Figure 19.15), but it is likely that they will move rapidly to standard instruments. To best understand the measures on a protractor or angle ruler, they need an approximate mental image of angle size. Then false readings of the protractor scale will be eliminated. One approach is to use a wheel. Rather than measuring hundredths, the wheel would be used as an "angle fixer." Two paper dessert plates, one white and the other a vivid color, would be cut and merged. You can then rotate the plates to create an "angle fixer" that can match angles of interest and eventually be used to estimate important benchmark angles such as 30, 45, 60, 90, 135, 180, and 270 degrees. If students have a strong grasp of the approximate sizes of angles, that will give them the background they need to move to standard measuring tools such as the protractor and angle ruler (see Figure 19.16).

Introducing Standard Units

As pointed out earlier, there are a number of reasons for teaching measurement using nonstandard units. However, measurement sense demands that children be familiar with standard measurement units and that they be able to make estimates in terms of these units and meaningfully interpret measures depicted with standard units.

Perhaps the biggest error in measurement instruction is the failure to recognize and separate two types of ob-

myeducationlab

Go to the Activities and Application section of Chapter 19 of MyEducationLab. Click on Lesson Resources and read **"Using Angle Rulers,"** a lesson plan for using angle rulers to measure degrees in a triangle.

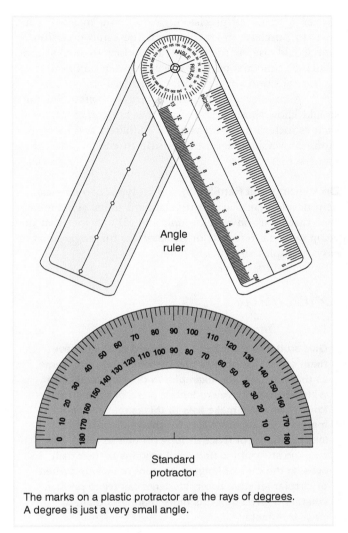

Angle ruler

Standard protractor

The marks on a plastic protractor are the rays of <u>degrees</u>. A degree is just a very small angle.

Figure 19.16 Different tools to measure angles (see Blackline Master 32).

jectives: (1) understanding the meaning and technique of measuring a particular attribute and (2) learning about the standard units commonly used to measure that attribute.

Instructional Goals

Teaching standard units of measure can be organized around three broad goals:

1. *Familiarity with the unit.* Students should have a basic idea of the size of commonly used units and what they measure. It is more important to know approximately how much 1 liter of water is or to be able to estimate a shelf as 5 feet long than to have the ability to measure either of these accurately.

2. *Ability to select an appropriate unit.* Students should know what is a reasonable unit of measure in a given situation. The choice of an appropriate unit is also a

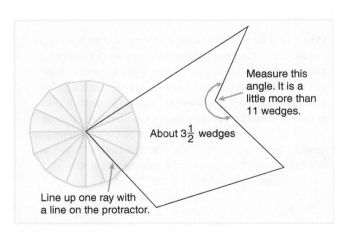

Measure this angle. It is a little more than 11 wedges.

About $3\frac{1}{2}$ wedges

Line up one ray with a line on the protractor.

Figure 19.15 Measuring angles in a polygon using a waxed-paper protractor.

matter of required precision. (Would you measure your lawn to purchase grass seed with the same precision as you would use in measuring a window to buy a pane of glass?) Students need practice in using common sense in the selection of appropriate standard units.

3. *Knowledge of relationships between units.* Students should know those relationships that are commonly used, such as inches, feet, and yards or milliliters and liters. Tedious conversion exercises do little to enhance measurement sense.

Developing Unit Familiarity. Two types of activities can help develop familiarity with standard units: (1) comparisons that focus on a single unit and (2) activities that develop personal referents or benchmarks for single units or easy multiples of units.

Activity **19.21**
About One Unit

Give students a model of a standard unit, and have them search for objects that measure about the same as that one unit. For example, to develop familiarity with the meter, give students a piece of rope 1 meter long. Have them make lists of things that are about 1 meter. Keep separate lists for things that are a little less (or more) or twice as long (or half as long). Encourage students to find familiar items in their daily lives. In the case of lengths, be sure to include curved or circular lengths. Later, students can try to predict whether a given object is more than, less than, or close to 1 meter.

The same activity can be done with other unit lengths. Families can be enlisted to help students find familiar distances that are about 1 mile or about 1 kilometer. Suggest in a letter that they check the distances around the neighborhood, to the school or shopping center, or along other frequently traveled paths. If possible, send home (or use in class) a 1-meter or 1-yard trundle wheel to measure distances.

For capacity units such as cup, quart, and liter, students need a container that holds or has a marking for a single unit. They should then find other containers at home and at school that hold about as much, more, and less. Remember that the shapes of containers can be very deceptive when estimating their capacity.

For the standard weights of gram, kilogram, ounce, and pound, students can compare objects on a two-pan balance with single copies of these units. It may be more effective to work with 10 grams or 5 ounces. Students can be encouraged to bring in familiar objects from home to compare on the classroom scale.

Standard area units are in terms of lengths such as square inches or square feet, so familiarity with lengths is important. Familiarity with a single degree is not as important as some idea of 30, 45, 60, and 90 degrees.

The second approach to unit familiarity is to begin with very familiar items and use their measures as references or benchmarks. A doorway is a bit more than 2 meters high and a doorknob is about 1 meter from the floor. A bag of flour is a good reference for 5 pounds. A paper clip weighs about a gram and is about 1 centimeter wide. A gallon of milk weighs a little less than 4 kilograms.

Activity **19.22**
Familiar References

Use the book *Measuring Penny* (Leedy, 2000) to get students interested in the variety of ways familiar items can be measured. In this book, the author bridges between nonstandard (e.g., dog biscuits) and standard units to measure Penny the pet dog. Have your students use the idea of measuring Penny to find something at home (or in class) to measure in as many ways as they can think using standard units. The measures should be rounded to whole numbers (unless children suggest adding a fractional unit to be more precise). Discuss in class the familiar items chosen and their measures so that different ideas and benchmarks are shared.

Of special interest for length are benchmarks found on our bodies. These become quite familiar over time and can be used as approximate rulers in many situations. Even though young children grow quite rapidly, it is useful for them to know the approximate lengths that they carry around with them.

Activity **19.23**
Personal Benchmarks

Measure your body. About how long is your foot, your stride, your hand span (stretched and with fingers together), the width of your finger, your arm span (finger to finger and finger to nose), the distance around your wrist and around your waist, and your height to waist, to shoulder, and to head? Some may prove to be useful benchmarks, and some may be excellent models for single units. (The average child's fingernail width is about 1 cm, and most people can find a 10-cm length somewhere on their hands.)

To help remember these references, they must be used in activities in which lengths, volumes, and so on are compared to the benchmarks to estimate measurements.

Choosing Appropriate Units. Should the room be measured in feet or inches? Should the concrete blocks be weighed in grams or kilograms? The answers to questions such as these involve more than simply knowing how big the units are, although that is certainly required. Another consideration involves the need for precision. If you were measuring your wall in order to cut a piece of molding or woodwork to fit, you would need to measure it very precisely. The smallest unit would be an inch or a centimeter, and you would also use small fractional parts. But if you were determining how many 8-foot molding strips to buy, the nearest foot would probably be sufficient.

Activity 19.24

Guess the Unit

Find examples of measurements of all types in newspapers, on signs, or in other everyday situations. Present the context and measures but without units. The task is to predict what units of measure were used. Have students discuss their choices.

Important Standard Units and Relationships

Both the customary and metric systems include many units that are rarely if ever used in everyday life. Your state or local curriculum is the best guide to help you decide which units your students should learn. NCTM's position statement on the metric system (2006) states: "To equip students to deal with diverse situations in science and other subject areas, and to prepare them for life in a global society, schools should provide students with rich experiences in working with both the metric and the customary systems of measurement while developing their ability to solve problems in either system." The statement goes on to explain that several countries have passed laws stating that international commerce must use metric units, as almost all nations in the world use the metric system. If U.S. students are going to be prepared for the global workplace, they must be knowledgeable and comfortable with commonly used metric units. Results of the 2004 NAEP reveal that only 40 percent of fourth graders were able to identify how many kilograms a bicycle weighed given the choices of 1.5, 15, 150, and 1500 kg. Among eighth graders, only 37 percent knew how many milliliters were in a liter (Perie, Moran, & Lutkus, 2005). Interestingly, although performance on national assessments reveals measurement as a weak area, U.S. students do better on metric units than customary units (Preston & Thompson, 2004).

The relationships between units within either the metric or customary systems are conventions. As such, students must simply be told what the relationships are,

and instructional experiences must be devised to reinforce them. It can be argued that knowing about how much liquid makes a liter, or being able to pace off 3 meters—unit familiarity—is more important than knowing how many cubic centimeters are in a liter. However, in the intermediate grades, knowing basic relationships becomes more important for testing purposes. Your curriculum should be your guide.

The customary system has very few patterns or rules to guide students in converting units. On the other hand, the metric system was designed systematically around powers of ten. An understanding of the role of the decimal point as indicating the units position is a powerful concept for making metric conversions. As students begin to appreciate the structure of decimal notation, the metric system can and should be developed with all seven places: three prefixes for smaller units (*deci-*, *centi-*, *milli-*) and three for larger units (*deka-*, *hecto-*, *kilo-*). Avoid mechanical rules such as "To change centimeters to meters, move the decimal point two places to the left." When the students themselves do not create conceptual, meaningful methods for conversions, arbitrary-sounding rules are bound to be misused and forgotten.

Exact conversions between the metric and the customary system should be avoided. As long as we live in a country that uses two systems of measurement, "friendly" conversions are useful. For example, a liter is a "gulp more" than a quart, and a meter is a bit longer than a yard. The same is true of familiar references. One hundred meters is about one football field plus one end zone, or about 110 yards.

 In assessing students' understanding and familiarity with standard units, there is a danger of focusing on the traditional conversion problems. Consider the following two tasks:

1. 4 feet = _____ inches.
2. Estimate the length of this rope in feet and then in inches. How did you decide on your estimate?

Both tasks relate feet and inches. However, the second task requires students to have a familiarity with the units as well. With the estimation task we can observe whether the student uses the first estimate to make the second (understanding and *using* the feet-inches relationship) or rather makes two separate estimates. This task also allows us to see how an estimate is made—information that is unavailable in the first task. ◆

Estimating Measures

Measurement estimation is the process of using mental and visual information to measure or make comparisons without the use of measuring instruments. It is a practical skill used almost every day. Do I have enough sugar to make cookies? Can you throw the ball 15 meters? Is this suitcase over the weight limit? About how long is the fence?

Besides its value outside the classroom, estimation in measurement activities helps students focus on the attribute being measured, adds intrinsic motivation, and helps develop familiarity with standard units. Therefore, measurement estimation both improves measurement understanding and develops a valuable life skill.

Strategies for Estimating Measurements

Just as for computational estimation, specific strategies exist for estimating measures. There are four strategies that can be taught specifically:

1. *Develop and use benchmarks or referents for important units.* Research has shown that students who have both acquired mental benchmarks or reference points for measurements *and* have practiced using them in class activities are much better estimators than students who have not learned to use benchmarks (Joram, 2003). Referents should be things that are easily envisioned by the student. One example is the height of a child, as shown in Figure 19.17. Students should have a good referent for single units and also useful multiples of standard units.

2. *Use "chunking" when appropriate.* Figure 19.17 shows an example. It may be easier to estimate the shorter chunks along the wall than to estimate the whole length. The weight of a stack of books is easier if some estimate is given to an "average" book.

3. *Use subdivisions.* This is a similar strategy to chunking, with the chunks imposed on the object by the estima-

tor. For example, if the wall length to be estimated has no useful chunks, it can be mentally divided in half and then in fourths or even eighths by repeated halving until a more manageable length is arrived at. Length, volume, and area measurements all lend themselves to this technique.

4. *Iterate a unit mentally or physically.* For length, area, and volume, it is sometimes easy to mark off single units visually. You might use your hands or make marks or folds to keep track as you go. If you know, for example, that your stride is about $\frac{3}{4}$ meter, you can walk off a length and then multiply to get an estimate. Hand and finger widths are useful for shorter measures.

Tips for Teaching Estimation

Each of the four strategies just listed should be taught directly and discussed with students. Suggested benchmarks for useful measures can be developed and recorded on a class chart. Include items found at home. But the best approach to improving estimation skills is to have students do a lot of estimating. Keep the following tips in mind:

1. Help students learn strategies by having them use a specified approach. Later activities should permit students to choose whatever techniques they wish.

2. Discuss how different students made their estimates. This will help students understand that there is no single right way to estimate and also remind them of different approaches that are useful.

3. Accept a range of estimates. Think in relative terms about what is a good estimate. Within 10 percent for length is quite good. Even 30 percent off may be reasonable for weights or volumes. Do not promote a "winning" estimate.

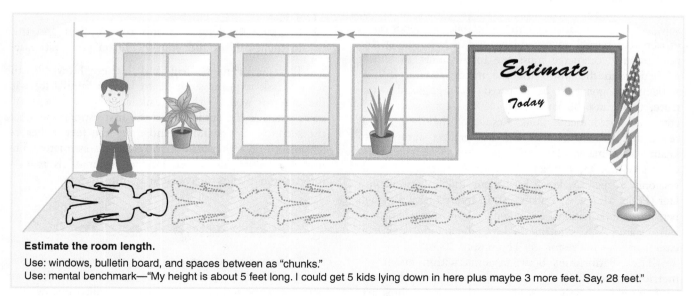

Estimate the room length.
Use: windows, bulletin board, and spaces between as "chunks."
Use: mental benchmark—"My height is about 5 feet long. I could get 5 kids lying down in here plus maybe 3 more feet. Say, 28 feet."

Figure 19.17 Estimating measures by using benchmarks and chunking.

4. Encourage students to give a range of measures that they believe includes the actual measure. This not only is a practical approach in real life but also helps focus on the approximate nature of estimation.

5. Make measurement estimation an ongoing activity. A daily measurement to estimate can be posted. Students can turn in their estimates on paper and discuss them in a 5-minute period. Older students can even be given the task of determining the measurements to estimate, with a student or team of students assigned this task each week.

Measurement Estimation Activities

Estimation activities need not be elaborate. Any measurement activity can have an "estimate first" component. For more emphasis on the process of estimation itself, simply think of measures that can be estimated, and have students estimate. Here are two suggestions.

Activity 19.25
Estimation Quickie

Select a single object such as a box, a pumpkin, a jar, or even the principal. Each day, select a different attribute or dimension to estimate. For a pumpkin, for example, students can estimate its height, circumference, weight, volume, and surface area.

Activity 19.26
Estimation Scavenger Hunt

Conduct estimation scavenger hunts. Give teams a list of measurements, and have them find things that are close to having those measurements. Do not permit the use of measuring instruments. A list might include the following items:

> A length of 3.5 m
>
> Something that weighs more than 1 kg but less than 2 kg
>
> A container that holds about 200 ml
>
> An angle of 45 degrees or 135 degrees

Let students suggest how to judge results in terms of accuracy.

Estimation tasks are a good way to assess students' understanding of both measurement and standard units. Use real objects and distances within the room as well as outside. Time and long distances should be estimated with comparisons to events and distances that are meaningful to the students.

Have students explain how they arrived at their estimates to get a more complete picture of their measurement knowledge. Asking only for a numeric estimate can mask a lack of understanding and will not give you the information you need to provide appropriate remediation. ◆

Developing Formulas for Area and Volume

Do not make the mistake of bypassing formula development with your students even if your state and local testing programs allow students access to formulas during the test. When students develop formulas, they gain conceptual understanding of the ideas and relationships involved and they engage in one of the real processes of doing mathematics. There is less likelihood that students will confuse area and perimeter or that they will select the incorrect formula on the test. General relationships are developed. For example, students can see how all area formulas are related to one idea: length of the base times the height. And students who understand where formulas come from do not see them as mysterious, tend to remember them, and reinforce the idea that mathematics makes sense. Rote use of formulas from a book offers none of these advantages.

Students' Misconceptions

The results of National Assessment of Educational Progress (NAEP) testing indicate clearly that students do not have a very good understanding of formulas. For example, in the 2007 NAEP, only 39 percent of fourth-grade students were able to give the area of a carpet 15 feet long and 12 feet wide. A common error is to confuse formulas for area and perimeter. Such results are largely due to an overemphasis on formulas with little or no conceptual background.

The tasks in Figure 19.18 cannot be solved with simple formulas; they require an understanding of concepts

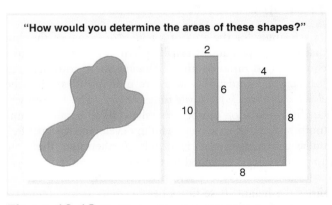

Figure 19.18 Understanding the attribute of area.

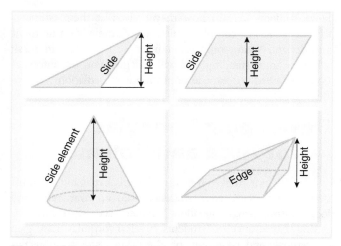

Figure 19.19 Heights of figures are not always measured along an edge or a surface.

and how formulas work. "Length times width" is not a definition of area.

Another common error when students use formulas comes from failure to conceptualize the meaning of height and base in both two- and three-dimensional geometric figures. The shapes in Figure 19.19 each have a slanted side and a height given. Students tend to confuse these two. Any side or flat surface of a figure can be called a *base* of the figure. For each base that a figure has, there is a corresponding height. If the figure were to slide into a room on a selected base, the *height* would be the height of the shortest door it could pass through without tipping—that is, the perpendicular distance to the base. Students have a lot of early experiences with the length-times-width formula for rectangles, in which the height is exactly the same as the length of a side. Perhaps this is the source of the confusion. Before formulas involving heights are discussed, students should be able to identify where a height could be measured for any base that a figure has.

Areas of Rectangles, Parallelograms, Triangles, and Trapezoids

The formula for the area of a rectangle is one of the first that is developed and is usually given as $A = L \times W$, "area equals length times width." Thinking ahead to other area formulas, an equivalent but more unifying idea might be $A = b \times h$, "area equals *base* times *height*." The base-times-height formulation can be generalized to all parallelograms (not just rectangles) and is useful in developing the area formulas for triangles and trapezoids. Furthermore, the same approach can be extended to three dimensions, where volumes of cylinders are given in terms of the *area of the base* times the height. Base times height, then, helps connect a large family of formulas that otherwise must be mastered independently.

Rectangles. Research suggests that it is a significant leap for students to move from counting squares inside of a rectangle to a conceptual development of a formula. Battista (2003) found that students often try to fill in empty rectangles with drawings of squares and then count the result one square at a time.

An important concept to review is the meaning of multiplication as seen in arrays. Show students rows and columns of objects or of squares and discuss why multiplication tells the total amount. We count either a single row or column and then find out how many columns or rows there are in all. This is the same concept that they will need to apply to the area of a rectangle. When we multiply a length times a width, we are not multiplying "squares times squares." Rather, the *length* of one side indicates how many squares will fit on that side. If this set of squares is taken as a unit, then the *length* of the other side (not a number of squares) will tell how many of these *rows of squares* can fit in the rectangle.

A good activity to begin your exploration of area formulas is to revisit Activity 19.11, "Rectangle Comparison—Square Units" (p. 379). Students who are drawing in all of the squares and counting them have not thought about a row of squares as a single row that can be replicated. Related tasks, based on the work of Battista (2003), are shown in Figure 19.20.

When your students have formulated an approach to area based on the idea of a row of squares (determined by the length of a side) multiplied by the number of these

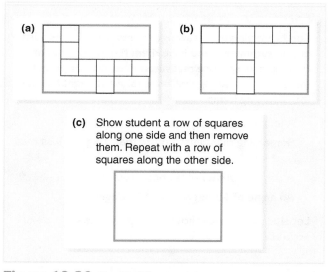

(c) Show student a row of squares along one side and then remove them. Repeat with a row of squares along the other side.

Figure 19.20 Three different activities in sequential order for determining area. Students in each case are to tell how many squares will fill the rectangles.

Source: Based on suggestions by Battista, M. T. (2003). "Understanding Students; Thinking about Area and Volume Measurement." In D. H. Clements (Ed.), *Learning and Teaching Measurement* (pp. 122–142). Reston, VA: NCTM.

rows that will fit the rectangle (determined by the length of the other side), it is time to consolidate these ideas. Explain to students that you like the idea of measuring one side to tell how many squares will fit in a row along that side. You would like them to call or think of this side as the *base* of the rectangle even though some people call it the length or the width. Then the other side you can call the *height*. But which side is the base? Be sure that students conclude that either side could be the base. If you use the formula $A = b \times h$, then the same area will result using either side as the base.

From Rectangles to Other Parallelograms. Once students understand the base-times-height formula for rectangles, the next challenge is to determine the areas of parallelograms. Do not provide a formula or other explanation. Rather, try the following activity, which again asks students to devise their own formula.

Activity 19.27

Area of a Parallelogram

Give students two or three parallelograms either drawn on grid paper or, for a slightly harder challenge, drawn on plain paper with all dimensions—the lengths of all four sides and the height. Their task is to use what they have learned about the area of rectangles to determine the areas of these parallelograms. Students should find a method that will work for any parallelogram, even if not drawn on a grid.

If students are stuck, ask them to examine ways that the parallelogram is like a rectangle or how it can be changed into a rectangle. As shown in Figure 19.21, a parallelogram can always be transformed into a rectangle

with the same base, the same height, and the same area. Thus, the formula for the area of a parallelogram is exactly the same as for a rectangle: base times height.

From Parallelograms to Triangles. With that background, the area of a triangle is relatively simple. Again, use a problem-based approach as in the next activity.

Activity 19.28

Area of a Triangle

Provide students with at least two triangles drawn on grid paper. Avoid right triangles because they are an easier special case. The challenge for students is to use what they have learned about the area of parallelograms to find the area of each of the triangles and to develop a method that will work for any triangle. They should be sure that their method works for all the triangles given to them as well as at least one more that they draw.

There are several hints that you might offer if students are stuck. *Can you find a parallelogram that is related to your triangle?* If this is not sufficient, suggest that they fold a piece of paper in half, draw a triangle on the folded paper, and cut it out, making two identical copies. They should use the copies to find out how a triangle is related to a parallelogram.

As shown in Figure 19.22 below, two congruent triangles can always be arranged to form a parallelogram with the same base and the same height as the triangle. The area of the triangle will, therefore, be one-half as much as that of the parallelogram. Have students further explore all three possible parallelograms, one for each triangle side that serves as a base. Will the computed areas always be the same?

From Parallelograms to Trapezoids. After developing formulas for parallelograms and triangles, your students may be interested in tackling trapezoids. (See Figure 3.1, p. 36, for an example of a completely open challenge.) There are at least ten different methods of arriving at a

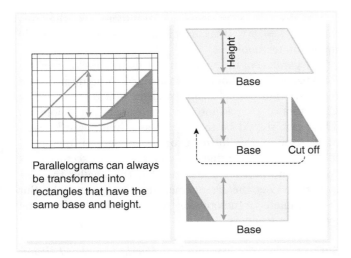

Parallelograms can always be transformed into rectangles that have the same base and height.

Figure 19.21 Transforming a parallelogram into a rectangle.

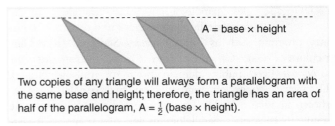

$A = \text{base} \times \text{height}$

Two copies of any triangle will always form a parallelogram with the same base and height; therefore, the triangle has an area of half of the parallelogram, $A = \frac{1}{2} (\text{base} \times \text{height})$.

Figure 19.22 Two congruent triangles always make a parallelogram.

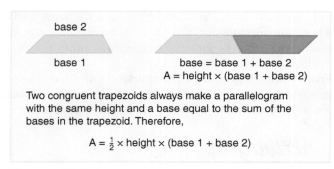

base 2

base 1

base = base 1 + base 2
A = height × (base 1 + base 2)

Two congruent trapezoids always make a parallelogram with the same height and a base equal to the sum of the bases in the trapezoid. Therefore,

$$A = \frac{1}{2} \times \text{height} \times (\text{base 1} + \text{base 2})$$

Figure 19.23 Two congruent trapezoids always form a parallelogram.

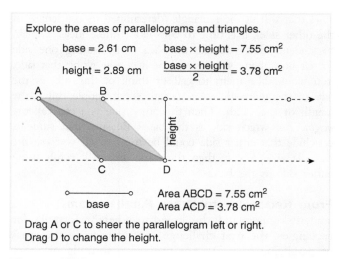

Explore the areas of parallelograms and triangles.

base = 2.61 cm   base × height = 7.55 cm²

height = 2.89 cm $\frac{\text{base} \times \text{height}}{2}$ = 3.78 cm²

base

Area ABCD = 7.55 cm²
Area ACD = 3.78 cm²

Drag A or C to sheer the parallelogram left or right.
Drag D to change the height.

Figure 19.24 Dynamic geometry software shows that figures with the same base and height maintain the same area.

formula for trapezoids, each related to the area of parallelograms or triangles. One method uses the same general approach that was used for triangles. Suggest that students try working with two trapezoids that are identical, just as they did with triangles. Figure 19.23 shows how this method results in the formula. Not only are all of these formulas connected, but similar methods were used to develop them as well.

Here are a few hints, each leading to a different approach to finding the area of a trapezoid.

- Make a parallelogram inside the given trapezoid using three of the sides.
- Make a parallelogram using three sides that surround the trapezoid.
- Draw a diagonal forming two triangles.
- Draw a line through the midpoints of the nonparallel sides. The length of that line is the average of the lengths of the two parallel sides.
- Draw a rectangle inside the trapezoid leaving two triangles and then put those two triangles together.

Pause and Reflect

Do you think that students should learn special formulas for the area of a square? Why or why not? Do you think students need formulas for the perimeters of squares and rectangles?

The relationship among the areas of rectangles, parallelograms, and triangles can be dramatically illustrated using a dynamic geometry program such as *The Geometer's Sketchpad* (Key Curriculum Press), *Cabri Geometry* (Texas Instruments), or *Wingeom* (free public domain program available online). Draw two congruent segments on two parallel lines, as shown in Figure 19.24. Then connect the endpoints of the segments to form a parallelogram and two triangles. A segment between the parallel lines and perpendicular to each indicates the height. Either of the two line segments can be

dragged left or right to "sheer" the parallelogram and triangle but without changing the base or height. All area measures remain fixed! ◆

Circumference and Area of Circles

The relationship between the *circumference* of a circle (the distance around or the perimeter) and the length of the *diameter* (a line through the center joining two points on the circle) is one of the most interesting that children can discover. The circumference of every circle is about 3.14 times as long as the diameter. The exact ratio is an irrational number close to 3.14 and is represented by the Greek letter π. So $\pi = C/D$, the circumference divided by the diameter. In a slightly different form, $C = \pi D$. Half the diameter is the radius (r), so the same equation can be written $C = 2\pi r$.

Figure 19.25 presents an argument for the area formula $A = \pi r^2$. This development is one commonly found in textbooks.

Regardless of the approach you use to develop the area formula, students should be challenged to figure it out on their own. For example, show students how to arrange 8 or 12 sectors of a circle into an approximate parallelogram. Their task should be to use this as a hint toward development of an area formula for the circle. You may need to help them notice that the arrangement of sectors is an approximate parallelogram and that the smaller the sectors, the closer the arrangement gets to a rectangle. But the complete argument for the formula should come from your students.

Surface Area. According to *Curriculum Focal Points* (NCTM, 2006), in the fifth grade students will explore

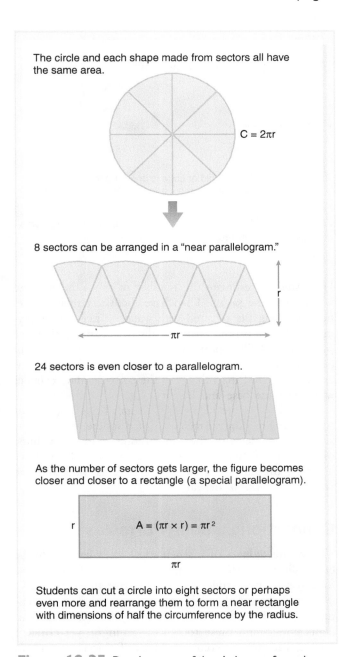

The circle and each shape made from sectors all have the same area.

$C = 2\pi r$

8 sectors can be arranged in a "near parallelogram."

r

πr

24 sectors is even closer to a parallelogram.

As the number of sectors gets larger, the figure becomes closer and closer to a rectangle (a special parallelogram).

r

$A = (\pi r \times r) = \pi r^2$

πr

Students can cut a circle into eight sectors or perhaps even more and rearrange them to form a near rectangle with dimensions of half the circumference by the radius.

Figure 19.25 Development of the circle area formula.

surface area of prisms and by seventh grade cylinders will be investigated. Build on the knowledge students have of the areas of two-dimensional figures. If they think of each face of a solid as its two-dimensional counterpart, they can find the area of each face and sum the amount. One of the best approaches to teaching the surface area of three-dimensional figures is to create several cardstock rectangular prisms, cubes, or cylinders that have sides held together by small pieces of Velcro. In this way students can think about the components or the "net" of the figure as they break the solid into faces and calculate the surface area.

Volumes of Common Solid Shapes

The relationships between the formulas for volume are completely analogous to those for area. As you read, notice the similarities between rectangles and prisms, between parallelograms and "sheered" (oblique) prisms, and between triangles and pyramids. Not only are the formulas related, but the process for developing the formulas is similar.

Volumes of Cylinders. A *cylinder* is a solid with two congruent parallel bases and sides with parallel elements that join corresponding points on the bases. There are several special classes of cylinders, including *prisms* (with polygons for bases), *right prisms, rectangular prisms,* and *cubes.* Interestingly, all of these solids have the same volume formula, and that one formula is analogous to the area formula for parallelograms.

Activity 19.29
Volume of a Box

Provide students with some cardboard shoe boxes or similar cardboard boxes, a few cubes of the same size, and a ruler. As was done with rectangles, the task is to determine how many cubes will fit inside the box. Most likely your boxes will not have whole-number dimensions, so tell students to ignore any fractional parts of cubes. Although they may have seen or used a volume formula before, for this task they may not rely on a formula. Rather, they must come up with a method using the cubes that they can explain or justify. If a hint is required, suggest that they begin by finding out how many cubes will fit on the bottom of the box.

The development of the volume formula from this box exploration is parallel to the development of the formula for the area of a rectangle, as shown in Figure 19.26. The *area* of the base (instead of *length* of the base for rectangles)

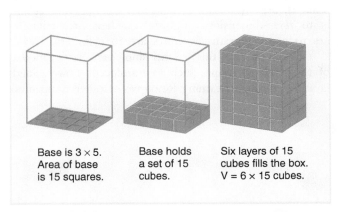

Base is 3×5. Area of base is 15 squares.

Base holds a set of 15 cubes.

Six layers of 15 cubes fills the box. $V = 6 \times 15$ cubes.

Figure 19.26 Volume of a right prism: *Area* of the base × height.

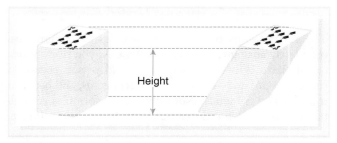

Figure 19.27 Two prisms with the same base and height have the same volume.

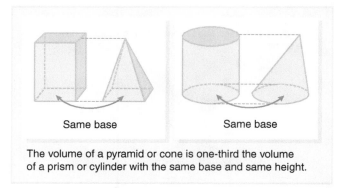

The volume of a pyramid or cone is one-third the volume of a prism or cylinder with the same base and same height.

Figure 19.28 Comparing volumes of pyramids to prisms and cones to cylinders.

determines how many *cubes* can be placed on the base forming a single unit—a layer of cubes. The *height* of the box then determines how many of these *layers* will fit in the box just as the height of the rectangle determined how many *rows* of squares would fill the rectangle.

Recall that a parallelogram can be thought of as a "sheered" rectangle, as was illustrated with the dynamic geometry software (see Figure 19.24). Show students a stack of three or four decks of playing cards (or a stack of books or paper). When stacked straight, they form a rectangular solid. The volume, as just discussed, is $V = A \times h$, with A equal to the area of one playing card. Now if the stack is sheered or slanted to one side as shown in Figure 19.27, what will the volume of this new figure be? Students should be able to argue that this figure has the same volume (and same volume formula) as the original stack.

What if the cards in this activity were some other shape? If they were circular, the volume would still be the area of the base times the height; if they were triangular, still the same. The conclusion is that the volume of *any* cylinder is equal to the *area of the base* times the *height*.

Volumes of Cones and Pyramids. Recall that when parallelograms and triangles have the same base and height, the areas are in a 2-to-1 relationship. Interestingly, the relationship between the volumes of cylinders and cones with the same base and height is 3 to 1. That is, *area* is to *two*-dimensional figures what *volume* is to *three*-dimensional figures. Furthermore, triangles are to parallelograms as cones are to cylinders.

To investigate this relationship use plastic models of these related shapes such as translucent Power Solids (available through Learning Resources or other companies).

Have students estimate the number of times the pyramid will fit into the prism. Then have them test their prediction by filling the pyramid with water or rice and emptying it into the prism. They will discover that exactly three pyramids will fill a prism with the same base and height (see Figure 19.28). The volume of a cone or pyramid is exactly one-third the volume of the corresponding cylinder with the same base and height.

Using the same idea of base times height, it is possible to explore the surface area of a sphere (4 times the area of a circle with the same radius) and the volume of a sphere ($\frac{1}{3}$ times the surface area times the radius). That is, the surface area of a sphere is $4\pi r^2$ and the volume is $\frac{1}{3}(4\pi r^2)r$ or $\frac{4}{3}\pi r^3$.

Connections among Formulas

The connectedness of mathematical ideas can hardly be better illustrated than with the connections of all of these formulas to the single concept of base times height.

As illustrated throughout this last section, a conceptual approach to the development of formulas helps students understand these tools as meaningful yet efficient ways to measure different attributes of objects around us. After having developed formulas in meaningful ways, students are no longer required to memorize them as isolated pieces of mathematical facts but can instead derive formulas from what they already know. Mathematics does make sense!

Reflections

Writing to Learn

1. Explain what it means to measure something. Does your explanation work equally well for length, area, weight, volume, and time?
2. A general instructional plan for measurement has three steps. Explain how the type of activity to use at each step accomplishes the instructional goal.
3. Four reasons were offered for using nonstandard units instead of standard units in instructional activities. Which of these seem most important to you, and why?
4. Develop in a connected way the area formulas for rectangles, parallelograms, triangles, and trapezoids. Draw pictures and provide explanations.

5. Explain how the area of a circle can be determined using the basic formula for the area of a parallelogram. (If you have a set of fraction circular pieces, these can be used as sectors of a circle.)

For Discussion and Exploration

1. Frequently, a textbook chapter on measurement will cover length, area, volume, and capacity with both metric and customary units. Get a teacher's edition of a textbook for any grade level, and look at the chapters on measurement. How well does the book cover metric measurement ideas? How would you modify or expand on the lessons found there?

Resources

Literature Connections

How Big Is a Foot? *Myller, 1990*

The story in this concept book is very attractive to young children. The king measures his queen using his feet and orders a bed made that is 6 feet long and 3 feet wide. The chief carpenter's apprentice, who is very small, makes the bed according to his own feet, demonstrating the need for standard units.

Every Minute on Earth: Fun Facts That Happen Every 60 Seconds *Murrie & Murrie, 2007*

This is an amazing book that is not just about the concept of time. The authors provide fun facts about what can happen in 60 seconds: a snow avalanche travels 4.2 miles (6.8 kilometers); the adult heart pumps 3.3 liters (3.5 quarts) of blood; movie film travels 90 feet (27.4 meters) through a projector; a garden snail moves 0.31 inches (7.8 millimeters); people in the United States throw away 18,315 pounds (8325 kilograms) of food; and consumers spend $954.00 on chewing gum. Students can use the facts provided or identify others as they think and discuss these relationships.

Inchworm and a Half *Pinczes, 2001*

In this wonderfully illustrated book, an inchworm happily goes about measuring various garden vegetables. One day a measurement does not result in a whole number, and the worm gets very upset. Fortunately, a smaller worm drops onto the vegetable and measures a half unit. Eventually, other fraction-measuring worms appear. (Be wary of the $\frac{1}{3}$ worm as $\frac{1}{3}$ is not a common measurement unit.) The story provides a great connection between fractions and measurement concepts, especially for the introduction of fractional units in measurement. Moyer and Mailley (2004) describe a nice series of activities inspired by the book.

Recommended Readings

Articles

Austin, R., Thompson, D., & Beckmann, C. (2005). Exploring measurement concepts through literature: Natural links across disciplines. *Mathematics Teaching in the Middle School, 10*(5), 218–224.
This article includes a rich collection of almost 30 children's books that emphasize overall systems of measurement, length, weight, capacity, speed, area, perimeter, and volume. Three books are described in detail as the authors share how to link measurement to science, history, geography, and economics.

National Council of Teachers of Mathematics. (2004). Measurement [Focus Issue]. *Mathematics Teaching in the Middle School, 9.*
This focus issue of NCTM's middle school journal is full of great information for teachers at that level. Of particular note are several articles that involve scale drawings or other aspects of proportional reasoning, which is a great way to integrate measurement into the curriculum.

Pumala, V. A., & Klabunde, D. A. (2005). Learning measurement through practice. *Mathematics Teaching in the Middle School, 10*(9), 452–460.
A mathematics teacher and a science teacher collaborated on a series of six activities to help their students learn about

measurement. Included in the article are descriptions of the activities and detailed rubrics, along with samples of student work.

Whitin, D. (2008). Learning our way to one million. *Teaching Children Mathematics, 14*(8), 448–453.

Through an exploration of the topic of one million, Whitin suggests ways for children in grades 2–5 to explore several mathematics topics, including length, area, and money. All investigations emphasize the need for active problem solving in real-world contexts that reflect students' interests.

Books

Clements, D. H. (Ed.). (2003). *Learning and teaching measurement: 2003 Yearbook.* Reston, VA: NCTM.

This book brings both a practical and a research perspective on measurement that expands and provides additional details concerning the ideas in this chapter. Discussions include beginning measurement in the pre-K–2 classroom, assessment strategies, and the importance of benchmarks in estimation.

Online Resources

Area Tool
http://illuminations.nctm.org/ActivityDetail.aspx?ID=108

There are three separate applets that explore how changes in the base and height of these shapes affect the area.

Clock Wise
www.shodor.org/interactivate/activities/clockwise

A clock face is shown and the user enters the digital time. Four difficulty levels.

Cubes
http://illuminations.nctm.org/ActivityDetail.aspx?ID=6

An excellent interactive applet that illustrates the volume of a rectangular prism (box). Units of single cubes, rows of cubes, or layers of cubes can be used to fill a prism.

Geoboard
http://nlvm.usu.edu/en/nav/frames_asid_279_g_4_t_3 .html

This electronic geoboard measures the area and perimeter of any shape made. What is nice is that the measures are not shown until the user clicks the Measure button. Students can be challenged to make shapes with specified areas and/or perimeters.

How High
http://nlvm.usu.edu/en/nav/frames_asid_275_g_3_t_4 .html

Two cylinders are shown along with the area of the base shown as a grid of squares. One cylinder is filled to a specified height. The task is to determine the height of this same liquid when it is poured into the second container.

Image Tool
www.shodor.org/interactivate/activities/imagetool/index .html

The user can measure angles, distances, and areas in several different images (choices include maps, aerial photos, and others). A scale feature allows the user to set the scale used for measuring distances and areas. Unique!

Money
http://nlvm.usu.edu/en/nav/frames_asid_325_g_2_t_4 .html

This site gives students an opportunity to make a dollar, find an exact amount, or fill in how much money is shown.

Perimeter Explorer
www.shodor.org/interactivate/activities/Perimeter Explorer

The user sets a fixed number of square units and the applet randomly creates shapes on a grid with this area. The object is to determine the perimeter. There is also an *Area Explorer* (fixes the perimeter) and a *Shape Explorer*, which asks the user for both the area and perimeter of the randomly produced shapes.

What Time Will It Be?
http://nlvm.usu.edu/en/nav/frames_asid_318_g_2_t_4 .html

Elapsed-time problems are presented in word format. Two clocks are shown, one with the start time and the other to be set. Some problems are digital, others analog.

Field Experience Guide Connections

Because measurement is so much a part of real-life experiences, lessons in measurement should be too. Use FEG 2.3 and 2.4 to analyze tasks or lessons to see whether they provide students with authentic opportunities to measure and understand measurement concepts. FEG Expanded Lessons 9.15 ("Crooked Paths") and 9.16 ("Fixed Areas") are engaging lessons about length and area and perimeter, respectively. FEG Activity 10.11 ("Cover All") uses manipulatives to explore area, and Balanced Assessment Task 11.3 ("Bolts and Nuts!") is a task to analyze student thinking about measuring length and analyzing patterns.

Geometric Thinking and Geometric Concepts

Geometry is a strand of the curriculum in nearly every state and district. This is due in large part to the influence of the NCTM standards movement beginning in 1989 and the growing use of geometry in everything from global positioning systems to computer animation. Increased attention to a theoretical perspective that has helped us understand how students reason about spatial concepts is another significant influence.

Big Ideas

1. What makes shapes alike and different can be determined by geometric properties. For example, shapes have sides that are parallel, perpendicular, or neither; they have line symmetry, rotational symmetry, or neither; they are similar, congruent, or neither.

2. Shapes can be moved in a plane or in space. These changes can be described in terms of translations (slides), reflections (flips), and rotations (turns).

3. Shapes can be described in terms of their location in a plane or in space. Coordinate systems can be used to describe these locations precisely. In turn, the coordinate view of shape offers ways to understand certain properties of shapes, changes in position (transformations), and how they appear or change size (visualization).

4. Shapes can be seen from various perspectives. The ability to perceive shapes from different viewpoints helps us understand relationships between two- and three-dimensional figures and mentally change the position and size of shapes.

Mathematics Content Connections

A rich understanding of geometry has clear and important implications for other areas of the curriculum. Take advantage of these connections whenever possible.

- **Algebra:** Coordinate graphing provides an analytic view of the concept of slope and, in turn, of perpendicular and parallel relationships. Transformations of shapes (slides, flips, and turns) can be described in terms of coordinates, allowing for the digital manipulation of shapes.

- **Proportional Reasoning:** Similar geometric objects have proportional dimensions and provide visual representations of proportionality.

- **Measurement:** Measurement is aligned in the development of area and volume formulas and in an understanding of area/perimeter and surface area/volume relationships. Coordinate geometry provides new ways to determine lengths, areas, and volumes. The Pythagorean relationship is at once an algebraic, geometric, and metric relationship.

- **Integers:** Both positive and negative numbers are used in the description of position in the plane and in space.

Geometry Goals for Students

It is useful to think about your geometry objectives in terms of two related frameworks: (1) spatial sense and geometric reasoning, and (2) the specific geometric content found in your state or district objectives. The first framework has to do with the way students think and reason about shape and space. There is a well-researched theoretical basis for organizing the development of geometric thought that guides this framework. The second framework is content in the more traditional sense—knowing about symmetry, triangles, parallel lines, and so forth. The NCTM *Principles and Standards for School Mathematics* and *Curriculum Focal Points* help describe content goals across the grades. We need to understand both aspects of geometry—reasoning and content—so that we can best help students grow.

From Chapter 20 of *Elementary and Middle School Mathematics: Teaching Developmentally*, 7/e. John A. Van de Walle. Karen S. Karp. Jennifer M. Bay-Williams. Copyright © 2010 by Pearson Allyn and Bacon. All rights reserved.

Spatial Sense and Geometric Reasoning

Spatial sense can be defined as an intuition about shapes and the relationships among shapes. Spatial sense includes the ability to mentally visualize objects and spatial relationships—to turn things around in your mind. It includes a comfort with geometric descriptions of objects and position. People with well-developed spatial sense appreciate geometric form in art, nature, and architecture. They are able to use geometric ideas to describe and analyze their world.

Some people say they aren't very good with shape or that they have poor spatial sense. The typical belief is that you either are or are not born with spatial sense. This simply is not true! We now know that rich experiences with shape and spatial relationships, when provided consistently over time, can and do develop spatial sense. Between 1990 and 2000, NAEP data indicated a steady, continuing improvement in students' geometric reasoning at grade 8 (Sowder & Wearne, 2006). Students did not just get smarter. Instead, there has been an increasing emphasis on geometry at all grades. Still, much more needs to be done if U.S. children are to rise to the same level as their European and Asian counterparts.

 ———————— *Pause and Reflect*

Reflect for a moment about your own beliefs concerning an individual's abilities in the area of spatial sense. What do you think causes some people to have better spatial sense than others?

NCTM Standards The *Standards* supports the notion that all students can grow in their geometric skills and understandings. "The notion of building understanding in geometry across the grades, from informal to more formal thinking, is consistent with the thinking of theorists and researchers" (p. 41). ◆

Geometric Content

For too long, the geometry curriculum in the United States has emphasized the learning of terminology. At the same time, however, the growing focus on geometry has spawned a huge assortment of wonderful tasks for students. As with each of the NCTM content standards, the geometry standard has a number of goals that apply to all grade levels. The four content goals for geometry can be summarized in the following four categories:

- *Shapes and Properties* includes a study of the properties of shapes in both two and three dimensions, as well as a study of the relationships built on properties.

- *Transformation* includes a study of translations, reflections, rotations (slides, flips, and turns), the study of symmetries, and the concept of similarity.
- *Location* refers primarily to coordinate geometry or other ways of specifying how objects are located in the plane or in space.
- *Visualization* includes the recognition of shapes in the environment, developing relationships between two- and three-dimensional objects, and the ability to draw and recognize objects from different perspectives.

Because of these content goals, a content framework finally exists that bridges grades so that both teachers and curriculum planners can examine growth from year to year. To assist you, the activities in this chapter are grouped according to these four categories.

The Development of Geometric Thinking

Although not all people think about geometric ideas in the same manner, we are all capable of growing and developing in our ability to think and reason in geometric contexts. The research of two Dutch educators, Pierre van Hiele and Dina van Hiele-Geldof (husband and wife), has provided insight into the differences in geometric thinking and how the differences come to be.

The van Hieles' work began in 1959 and immediately attracted a lot of attention in the former Soviet Union but for nearly two decades got little notice in the United States (Hoffer & Hoffer, 1992). But today, the van Hiele theory has become the greatest influence in the American geometry curriculum.

The van Hiele Levels of Geometric Thought

The most prominent feature of the model is a five-level hierarchy of ways of understanding spatial ideas. Each of the five levels describes the thinking processes used in geometric contexts (see Figure 20.1). The levels describe how we think and what types of geometric ideas we think about, rather than how much knowledge we have. A significant difference from one level to the next is the objects of thought—what we are able to think about geometrically.

Level 0: Visualization

The objects of thought at level 0 are shapes and what they "look like."

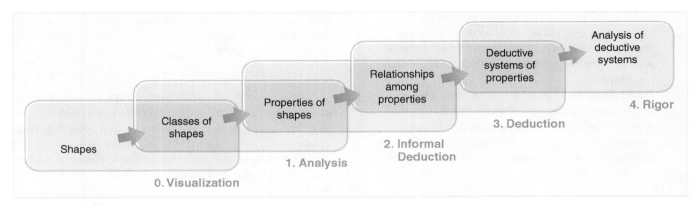

Figure 20.1 The van Hiele theory of geometric thought.

Students at level 0 recognize and name figures based on the global visual characteristics of the figure. For example, a square is defined by a level 0 student as a square "because it looks like a square." Because appearance is dominant at this level, appearances can overpower properties of a shape. For example, a square that has been rotated so that all sides are at a 45-degree angle to the vertical may now be a diamond and no longer a square. Students at this level will sort and classify shapes based on their appearances—"I put these together because they are all pointy" (or "fat," or "look like a house," and so on). With a focus on the appearances of shapes, students are able to see how shapes are alike and different. As a result, students at this level can create and begin to understand classifications of shapes.

The products of thought at level 0 are classes or groupings of shapes that seem to be "alike."

The emphasis at level 0 is on the shapes that students can observe, feel, build, take apart, or work with in some manner. The general goal is to explore how shapes are alike and different and to use these ideas to create classes of shapes (both physically and mentally). Some of these classes of shapes have names—rectangles, triangles, prisms, cylinders, and so on. Properties of shapes, such as parallel sides, symmetry, right angles, and so on, are included at this level but only in an informal, observational manner.

Although the van Hiele theory applies to students of all ages learning any geometric content, it may be easier to apply the theory to the shapes-and-property category. The following is a good representation of an activity appropriate for level 0.

Activity 20.1

Shape Sorts

Have students work in groups of four with a set of 2-D shapes similar to those in Figure 20.2, doing the following related activities in order:

- **Each child selects a shape. In turn, the students tell one or two things they find interesting about their shape. There are no right or wrong responses.**
- **Children each randomly select two shapes and try to find something that is alike about their two shapes and something that is different.**
- **The group selects one shape at random and places it in the center of the workspace. Their task is to find all other shapes that are like the target shape according to the same rule. For example, if they say "This shape is like the target shape because it has a**

Figure 20.2 An assortment of shapes for sorting. See Blackline Masters 41–47 for a larger collection of shapes.

curved side and a straight side," then all other shapes that they put in the collection must have these properties. Challenge them to do a second sort with the same target shape but using a different property.

- Do a "secret sort." You (or one of the students) create a small collection of about five shapes that fit a secret rule. Leave others that belong in your group in the pile. The other students try to find additional pieces that belong to the set and/or guess the secret rule.

Depending on the grade level, these activities will elicit a wide variety of ideas as students examine the shapes. For the most part these will be ideas such as "curvy" or "looks like a rocket" rather than typical geometric concepts. But students may begin to notice more sophisticated properties and the teacher can take the opportunity to attach appropriate names to them as the students describe them. For example, students may notice that some shapes have corners "like a square" (right angles) or that "these shapes are the same on both sides" (line symmetry).

What clearly makes this a level-0 activity, however, is not the presence or the absence of traditional geometric properties or terms. Rather, students are operating on the shapes that they see in front of them. Furthermore, for level-0 students, the shapes may even "change" or have different properties as they are rearranged or rotated. The objective of the activity is for students to begin to see that there are likenesses and differences in shapes. By forming groups of shapes, they may begin to imagine shapes belonging to these classes that are not there.

Level 1: Analysis

The objects of thought at level 1 are classes of shapes rather than individual shapes.

Students at the analysis level are able to consider all shapes within a class rather than a single shape on their desk. Instead of talking about *this* rectangle, it is possible to talk about *all* rectangles. By focusing on a class of shapes, students are able to think about what makes a rectangle a rectangle (four sides, opposite sides parallel, opposite sides same length, four right angles, congruent diagonals, etc.). The irrelevant features (e.g., size or orientation) fade into the background and students begin to appreciate that a collection of shapes goes together because of properties. If a shape belongs to a particular class such as cubes, it has the corresponding properties of that class. "All cubes have six congruent faces, and each of those faces is a square." These properties were only implicit at level 0. Students operating at level 1 may be able to list all the properties of squares, rectangles, and parallelograms but may not see that these are subclasses of one another, that all squares are rectangles

and all rectangles are parallelograms. In defining a shape, level-1 thinkers are likely to list as many properties of a shape as they know.

The products of thought at level 1 are the properties of shapes.

A significant difference between level 1 and level 0 is the object of students' thought. While level-1 students will continue to use models and drawings of shapes, they begin to see these as representatives of classes of shapes. Their understanding of the properties of shapes—such as symmetry, perpendicular and parallel lines, and so on—continues to be refined.

In the following activity, students use the properties of shapes they learned in earlier activities, possibly while operating at level 0. These include ideas such as symmetry, angle classification (right, obtuse, acute), parallel and perpendicular, and the concept of congruent line segments and angles.

Activity 20.2
Property Lists for Quadrilaterals

Prepare worksheets for parallelograms, rhombi, rectangles, and squares. (See Blackline Masters 54–57 and Figure 20.3.) Assign students working in groups of three or four to one type of quadrilateral. Their task is to list as many properties as they can that are applicable to all of the shapes on their sheet. They will need an index card to check right angles, to compare

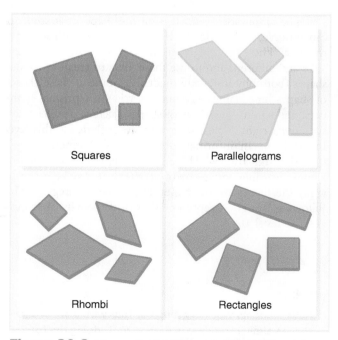

Figure 20.3 Shapes for the "Property Lists for Quadrilaterals" activity (see Blackline Masters 54–57).

side lengths, and to draw straight lines. Mirrors (to check line symmetry) and tracing paper (for angle congruence and rotational symmetry) are also useful tools. Encourage students to use the words "at least" when describing how many of something: for example, "rectangles have at least two lines of symmetry," because squares—included in the rectangles—have four.

Have students prepare their property lists under these headings: Sides, Angles, Diagonals, and Symmetries. Groups then share their lists with the class and eventually a class list for each category of shape will be developed.

Both this activity and the earlier classification activity involve an examination of shapes focusing on geometric properties. What distinguishes this activity from the level-0 classification activity is the object of students' thinking. Students must assess whether the properties apply to all shapes in the category. If they are working on the squares, for example, their observations must apply to a square mile as well as a square centimeter.

Level 2: Informal Deduction

The objects of thought at level 2 are the properties of shapes.

As students begin to be able to think about properties of geometric objects without the constraints of a particular object, they are able to develop relationships between and among these properties. "If all four angles are right angles, the shape must be a rectangle. If it is a square, all angles are right angles. If it is a square, it must be a rectangle." With greater ability to engage in "if-then" reasoning, shapes can be classified using only minimum defining characteristics. For example, four congruent sides and at least one right angle can be sufficient to define a square. Rectangles are parallelograms with a right angle. Observations go beyond properties themselves and begin to focus on logical arguments *about* the properties. Students at level 2 will be able to follow and appreciate an informal deductive argument about shapes and their properties. "Proofs" may be more intuitive than rigorously deductive; however, there is an appreciation that a logical argument is compelling. An appreciation of the axiomatic structure (an agreed-on set of rules) of a formal deductive system, however, remains under the surface.

The products of thought at level 2 are relationships among properties of geometric objects.

The hallmark of level-2 activities is the inclusion of informal logical reasoning. Since students have developed an understanding of various properties of shapes, it is now time to encourage conjecture and to ask "Why?" or "What if?" Contrast the required thinking in the following activity.

Activity 20.3
Minimal Defining Lists

(This activity must be done as a follow-up to Activity 20.2, "Property Lists.") Once property lists for the parallelogram, rhombus, rectangle, and square (and possibly the kite and trapezoid) have been agreed on by the class, have these lists posted. Have students work in groups to find "minimal defining lists," or MDLs, for each shape. An MDL is a subset of the properties for a shape that is defining and "minimal." "Defining" here means that any shape that has all the properties on the MDL must be that shape. "Minimal" means that if any single property is removed from the list it is no longer defining. For example, one MDL for a square is a quadrilateral with four congruent sides and four right angles. Students should try to find at least two or three MDLs for their shape. A proposed list can be challenged as either not minimal or not defining. A list is not defining if a counterexample—a shape other than one being described—can be produced using only the properties on the list.

The hallmark of this and other level-2 activities is the logic component. "*If* a quadrilateral has these properties, *then* it must be a square." Logic is also involved in proving that a list is faulty—either not minimal or not defining. Here students begin to learn the nature of a definition and the value of counterexamples. In fact, any minimal defining list (MDL) is a potential definition. The other aspect of this activity that clearly sets it into the level-2 category is that students focus on the lists of properties of the shapes—the very factors that were products of the earlier level-1 activity. As a result of the MDL activity, students are creating a collection of new relationships that exist between and among properties.

Level 3: Deduction

The objects of thought at level 3 are relationships among properties of geometric objects.

At level 3, students are able to examine more than just the properties of shapes. Their earlier thinking has produced conjectures concerning relationships among properties. Are these conjectures "true"? As this analysis of the informal arguments takes place, the structure of a system complete with axioms, definitions, theorems, corollaries, and postulates begins to develop and can be appreciated as the necessary means of establishing geometric truth. The student at this level is able to work with abstract statements about geometric properties and make conclusions based more on logic than intuition. A student operating at level 3 is aware that the diagonals of a rectangle bisect each other. However, at level 3, there is an appreciation of the need to prove this from a series of deductive arguments. The level-2 thinker, by contrast, follows the argument but fails to appreciate the need for more.

The products of thought at level 3 are deductive axiomatic systems for geometry.

The type of reasoning that characterizes a level-3 thinker is the same that is required in a typical high school geometry course. There students build on a list of axioms and definitions to create theorems. They also prove theorems using clearly articulated logical reasoning, whereas the reasoning at level 2 may be quite informal. In the best geometry courses, students would engage in activities in which they would discover the relationships they later prove.

In a very global sense, high school geometry students are working on the creation of a complete geometric deductive system. Usually this is the Euclidean system that describes best the world in which we live. They may also explore other geometric systems, such as the geometry where all lines are drawn on the surface of a sphere or "taxicab geometry" where lines may only follow a rectangular grid of "streets."

Level 4: Rigor

The objects of thought at level 4 are deductive axiomatic systems for geometry.

At the highest level of the van Hiele hierarchy, the objects of attention are axiomatic systems themselves, not just the deductions within a system. There is an appreciation of the distinctions and relationships between different axiomatic systems. For example, spherical geometry is based on lines drawn on a sphere rather than in a plane or ordinary space. This geometry has its own set of axioms and theorems. This is generally the level of a college mathematics major who is studying geometry as a branch of mathematical science.

The products of thought at level 4 are comparisons and contrasts among different axiomatic systems of geometry.

Characteristics of the van Hiele Levels. You no doubt noticed that the products of thought at each level are the same as the objects of thought at the next. This object-product relationship between levels of the van Hiele theory is illustrated in Figure 20.1. The objects (ideas) must be created at one level so that relationships among these objects can become the focus of the next level. In addition, the van Hiele levels have several common characteristics:

- The levels are sequential. To arrive at one level, students must move through prior levels.
- The products of thought at each level are the same as the objects of thought at the next.
- The levels are not age dependent. A third grader or a high school student could be at level 0.

- Geometric experiences are the greatest single factor influencing advancement through the levels. Students should explore, talk about, and interact with content at the next level while increasing experiences at their current level.
- When instruction or language is at a level higher than that of the student, there will be a lack of communication. A student can memorize a fact (e.g., all squares are rectangles) without having constructed that relationship.

The first three of the five van Hiele levels will continue as the focus of this chapter. Most students in pre-K through grade 8 will fall within these three categories. The emphasis of your work in geometry will be reflected by these ideas.

Implications for Instruction

If the van Hiele theory is correct—and there is much evidence to support it—then a major goal of the pre-K–8 curriculum must be to advance students' level of geometric thought. If students are to be adequately prepared for the deductive geometry curriculum of high school and beyond, then it is important for their thinking to have grown to at least level 2 by the end of the eighth grade.

All teachers should be aware that the experiences they provide are the single most important factor in moving children up this developmental ladder. Every teacher should be able to see some growth in students' geometric thinking over the course of the year.

The van Hiele theory and the developmental perspective of this book highlight the necessity of teaching at the child's level of thought. However, almost any activity can be modified to span two levels of thinking, even within the same classroom. For many activities, how we interact with individual children will adapt the activity to their levels while challenging them to operate at the next higher level.

The following sections contain descriptions of the types of activity and questioning that are appropriate for each of the first three levels. Apply these descriptors to the tasks that you pose to students, and use them to guide your interaction with students. The use of physical materials, drawings, and computer models is a must at every level.

Instruction at Level 0. Instructional activities in geometry appropriate for level 0 should:

- Involve lots of sorting and classifying. Seeing how shapes are alike and different is the primary focus of level 0. As students learn more content, the relationships that they notice will become more sophisticated.

- Students need ample opportunities to draw, build, make, put together (compose), and take apart (decompose) shapes in both two and three dimensions. These activities should be built around specific characteristics or properties so that students develop an understanding of geometric properties and begin to use them naturally.

To help students move from level 0 to level 1, students should be challenged to test ideas about shapes for a variety of examples from a particular category. Say to them, "Let's see if that is true for other rectangles," or "Can you draw a triangle that does *not* have a right angle?" In general, students should be challenged to see if observations made about a particular shape apply to other shapes of a similar kind.

Instruction at Level 1.
Instructional activities in geometry appropriate for level 1 should:

- Focus more on the properties of figures rather than on simple identification. As new geometric concepts are learned, the number of properties that figures have can be expanded.
- Apply ideas to entire classes of figures (e.g., *all* rectangles, *all* prisms) rather than on individual models. For example, find ways to sort all possible triangles into groups. From these groups, define types of triangles.

To assist students in moving from level 1 to level 2, challenge them with questions such as "Why?" and those that involve reasoning. For example, "If the sides of a four-sided shape are all congruent, will you always have a square?" and "Can you find a counterexample?"

Instruction at Level 2.
Instructional activities in geometry appropriate for level 2 should:

- Encourage the making and testing of hypotheses or conjectures. "Do you think that will work all the time?" "Is that true for all triangles or just equilateral ones?"
- Examine properties of shapes to determine necessary and sufficient conditions for different shapes or concepts. "What properties of diagonals do you think will guarantee that you will have a square?"
- Use the language of informal deduction: *all, some, none, if . . . then, what if,* and so on.
- Encourage students to attempt informal proofs. As an alternative, require them to make sense of informal proofs that other students or you have suggested.

Task Selection and Levels of Thought.
If you teach at the pre-K–3 level, nearly all of your students will be at level 0. In the upper grades you may have children at two or even three levels within the same classroom. How do you discover the level of each student? Once you know, how will you select the right activities to match your students' levels?

No simple assessment exists to identify the exact level at which a student is functioning. However, examine the descriptors for the first two levels. As you conduct an activity, listen to students' observations. Can they talk about shapes as classes? Do they refer, for example, to "rectangles" rather than basing discussion around a particular rectangle? Do they understand that shapes do not change when the orientation or size changes? With careful observations such as these, you will soon be able to distinguish between levels 0 and 1.

At the upper grades, attempt to move students from level 1 to level 2. If students are not able to follow or appreciate logical arguments and are not comfortable with conjectures and if-then reasoning, these students are likely still at level 1 or below.

The remainder of this chapter offers a sampling of activities organized broadly around the four content goals of the NCTM standards: Shapes and Properties, Location, Transformations, and Visualization. Within each of these content groupings, activities are further sorted according to the first three van Hiele levels. Understand that all of these subdivisions are quite fluid. An activity found at one level can easily be adapted to an adjacent level simply by the way it is presented to the students.

Learning about Shapes and Properties

This is the content area that most people think about when they think about geometry in the pre-K–8 classroom; children are working with both two- and three-dimensional shapes. They are finding out what makes these shapes alike and different and in the process they begin to discover properties of the shapes, including the conventional names for these properties. With sufficient experiences, students develop classifications of special shapes—triangles, parallelograms, cylinders, pyramids, and so on—and learn that some properties apply to full classes. Eventually, they will investigate how properties of shapes impose logical consequences on geometric relationships and the ability to reason about shapes and properties will be developed.

Shapes and Properties for Level-0 Thinkers

Young children need experience with a rich variety of both two- and three-dimensional shapes. Triangles should be more than just equilateral and not always shown with the vertex at the top. Shapes should have curved sides, straight sides, and combinations of these. Along the way, the names of shapes and their properties can be introduced.

Sorting and Classifying. As young students work at classification of shapes, be prepared for them to notice features that you do not consider to be "real" geometric attributes, such as "dented" or "looks like a tree." Children at this level will also attribute to shapes ideas that are not part of the shape, such as "points up" or "has a side that is the same as the edge of the board."

For variety in two-dimensional shapes, create your own materials. A good set of assorted shapes is found in Blackline Masters 41–47. Make multiple copies so that groups of children can all work with the same shapes. Once you have your sets constructed, a good beginning is Activity 20.1, "Shape Sorts."

In any sorting activity, the students should decide how to sort, not the teacher. This allows the students to do the activity using ideas *they* own and understand. By listening to the kinds of attributes that they use in their sorting, you will be able to tell what properties they know and use and how they think about shapes. Figure 20.4 illustrates a few of the many possible ways a set might be sorted.

The secret sorting portion of Activity 20.1 is one option for introducing a new property. For example, sort the shapes so that all have at least one right angle or "square corner." When students discover your rule, you have an opportunity to talk more about that property.

The following activity is also done with the 2-D shapes.

Activity 20.4

What's My Shape?

From Blackline Masters 41–47, make a double set of 2-D assorted shapes on cardstock. Cut out one set of shapes and glue each inside a folded half-sheet of construction paper to make "secret shape" folders.

In a group, one student is designated the leader and given a secret-shape folder. The other students are to find the shape that matches the shape in the folder by asking questions to which the leader can answer only "yes" or "no." The group can eliminate shapes as they ask questions to help narrow down the possibilities. They are not allowed to point to a piece and ask, "Is it this one?" Rather, they must continue to ask questions about properties or characteristics that reduce the choices to one shape. The final piece is checked against the one in the leader's folder.

The difficulty of Activity 20.4 is largely dependent on the shape in the folder. The more shapes in the collection that resemble the secret shape, the more difficult the task.

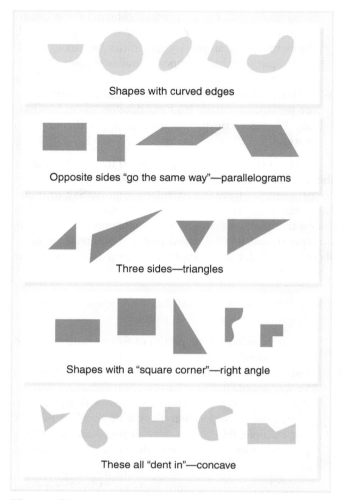

Figure 20.4 By sorting shapes, students begin to recognize properties.

Most of the activities in "Shape Sorts" can and should be done with three-dimensional shapes. The difficulty is finding or making a collection that has sufficient variability. Geoblocks are a large set of wooden blocks available through various distributors. The variety is good, but no blocks have curved surfaces. Check catalogs for other collections. Consider combining several different sets to get variation. Another option is to collect real objects such as cans, boxes, balls, and Styrofoam shapes. Figure 20.5 illustrates some classifications of solids.

The ways in which children describe shapes in "Shape Sorts" and similar activities with three-dimensional shapes are good evidence of their level of thinking. The classifications made by level-0 thinkers will generally be restricted to the shapes that they have in front of them. As they begin to think in terms of the properties of shapes, they will create categories based on properties and their language will indicate that there are many more shapes in the group than those that

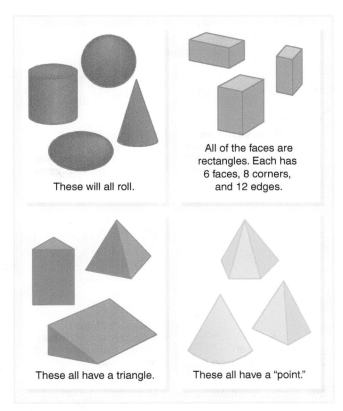

These will all roll.

All of the faces are rectangles. Each has 6 faces, 8 corners, and 12 edges.

These all have a triangle.

These all have a "point."

Figure 20.5 Early classifications of three-dimensional shapes.

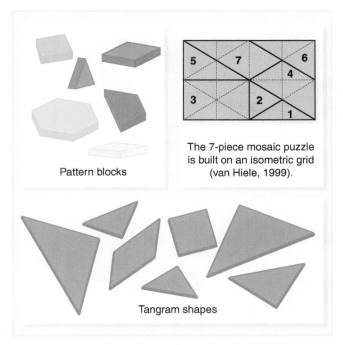

Pattern blocks

The 7-piece mosaic puzzle is built on an isometric grid (van Hiele, 1999).

Tangram shapes

Figure 20.6 Assorted tiles for activities.

are physically present (Mack, 2007). Students may say things like, "These shapes have square corners sort of like rectangles," or "These look like boxes. All the boxes have square [rectangular] sides." ◆

Composing and Decomposing Shapes. Children need to freely explore how shapes fit together to form larger shapes and how larger shapes can be made of smaller shapes. Among two-dimensional shapes for these activities, pattern blocks and tangrams are the best known. In a 1999 article, Pierre van Hiele describes an interesting set of tiles he calls the mosaic puzzle (see Figure 20.6). Patterns for the mosaic puzzle and tangrams can be found in Blackline Master 51.

Figure 20.7 shows four different types of tangram puzzles in increasing order of difficulty. NCTM's e-Examples includes a tangram applet (Example 4.4) with a set of challenges. One form of the applet includes eight puzzle figures that can be made using all seven of the pieces. The e-version of tangrams has the advantage of motivation and the fact that you must be much more deliberate in arranging the shapes.

The value of van Hiele's mosaic puzzle is partly due to the fact that the set contains five different angles (see Figure 20.8). You can use the pieces to talk about square corners (*right* angles) and angles that are more and less than a right angle (*obtuse* and *acute* angles).

The geoboard is one of the best devices for "drawing" two-dimensional shapes. The following activities are just three of many possible activities appropriate for level 0.

Activity 20.5

Geoboard Copy

Copy shapes, designs, and patterns from an overhead or projected geoboard. Begin with designs using one band; then create more complex designs (see Figure 20.9).

Activity 20.6

Congruent Parts

Copy a shape from a card, and have students subdivide or decompose it into smaller shapes on their geoboards. Specify the number of smaller shapes. Also specify whether they are all to be congruent or simply of the same type as shown in Figure 20.10.

Have lots of geoboards available in the classroom. It is better for two or three children to have 10 or 12 boards at a station than for each to have only one. That way, a variety of shapes can be made and compared before they are changed.

Teach students from the very beginning to record their geoboard designs. Paper copies (see Blackline Masters 49–50) permit students to create complete sets of

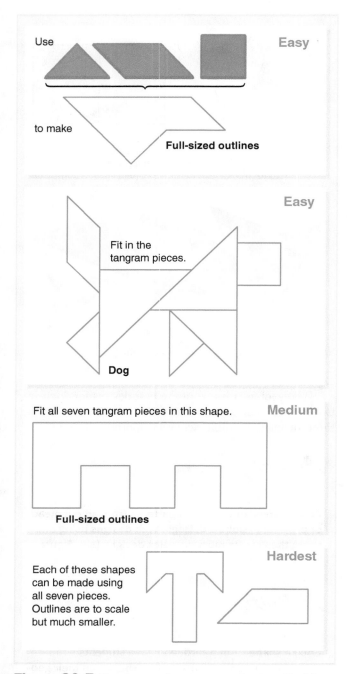

Figure 20.7 Four types of tangram puzzles (see Blackline Master 51).

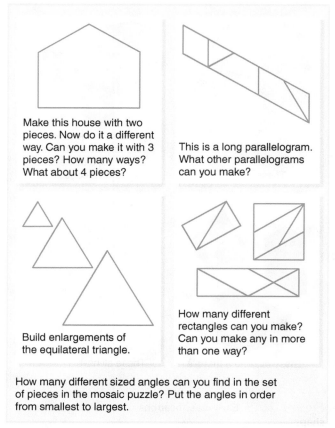

Figure 20.8 A sample of activities with the mosaic puzzle (see Blackline Master 51).

Source: Based on van Hiele, P. M. (1999). "Developing Geometric Thinking Through Activities That Begin with Play." *Teaching Children Mathematics,* 5(6), 310–316. Reprinted with permission. Copyright © 1999 by the National Council of Teachers of Mathematics, Inc. www.nctm.org. All rights reserved.

Tech NOTES The e-Examples found at the NCTM website under "Standards Focal Points" provide a good electronic geoboard (Applet 4.2). Although found in the K–2 section and entitled "Investigating the Concept of a Triangle," this is a great geoboard applet for any grade. It allows you to select and delete bands and vertices. The *Geoboard* applet from the National Library of Virtual Manipulatives (http://nlvm.usu.edu/en/nav/vlibrary .html) is essentially the same but with instant calculation of perimeter and area by clicking the "measures" button. ◆

Pause and Reflect

If you have never used a geoboard, explore one of these electronic geoboards. If you know about geoboards but have never used an e-geoboard, now would be a good time to try one.

drawings that fulfill a particular task. To help children in the very early grades copy geoboard designs, suggest that they first mark the dots for the corners of their shape ("second row, end peg"). With the corners identified, it is much easier for them to draw lines to make the shape.

Drawings can be placed in groups for classification and discussion, made into booklets illustrating a new idea that is being discussed, and sent home to families.

Building three-dimensional shapes is a little more difficult compared with two-dimensional shapes. A variety of

Have children copy shapes from pattern cards onto a geoboard.

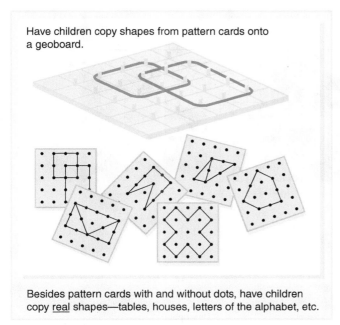

Besides pattern cards with and without dots, have children copy <u>real</u> shapes—tables, houses, letters of the alphabet, etc.

Figure 20.9 Shapes on geoboards (see Blackline Masters 49 and 50).

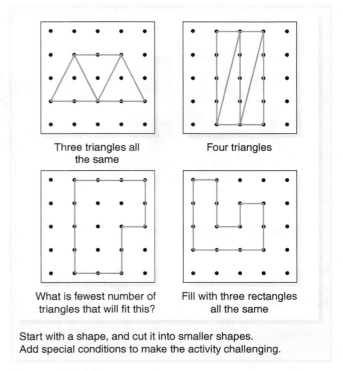

Three triangles all the same

Four triangles

What is fewest number of triangles that will fit this?

Fill with three rectangles all the same

Start with a shape, and cut it into smaller shapes. Add special conditions to make the activity challenging.

Figure 20.10 Subdividing shapes (see Blackline Masters 49 and 50).

commercial materials permit fairly creative construction of geometric solids (for example, 3D Geoshapes, Polydron, and the Zome System). The following are three highly recommended handmade approaches to skeletal models.

- *Plastic coffee stirrers with twist ties or modeling clay.* Plastic stirrers can be easily cut to different lengths. Use twist ties inserted into the ends or small chunks of clay (about 2 cm in diameter) to connect the corners.
- *Plastic drinking straws.* Cut the straws lengthwise with scissors from the top down to the flexible joint. These slit ends can then be inserted into the uncut bottom ends of other straws, making a strong but flexible joint. Three or more straws are joined in this fashion to form two-dimensional polygons. Use tape or twist ties to join polygons.
- *Rolled newspaper rods.* Fantastic super large skeletons can be built using newspaper and masking or duct tape (see Figure 20.11).

With these handmade models, students should compare the rigidity of a triangle with the lack of rigidity of polygons with more than three sides. Point out that triangles are used in many bridges, in the long booms of construction cranes, and in the structural parts of buildings. Discuss why this may be so. As children build large skeleton structures, they will find that they need to add diagonal pieces to form triangles for strength. The more triangles, the less likely their structure will collapse. Primary-grade students can benefit from creating free-form structures. Older students can be challenged to make more well-defined shapes.

Roll three full sheets of newspaper very tightly on the diagonal. Secure with tape. Tight rolls make stronger sticks.

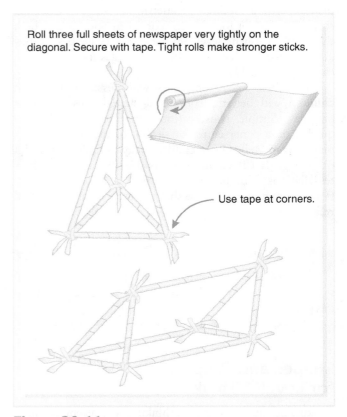

Use tape at corners.

Figure 20.11 Large skeletal structures and special shapes can be built with tightly rolled newspaper.

Tessellations can be made of construction paper tiles or drawn on grids.

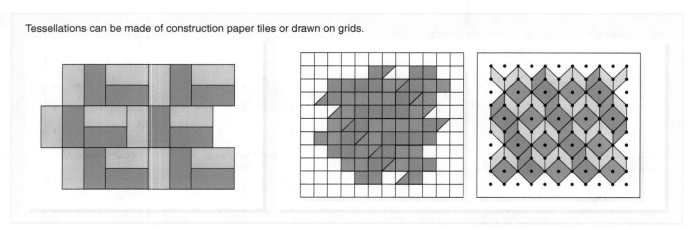

Figure 20.12 Tessellations (see Blackline Masters 34–40).

Tessellations.   A *tessellation* is a tiling of the plane using one or more shapes in a repeated pattern with no gaps or overlaps. Making tessellations is an artistic way for level-0 students from first grade to eighth grade to explore patterns in shapes and to see how shapes combine to form other shapes. Tessellation activities can vary considerably in difficulty.

Single-shape tessellations are more easily made with some shapes than others. For example, squares or equilateral triangles self-tessellate quite easily, although these provide only a minimal geometric challenge. When the shapes can be put together in more than one pattern, both the problem-solving level and the creativity increase. Literally hundreds of shapes can be used as tiles for tessellations (see Figure 20.12).

For their first experiences with tessellations, most children will benefit from using actual tiles to create patterns. Simple construction paper tiles can be cut quickly on a paper cutter or several of the pattern block pieces work well. Older children may be able to use dot or line grids (Blackline Masters 34–40) and plan their tessellations with pencil and paper. To plan a tessellation, use only one color so that the focus is on the spatial relationships.

❚❚ ———————— *Pause and Reflect*

Look at the center tessellation in Figure 20.12. What single tile (a combination of squares and half squares) made this pattern?

Shapes and Properties for Level-1 Thinkers

As students move to level-1 thinking, the attention turns more to properties possessed by the traditional classifi-

Table 20.1

Categories of Two-Dimensional Shapes	
Shape	Description
Simple Closed Curves	
Concave, convex	An intuitive definition of *concave* might be "having a dent in it." If a simple closed curve is not concave, it is *convex*. A more precise definition of *concave* may be interesting to explore with older students.
Symmetrical, nonsymmetrical	Shapes may have one or more lines of symmetry and may or may not have rotational symmetry. These concepts will require more detailed investigation.
Polygons	Simple closed curves with all straight sides.
Concave, convex	
Symmetrical, non-symmetrical	
Regular	All sides and all angles are congruent.
Triangles	
Triangles	Polygons with exactly three sides.
Classified by sides	
Equilateral	All sides are congruent.
Isosceles	At least two sides are congruent.
Scalene	No two sides are congruent.
Classified by angles	
Right	Has a right angle.
Acute	All angles are smaller than a right angle.
Obtuse	One angle is larger than a right angle.
Convex Quadrilaterals	
Convex quadrilaterals	Convex polygons with exactly four sides.
Kite	Two opposing pairs of congruent adjacent sides.
Trapezoid	At least one pair of parallel sides.
Isosceles trapezoid	A pair of opposite sides is congruent.
Parallelogram	Two pairs of parallel sides.
Rectangle	Parallelogram with a right angle.
Rhombus	Parallelogram with all sides congruent.
Square	Parallelogram with a right angle and all sides congruent.

cations of shapes. During this period it makes sense for students to learn the proper names for shapes and their properties.

For the sake of clarity, the important definitions of two- and three-dimensional shapes are provided here. You will notice that shape definitions include relationships between and among shapes.

Special Categories of Two-Dimensional Shapes.
Table 20.1 lists some important categories of two-dimensional shapes. Examples of these shapes can be found in Figure 20.13.

In the classification of quadrilaterals and parallelograms, some subsets overlap. For example, a square is a rectangle and a rhombus. All parallelograms are trapezoids,

but not all trapezoids are parallelograms.* Children at level 1 continue to have difficulty seeing this type of subrelationship. They may quite correctly list all the properties of a square, a rhombus, and a rectangle and still might classify a square as a "nonrhombus" or a "nonrectangle." By fourth or fifth grade, encourage students to be more precise in their classifications. Burger (1985) points out that upper elementary students correctly use such classification

---

*Some definitions of trapezoid specify *only one* pair of parallel sides, in which case parallelograms would not be trapezoids. The University of Chicago School Mathematics Project (UCSMP) uses the "at least one pair" definition, meaning that parallelograms and rectangles are trapezoids.

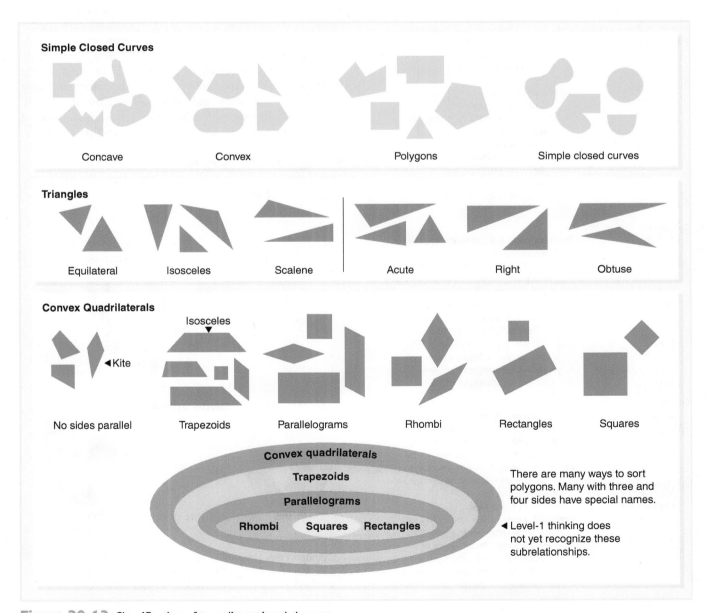

Figure 20.13 Classification of two-dimensional shapes.

schemes in other contexts. For example, individual students in a class can belong to more than one club. A square is an example of a quadrilateral that belongs to two other clubs.

Table 20.2

Categories of Three-Dimensional Shapes	
Shape	**Description**
Sorted by Edges and Vertices	
Spheres and "egglike" shapes	Shapes with no *edges* and no *vertices* (corners).
	Shapes with *edges* but no *vertices* (e.g., a flying saucer).
	Shapes with *vertices* but no *edges* (e.g., a football).
Sorted by Faces and Surfaces	
Polyhedron	Shapes made of all faces (a *face* is a flat surface of a solid). If all surfaces are faces, all the edges will be straight lines.
	Some combination of faces and rounded surfaces (circular cylinders are examples, but this is not a definition of a cylinder).
	Shapes with all curved surfaces.
	Shapes with and without edges and with and without vertices.
	Faces can be parallel. Parallel faces lie in planes that never intersect.
Cylinders	
Cylinder	Two congruent, parallel faces called *bases*. Lines joining corresponding points on the two bases are always parallel. These parallel lines are called *elements* of the cylinder.
Right cylinder	A cylinder with elements perpendicular to the bases. A cylinder that is not a right cylinder is an *oblique cylinder.*
Prism	A cylinder with polygons for bases. All prisms are special cases of cylinders.
Rectangular prism	A cylinder with rectangles for bases.
Cube	A square prism with square sides.
Cones	
Cone	A solid with exactly one face and a vertex that is not on the face. Straight lines (elements) can be drawn from any point on the edge of the base to the vertex. The base may be any shape at all. The vertex need not be directly over the base.
Circular cone	Cone with a circular base.
Pyramid	Cone with a polygon for a base. All faces joining the vertex are triangles. Pyramids are named by the shape of the base: *triangular* pyramid, *square* pyramid, *octagonal* pyramid, and so on. All pyramids are special cases of cones.

Special Categories of Three-Dimensional Shapes. Important and interesting shapes and relationships also exist in three dimensions. Table 20.2 describes classifications of solids. Figure 20.14 shows examples of cylinders and prisms. Note that prisms are defined here as a special category of cylinder—a cylinder with a polygon for a base. Figure 20.15 shows a similar grouping of cones and pyramids.

Pause and Reflect

Explain the following: Prisms are to cylinders as pyramids are to cones. How is this relationship helpful in learning volume formulas?

Many textbooks define cylinders strictly as circular cylinders. These books do not have special names for other cylinders. Under that definition, the prism is not a special case of a cylinder. This points to the fact that definitions are conventions, and not all conventions are universally agreed on. If you return to the volume formulas in the previous chapter, you will see that the more inclusive definition of cylinders and cones given here allows one formula for any type of cylinder—hence, prisms—with a similar statement that is true for cones and pyramids.

Sorting and Classifying Activities. The next activity provides a good method when you want to introduce a category of shapes.

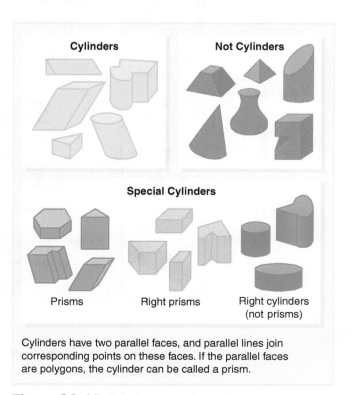

Cylinders have two parallel faces, and parallel lines join corresponding points on these faces. If the parallel faces are polygons, the cylinder can be called a prism.

Figure 20.14 Cylinders and prisms.

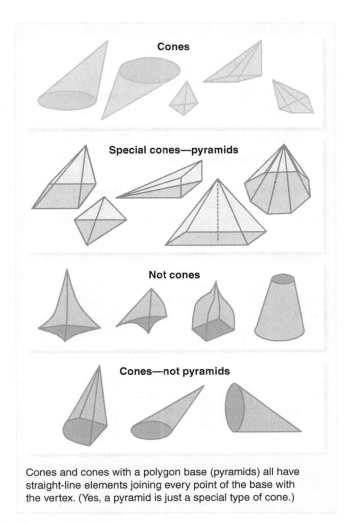

Cones

Special cones—pyramids

Not cones

Cones—not pyramids

Cones and cones with a polygon base (pyramids) all have straight-line elements joining every point of the base with the vertex. (Yes, a pyramid is just a special type of cone.)

Figure 20.15 Cones and pyramids.

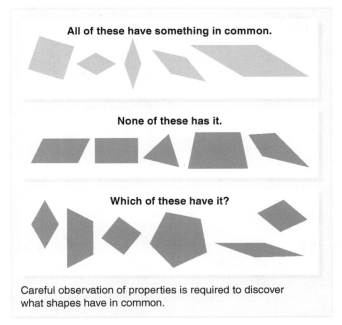

All of these have something in common.

None of these has it.

Which of these have it?

Careful observation of properties is required to discover what shapes have in common.

Figure 20.16 A mystery definition.

Activity 20.7
Mystery Definition

Use the overhead or whiteboard to conduct logic activities such as the example in Figure 20.16. For your first collection be certain that you have allowed for all possible variables. In Figure 20.16, for example, a square is included in the set of rhombi. Similarly, choose nonexamples to be as close to the positive examples as is necessary to help with an accurate definition. The third or mixed set should also include those nonexamples with which students are most likely to be confused. Students should justify their choices.

The value of the "Mystery Definition" approach is that students develop ideas and definitions based on their own concept development. After their definitions have been

discussed and compared, you can offer the usual "book" definition for the sake of clarity.

For defining types or categories of triangles, the next activity is especially good and uses a different approach.

Activity 20.8
Triangle Sort

Make copies of the Assorted Triangles sheet (see Blackline Master 58). Note the examples of right, acute, and obtuse triangles; examples of equilateral, isosceles, and scalene triangles; and triangles that represent every possible combination of these categories. Have students cut them out. The task is to sort the entire collection into three discrete groups so that no triangle belongs to two groups. When this is done and descriptions of the groupings have been written, students should then find a second criterion for creating three different groupings. Students may need a hint to look only at angle sizes or only at the issue of congruent sides, but hold these hints if you can.

"Triangle Sort" results in definitions of the six different types of triangles without having to list these definitions on the board and have students memorize them. As a follow-up activity, make a chart such as the following.

Challenge students to sketch a triangle in each of the nine cells.

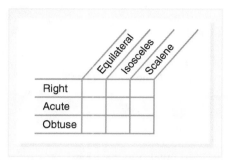

❚❚ ——————— *Pause and Reflect*

Of the nine cells in the chart, two of them are impossible to fill. Can you tell which ones and why?

Quadrilaterals (polygons with four sides) are an especially rich source of investigations. Once students are familiar with the concepts of right, obtuse, and acute angles, congruence of line segments and angles, and symmetry (both line and rotational), Activity 20.2 "Property Lists for Quadrilaterals," is a good way to bring these ideas together and begin to see how different collections of properties apply to special classes of shapes. In this activity, students work to create lists of all the properties that they can find for a particular class of shapes. Students should share lists beginning with parallelograms, then rhombi, then rectangles, and finally squares.

The class must agree with everything that is put on the list. As new relationships come up in this presentation-and-discussion period, you can introduce proper terminology. For example, if two diagonals intersect in a square corner, then they are *perpendicular*. Other terms such as *parallel*, *congruent*, *bisect*, *midpoint*, and so on can be clarified as you help students write their descriptions. This is also a good time to introduce symbols such as ≅ for "congruent" or ‖ for "parallel." As an extension, repeat Activity 20.2 using kites and trapezoids. Furthermore, similar activities can be used to introduce three-dimensional shape definitions.

Construction Activities. Students' building or drawing shapes continue to be important at level 1. Dynamic geometry software (*The Geometer's Sketchpad*, *Cabri*, and *Wingeom*) dramatically enhances the exploration of shapes at this level.

In the next activity, students examine the diagonals of various classes of quadrilaterals.

Activity 20.9
Diagonal Strips

For this activity, students need three strips of tagboard about 2 cm wide. Two should be the same length (about 30 cm) and the third somewhat shorter (about 20 cm). Punch nine holes equally spaced along the strip. Use a brass fastener to join two strips. A quadrilateral is formed by joining the four end holes as shown in Figure 20.17. Provide students with the list of possible relationships for angles, lengths, and ratios of parts. Their task is to use the strips to determine the properties of diagonals that will produce different quadrilaterals. Students may want to make drawings on dot grids to test the various hypotheses.

Every type of quadrilateral can be uniquely described in terms of its diagonals using only the conditions of length, ratio of parts, and whether or not they are perpendicular. A dynamic geometry program is also an excellent vehicle for this investigation.

Circles. Many interesting relationships can be observed among measures of different parts of the circle. One of the most astounding and important is the ratio between measures of the circumference and the diameter.

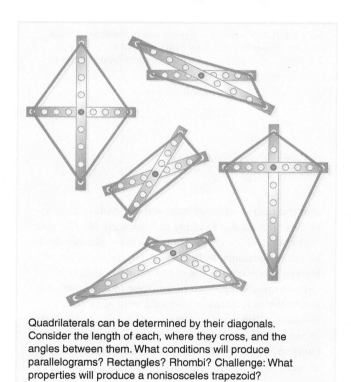

Quadrilaterals can be determined by their diagonals. Consider the length of each, where they cross, and the angles between them. What conditions will produce parallelograms? Rectangles? Rhombi? Challenge: What properties will produce a nonisosceles trapezoid?

Figure 20.17 Diagonals of quadrilaterals.

Activity 20.10

Discovering Pi

Have groups of students carefully measure both the circumference and diameter of circular items such as jar lids, tubes, cans, and wastebaskets. To measure circumference, wrap string once around the object and then measure that length of string. Also measure large circles marked on gym floors and playgrounds. Use a trundle wheel or rope to measure the circumference.

Collect measures of circumference and diameter from all groups and enter them in a table. Ratios of the circumference to the diameter should also be computed for each circle. A scatter plot of the data should be made with the horizontal axis representing diameters and the vertical axis circumferences.

Most ratios should be in the neighborhood of 3.1 or 3.2. The scatter plot should approximate a straight line through the origin. The slope of the line should also be close to 3.1. (Recall that graphs of equivalent ratios are always straight lines through the origin.) The exact ratio is an irrational number, about 3.14159, represented by the Greek letter ο (pi).

What is most important in Activity 20.10 is that students develop a clear understanding of π as the ratio of circumference to diameter in any circle. The quantity π is not some strange number that appears in math formulas; it is a naturally occurring and universal ratio.

Dynamic Geometry Software. In a dynamic geometry program, points, lines, and geometric figures are easily constructed on the computer using only a mouse or a stylus. Once drawn, the geometric objects can be moved about and manipulated in endless variety. Distances, lengths, areas, angles, slopes, and perimeters can be measured. As the figures are changed, the measurements update instantly.

Lines can be drawn perpendicular or parallel to other lines or segments. Angles and segments can be drawn congruent to other angles and segments. A point can be placed at the midpoint of a segment. A figure can be produced that is a reflection, rotation, or dilation of another figure. The most significant idea is that when a geometric object is created with a particular relationship to another, that relationship is maintained no matter how either object is moved or changed.

> **myeducationlab**
>
> Go to the Building Teaching Skills and Dispositions section of Chapter 20 of MyEducationLab. Click on Videos and watch the video entitled **"Geometer's Sketchpad"** to see a teacher work with dynamic geometry software.

The best known dynamic geometry programs are *The Geometer's Sketchpad* (Key Curriculum Press), *Wingeom* (open source from Peanut Software), *Geogebra* (open source), and *Cabri Geometry II* (Texas Instruments). Originally designed for high school students, all can be used starting about grade 4.

Dynamic Geometry Examples. To appreciate the potential (and the fun) of dynamic geometry software, you really need to experience it. In the meantime, an example is offered here in an attempt to illustrate how these programs work.

In Figure 20.18, the midpoints of a freely drawn quadrilateral ABCD have been joined. The diagonals of the resulting quadrilateral (EFGH) are also drawn and measured. No matter how the points A, B, C, and D are dragged around the screen, even inverting the quadrilateral, the other lines will maintain the same relationships (joining midpoints and diagonals), and the measurements will be instantly updated.

Remember that at level 1, the objects of thought are *classes* of shapes. In a dynamic geometry program, if a quadrilateral is drawn, only one shape is observed, as would be the case on paper or on a geoboard. But now that quadrilateral can be stretched and altered in endless ways, so students actually explore not one shape but an enormous number of examples from that class of shapes. If a property or constructed relationship does not change when the figure changes, the property is attributable to the *class* of shapes rather than any particular shape.

Another example in Figure 20.19 shows how dynamic geometry software can be used to investigate quadrilaterals starting with the diagonals. By creating the drawing in this manner, the diagonals of ACBD will always bisect each

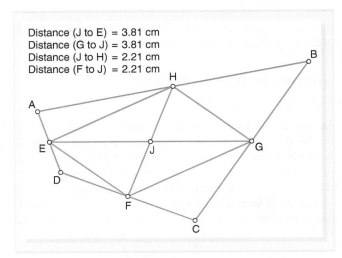

Distance (J to E) = 3.81 cm
Distance (G to J) = 3.81 cm
Distance (J to H) = 2.21 cm
Distance (F to J) = 2.21 cm

Figure 20.18 A *Sketchpad* construction illustrating an interesting property of quadrilaterals.

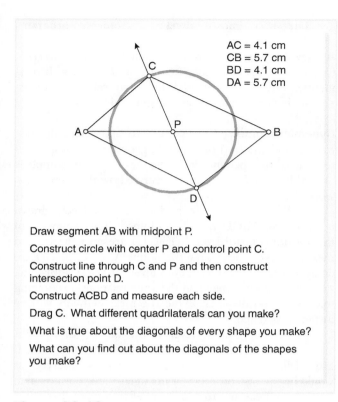

Draw segment AB with midpoint P.

Construct circle with center P and control point C.

Construct line through C and P and then construct intersection point D.

Construct ACBD and measure each side.

Drag C. What different quadrilaterals can you make?

What is true about the diagonals of every shape you make?

What can you find out about the diagonals of the shapes you make?

Figure 20.19 Quadrilaterals with diagonals that bisect each other.

other no matter how the drawing is altered. By dragging point C around, ACBD can be made into a parallelogram, rectangle, rhombus, and square. For each of these figures, additional information about the diagonals can be determined by looking at the drawing.

Dynamic geometry programs are also powerful for investigating concepts of symmetry and transformations (slides, flips, and turns). There are many excellent activities that are appropriate for level-1 investigations found in NCTM journals publications and on the Web.

Shapes and Properties for Level-2 Thinkers

At level 2, the focus shifts from simply examining properties of shapes to explorations that include logical reasoning. As students develop an understanding of various geometric properties and attach these properties to important categories of shapes, it is essential to encourage conjecture and to explore informal deductive arguments. Students should begin to attempt—or at least follow—simple proofs and explore ideas that connect directly to algebra.

Definitions and Proofs. The previously described activities of "Property Lists for Quadrilaterals" (Activity

20.2), which is a level-1 activity, and "Minimal Defining Lists" (Activity 20.3), a level-2 activity, really clarify the distinction between these two levels. (See Groth, 2006, for more information.) The parallelogram, rhombus, rectangle, and square each has at least four MDLs. One of the most interesting MDLs for each shape consists only of the properties of its diagonals. For example, a quadrilateral with diagonals that bisect each other and are perpendicular (intersect at right angles) is a rhombus.

Notice that the MDL activity is actually more involved with logical thinking than in examining shapes. Students are engaged in the general process of deciding, "*If* we specify only this list of properties, will that guarantee this particular shape?" A second feature is the opportunity to discuss what constitutes a definition. In fact, any MDL could be the definition of the shape. The definitions we usually use are MDLs that have been chosen probably due to the ease with which we can understand them. A quadrilateral with diagonals that bisect each other does not immediately call to mind a parallelogram although that is a defining list of properties.

The next activity is also a good follow-up to the "Property Lists" activity, although it is not restricted to quadrilaterals and can include three-dimensional shapes as well. Notice again the logic involved.

Activity 20.11

True or False?

Prepare a set of true and false statements of the following forms: "If it is a _____, then it is also a _____." "All _____ are _____." "Some _____ are _____."

A few examples are suggested here but numerous possibilities exist.

- **If it is a square, then it is a rhombus.**
- **All squares are rectangles.**
- **Some parallelograms are rectangles.**
- **All parallelograms have congruent diagonals.**
- **If it has exactly two lines of symmetry, it must be a quadrilateral.**
- **If it is a cylinder, then it is a prism.**
- **All prisms have a plane of symmetry.**
- **All pyramids have square bases.**
- **If a prism has a plane of symmetry, then it is a right prism.**

The task is to decide if the statements are true or false and to present an argument to support the decision. Four or five true-or-false statements will make a good lesson. Once this format is understood, let students challenge their classmates by making their own lists of

five statements. Each list should have a mix of true and false statements. See the suggested article by Renne (2004) for additional ideas. Students' lists can then be used in subsequent lessons.

II ———————— *Pause and Reflect*

Use the property list for squares and rectangles to prove "All squares are rectangles." Notice that you must use logical reasoning to understand this statement. It does little good to simply force it on students who are not ready to develop the relationship.

The following activity was designed by Sconyers (1995) to demonstrate that students can create proofs in geometry well before high school.

Activity 20.12

Two Polygons from One

Pose the following problem:

> Begin with a convex polygon with a given number of sides. Connect two points on the polygon with a line segment forming two new polygons. How many sides do the two resulting polygons have together?

Demonstrate with a few examples (see Figure 20.20). Have students explore by drawing polygons and slicing them. Encourage students to make a table showing sides in the original and resulting sides. Students should first make conjectures about a general rule. When groups are comfortable with their conjecture, they should try to reason why their statement is correct—that is, prove their conjecture.

Obviously, the number of resulting sides depends on where the slice is made. With the exception of triangles, there are three possibilities. For each case, a clear argument can be made. The appropriate conjecture and proof are left to you, but trust that students working together can do this task.

Notice that in this task, as in others we have explored, the statements to be proved come from students. If you write a theorem on the board and ask students to prove it, you have already told them that it is true. If, by contrast, a student makes a statement about a geometric situation the class is exploring, it can be written on the board with a question mark as a *conjecture*, a statement whose truth has not yet been determined. You can ask, "Is it true? Always? Can we prove it? Can we find a counterexample?" Reasonable deductive arguments can be forged out of discussions (Boats, Dwyer, Laing, & Fratella, 2003).

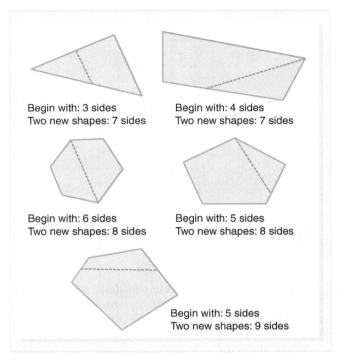

Begin with: 3 sides
Two new shapes: 7 sides

Begin with: 4 sides
Two new shapes: 7 sides

Begin with: 6 sides
Two new shapes: 8 sides

Begin with: 5 sides
Two new shapes: 8 sides

Begin with: 5 sides
Two new shapes: 9 sides

Figure 20.20 Start with a polygon, and draw a segment to divide it into two polygons. How many sides will the two new polygons have?

The Pythagorean Relationship. The *Pythagorean relationship* is so important that it deserves special attention. In geometric terms, this relationship states that if a square is constructed on each side of a right triangle, the areas of the two smaller squares will together equal the area of the square on the longest side, the hypotenuse. To discover this relationship, consider the following activity.

Activity 20.13

The Pythagorean Relationship

Have students draw a right triangle on half-centimeter grid paper (see Blackline Master 36). Assign each student a different triangle by specifying the lengths of the two legs. Students are to draw a square on each leg and the hypotenuse and find the area of all three squares. (For the square on the hypotenuse, the exact area can be found by making each of the sides the diagonal of a rectangle. See Figure 20.21.) Make a table of the area data (Sq. on leg 1, Sq. on leg 2, Sq. on hyp.), and ask students to look for a relationship between the squares.

As an extension to the last activity, students can explore drawing other figures on the legs of right triangles

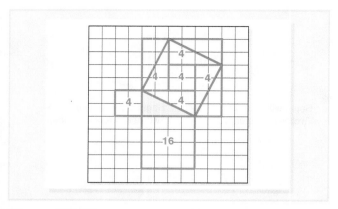

Figure 20.21 The Pythagorean relationship. Note that if drawn on a grid, the area of all squares is easily determined. Here 4 + 16 = area of the square on the hypotenuse.

and computing areas. For example, draw semicircles or equilateral triangles instead of squares. The areas of any regular polygons drawn on the three sides of right triangles will have the same relationship.

What about proof? Both large congruent squares in Figure 20.22 together show a nonverbal proof of the Pythagorean theorem (Nelson, 2001). Note that both squares contain four triangles that are the same but arranged differently. By adding up the areas of the squares and the triangles and setting them equal, the Pythagorean relationship can be found by subtracting out the common areas in both squares. An algebraic recording of the thinking process is shown below the drawings.

Ⅱ ———————— *Pause and Reflect*

Use the two drawings in Figure 20.22 to create a proof of the Pythagorean relationship.

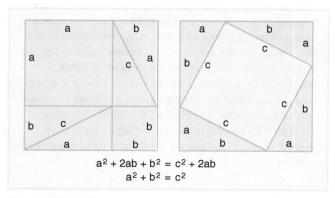

$$a^2 + 2ab + b^2 = c^2 + 2ab$$
$$a^2 + b^2 = c^2$$

Figure 20.22 The two squares together are a "proof without words." Can you supply the words?

The e-Examples found at the NCTM website under "Standards & Focal Points" includes a dynamic proof without words that is worth sharing with your students (Applet 6.5). Because it requires knowing that parallelograms and rectangles with the same base and height have the same area, it is also a good review. ◆

Finding Versus Explaining Relationships. At level 2, the focus is on reasoning or deductive thinking. Can dynamic geometry software programs help students develop deductive arguments to support the relationships they come to believe through inductive reasoning? Consider the following situation.

Suppose that you have students use a dynamic geometry program to draw a triangle, measure all of the angles, and add them up. As the triangle vertices are dragged around, the sum of the angles would remain steadfast at 180 degrees. Students can conjecture that the sum of the interior angles of a triangle is always 180 degrees, and they would be completely convinced of the truth of this conjecture based on this inductive experience. (Several noncomputer activities lead to the same conclusion.) However, the experience just described fails to explain *why it is so*. Consider the following activity, which can be done easily with paper and scissors or quite dramatically with a dynamic geometry program.

Activity 20.14

Angle Sum in a Triangle

Have all students cut out three congruent triangles. (Stack three sheets of paper, and cut three shapes at one time.) Place one triangle on a line and the second directly next to it in the same orientation. Place the third triangle in the space between the triangles as shown in Figure 20.23(a). Based on this experience, what conjecture can you make about the sum of the angles in a triangle?

In a dynamic geometry program, the three triangles in Figure 20.23(a) can be drawn by starting with one triangle, translating it to the right the length of AC, and then rotating the same triangle about the midpoint of side BC. When vertices of the original triangle are dragged, the other triangles will change accordingly and remain congruent. We still do not know why the angle sum is always a straight angle, but this exploration allows students to see why it might be so. In the figure, there are lines parallel to each side of the original triangle. By using properties of angles formed by cutting parallel lines with a transverse

(a) Three congruent triangles can be arranged to show that the sum of the interior angles will always be a straight angle or 180 degrees.

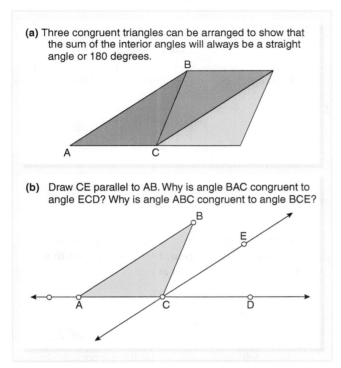

(b) Draw CE parallel to AB. Why is angle BAC congruent to angle ECD? Why is angle ABC congruent to angle BCE?

Figure 20.23 Deductive, logical reasoning is necessary to prove relationships that appear true from observations.

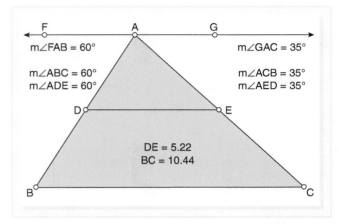

Figure 20.24 The midsegment of a triangle is always parallel to the base and half as long.

line, it is easy to argue that the sum of the angles will always be a straight line. See Figure 20.23(b); the proof is left to you.

Dynamic geometry software can be enormously powerful for helping students observe geometric relationships and make conjectures. The truth of the conjectures will often be obvious. At level 2, however, we must begin to ask why. The following activity further illustrates the point.

Activity 20.15

Triangle Midsegments

Using a dynamic geometry program, draw a triangle, and label the vertices A, B, and C. Draw the segment joining the midpoints of AB and AC, and label this segment DE, as in Figure 20.24. Measure the lengths of DE and BC. Also measure angles ADE and ABC. Drag points A, B, and C. What conjectures can you make about the relationships between segment DE, the *midsegment* of ABC, and BC, the base of ABC?

It is very clear that the midsegment is half the length of the base and parallel to it, but why is this so? Students will

need a bit more guidance, but you should not necessarily have to provide the argument for them. Suggest that they draw a line through A parallel to BC. List all pairs of angles that they know are congruent. Why are they congruent? Note that triangle ABC is similar to triangle ADE. Why is it similar? With hints such as these, many middle grade students can begin to make logical arguments for why the things they observe to be true are in fact true.

Learning about Transformations

Transformations are changes in position or size of a shape. Movements that do not change the size or shape of the object moved are called "rigid motions." Usually, three rigid-motion transformations are discussed: *translations* or slides, *reflections* or flips, and *rotations* or turns. Interestingly, the study of symmetry is also included under the study of transformations. Do you know why?

Transformations for Level-0 Thinkers

Transformations at this level involve an introduction to the basic concepts of slides, flips, and turns and the initial development of line symmetry and rotational symmetry.

Slides, Flips, and Turns. At the primary level, the terms *slide, flip,* and *turn* are adequate. The early goal is to help students recognize these transformations and to begin to explore their effects on simple shapes. You can use a nonsymmetric shape to introduce these terms (see Figure 20.25). Most likely your textbook will use only the center of a shape as the point of rotation and restrict reflections to vertical

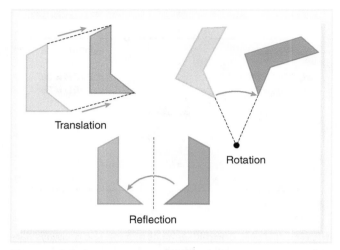

Figure 20.25 Translation (slide), reflection (flip), rotation (turn).

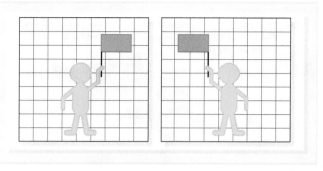

Figure 20.26 Motion Man is used to show slides, flips, and turns (see Blackline Masters 52 and 53).

and horizontal lines through the center. These restrictions are not necessary and may even be misleading.

The Motion Man activity described next can also be used to introduce students to the terms *slide*, *flip*, and *turn*. In the activity, rotations are restricted to $\frac{1}{4}$, $\frac{1}{2}$, and $\frac{3}{4}$ turns in a clockwise direction. The center of the turn will be the center of the figure. Reflections will be flips over vertical or horizontal lines. These restrictions are for simplicity. In the general case, the center of rotation can be anywhere on or off the figure. Lines of reflection can also be anywhere.

Activity 20.16

Motion Man

Using Blackline Masters 52–53, make copies of the first Motion Man and then copy the mirror image on the backs of these copies. (See Figure 20.26.) Experiment first. You want the back image to match the front image when held to the light. Cut off the excess paper to leave a square. Give all students a two-sided Motion Man.

Demonstrate each of the possible motions. A slide is simply that. The figure does not rotate or turn over. Demonstrate turns. Emphasize that only clockwise turns will be used for this activity. Similarly, demonstrate a horizontal flip (top goes to bottom) and a vertical flip (left goes to right). Practice by having everyone start with his or her Motion Man in the same orientation. As you announce one of the moves, students slide, flip, or turn Motion Man accordingly.

Then display two Motion Men side by side in any orientation. The task is to decide what motion or combination of motions will get the man on the left to match the man on the right. Students use their own man to work out a solution. Test the solutions that students offer. If both men are in the same position, call that a slide.

⏸ ———————————————— *Pause and Reflect*

Begin with the Motion Man in the left position shown in Figure 20.26. Now place a second Motion Man next to the first. Will it take one move or more than one move (transformation) to get from the first to the second Motion Man? Can you describe all of the positions that require more than one move? Are there any positions that require more than two moves?

At first, students will be confused when they can't get their Motion Man into the new position with one move. This causes an excellent problem. Don't be too quick to suggest that it may take two moves. If flips across each of the two diagonals are added to the motions along with vertical and horizontal flips, Motion Man can assume any new position in exactly one move. This provides a challenge for students. Two students begin with their Motion Man figures in the same position. One student then changes his or her Motion Man and challenges the other student to say what motion is required to make the two Motion Men match. The solution is then tested and the roles reversed.

Line and Rotational Symmetry. If a shape can be folded on a line so that the two halves match, then it is said to have *line symmetry* (or mirror symmetry). Notice that the fold line is actually a line of reflection—the portion of the shape on one side of the line is reflected onto the other side, demonstrating a connection between line symmetry and transformations.

One way to introduce line symmetry to children is to show examples and nonexamples using an all-of-these/none-of-these approach as in Figure 20.16. Another possibility is to have students fold a sheet of paper in half and cut out a shape of their choosing. When they open the paper, the fold line will be a line of symmetry. A third way is to use mirrors or Miras. (The Mira is a red, plastic image reflector that can be used to explore concepts of symmetry and congruence.) When you place a mirror on a picture or design so that the mirror is perpendicular to the table, you see a shape with symmetry when you look in the mirror.

The following activity explores line symmetry.

Activity 20.17

Pattern Block Mirror Symmetry

Students need a plain sheet of paper with a straight line through the middle. Using about six to eight pattern blocks, students make a design completely on one side of the line that touches the line in some way. The task is to make the mirror image of their design on the other side of the line. When finished, they use a mirror (or Mira) to check their work. They place the mirror on the line and look into it from the side of the original design. With the mirror in place they should see exactly the same image as they see when they lift the mirror. You can also challenge them to make designs with more than one line of symmetry.

Building symmetrical designs with pattern blocks tends to be easier if the line is vertical. With the line oriented horizontally or diagonally, the task is harder.

The same task can be done with a geoboard. First, stretch a band down the center or from corner to corner. Make a design on one side of the line and its mirror image on the other. Check with a mirror. This can also be done on either isometric or square dot grids (Blackline Masters 34 and 38) as shown in Figure 20.27 or with dynamic geometry software.

A plane of symmetry in three dimensions is analogous to a line of symmetry in two dimensions. Figure 20.28 illustrates a shape built with cubes that has a plane of symmetry.

Activity 20.18

Plane Symmetry Buildings

With cubes, build a building that has a plane of symmetry. If the plane of symmetry goes between cubes, slice the shape by separating the building into two symmetrical parts. Try making buildings with two or three planes of symmetry. Build various prisms. Do not forget that a plane can slice diagonally through the blocks.

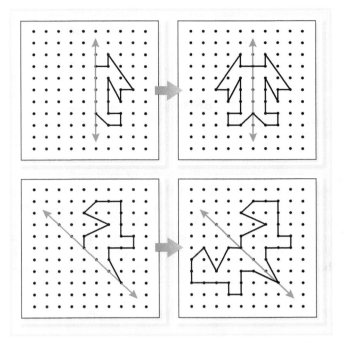

Figure 20.27 Exploring symmetry on dot grids (Blackline Masters 37 and 39).

A shape has *rotational symmetry* (also referred to as *point symmetry*) if it can be rotated about a point and land in a position exactly matching the one in which it began. A square has rotational symmetry as does an equilateral triangle.

A good way to understand rotational symmetry is to take a shape with rotational symmetry, such as a square, and trace around it on a piece of paper. Call this tracing

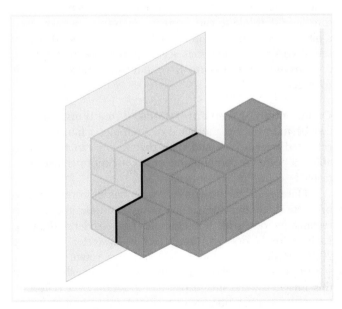

Figure 20.28 A block building with one plane of symmetry.

Figure 20.29 This parallelogram fits in its footprint two ways without flipping it over. Therefore, it has rotational symmetry of order 2.

the shape's "footprint." The order of rotational symmetry will be the number of ways that the shape can fit into its footprint without flipping it over. A square has rotational symmetry of *order* 4, whereas an equilateral triangle has rotational symmetry of *order* 3. The parallelogram in Figure 20.29 has rotational symmetry of order 2. Some books would call order-2 symmetry "180-degree symmetry." The degrees refer to the smallest angle of rotation required before the shape matches itself or fits into its footprint. A square has 90-degree rotational symmetry.

Activity 20.19

Pattern Block Rotational Symmetry

Have students construct designs with pattern blocks having different rotational symmetries. They should be able to make designs with order 2, 3, 4, 6, or 12 rotational symmetry. Which of the designs have mirror symmetry as well?

Transformations for Level-1 Thinkers

Within the context of transformations, students moving into level-1 thinking can begin to analyze transformations a bit more analytically and to apply them to shapes that they see. Two types of activities seem appropriate at this level: compositions of transformations and using transformations to create tessellations.

Composition of Transformations. One transformation can be followed by another. For example, a figure can be reflected over a line, and then that figure can be rotated about a point. A combination of two or more transformations is called a *composition*.

Have students experiment with compositions of two or even three transformations using a simple shape on a rectangular dot grid. For example, have students draw an L-shape on a dot grid and label it L_1 (refer to Figure 20.30). Reflect it through a line, and then rotate the image $\frac{1}{4}$ turn clockwise about a point not on the shape. Call this image L_2, the image of a composition of a reflection followed by a rotation. Notice that if L_1 is rotated $\frac{1}{4}$ turn clockwise about the same point used before to L_3 there is a relationship between L_2 and L_3. Continue to explore

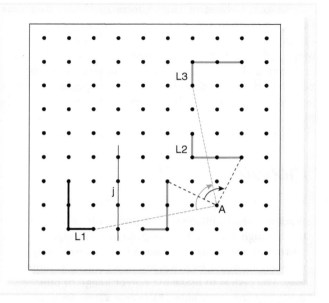

Figure 20.30 Shape L_1 was reflected across line j and rotated $\frac{1}{4}$ turn about point A resulting in L_2. L_1 was also rotated $\frac{1}{4}$ turn about point A. How are L_2 and L_3 related? Will this always work?

different combinations of transformations. Don't forget to include translations (slides) in the compositions. Compositions do not have to involve different types of transformations. For example, a reflection can be followed by another reflection.

 In NCTM's e-Examples found at the NCTM website under "Standards & Focal Points," "Understanding Congruence, Similarity, and Symmetry" (Applet 6.4) is one of the best examples of a simple yet valuable interactive applet. In the first part of the applet, students develop an understanding of all three rigid motions. In the second part, a transformation is complete and the student uses a guess-and-check procedure to determine what exact transformation was done. In the last two parts, students can explore compositions of reflections and then other compositions of up to three transformations. This applet is strongly recommended. ◆

Similar Figures and Proportional Reasoning. In a previous chapter on proportional reasoning, we saw a good first definition of similar figures as shapes that "look alike but are different sizes." More precisely, two figures are *similar* if all of their corresponding angles are congruent and the corresponding sides are proportional. Other proportional reasoning activities are also good connections to geometry, which involves scale drawings and proportional relationships in figures that are similar.

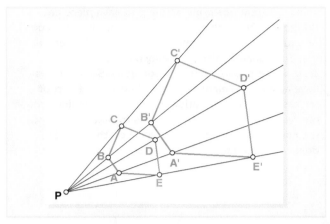

Figure 20.31 Begin with figure ABCDE and place point P anywhere at all. Draw lines from P through each vertex. Place point A' twice as far from P as A is from P (scale factor of 2). Do similarly for the other points. ABCDE is congruent with A'B'C'D'E'.

A *dilation* is a nonrigid transformation that produces similar figures. Figure 20.31 shows how a given figure can be *dilated* to make larger or smaller figures. If different groups of students dilate the same figure using the same scale factor, they will find that the resulting figures are all congruent, even with each group using different dilation points. Dynamic geometry software makes the results of this exercise quite dramatic. The software allows for the scale factors to be set at any value. Once a dilation is made, the dilation point can be dragged around the screen and the size and shape of the image clearly stay unchanged. Scale factors less than 1 produce smaller figures.

Tessellations Revisited. Either by using transformations or by combining compatible polygons, students at level 1 can create tessellations that are artistic and quite complex.

The Dutch artist M. C. Escher is well known for his tessellations, where the tiles are very intricate and often take the shape of things like birds, horses, angels, or lizards. Escher took a simple shape such as a triangle, parallelogram, or hexagon and performed transformations on the sides. For example, a curve drawn along one side might be translated (slid) to the opposite side. Another idea was to draw a curve from the midpoint of a side to the adjoining vertex. This curve was then rotated about the midpoint to form a totally new side of the tile. These two ideas are illustrated in Figure 20.32. Dot paper is used to help draw the lines. *Escher-type tessellations*, as these have come to be called, are important applications of transformations for students in grades 5 and up. Once a tile has been designed, it can be cut from two different colors of construction paper instead of drawing the tessellation on a dot grid.

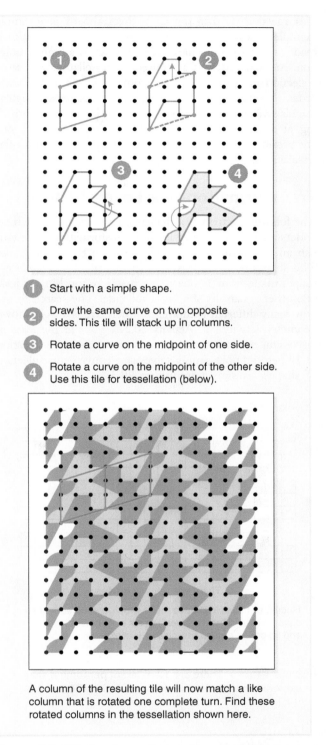

1. Start with a simple shape.

2. Draw the same curve on two opposite sides. This tile will stack up in columns.

3. Rotate a curve on the midpoint of one side.

4. Rotate a curve on the midpoint of the other side. Use this tile for tessellation (below).

A column of the resulting tile will now match a like column that is rotated one complete turn. Find these rotated columns in the tessellation shown here.

Figure 20.32 Creating an Escher-type tessellation (see Blackline Master 37).

A *regular tessellation* is made of a single tile that is a regular polygon (all sides and angles congruent). Each vertex of a regular tessellation has the same number of tiles meeting at that point. A checkerboard is a simple example of a regular tessellation. A *semiregular tessellation* is made of two or more tiles, each of which is a regular polygon. At each vertex of a semiregular tessellation, the same collection of regular polygons come together in the same order. A vertex (and, therefore, the complete semiregular tessellation) can be described by the series of shapes meeting at a vertex. Students can figure out which polygons are possible at a vertex and design their own semiregular tessellations.

Transformations for Level-2 Thinkers

The following activity is a challenge for students to use their understanding of symmetries and transformations to establish an interesting relationship between these two ideas. The shapes used for this activity are called *pentominoes*—shapes made from 5 squares, each square touching at least one other square by sharing a full side. The search to see how many different pentominoes there are is a well-known geometry activity (see Activity 20.27). For our purposes in discussing transformations and symmetries, the collection of 12 pentominoes simply serves as a convenient collection of shapes, as shown in Figure 20.33.

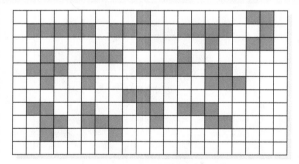

There are 12 pentominoes.

Finding all possible shapes made with five squares—or six squares (called "hexominoes") or six equilateral triangles and so on—is a good exercise in spatial problem solving.

Figure 20.33 There are 12 different pentomino shapes. An exploration to find these shapes is Activity 20.27.

Activity 20.20

Pentomino Positions

Have students cut out a set of 12 pentominoes from 2-cm grid paper (see Figure 20.33). Mark one side of each piece to help remember if it has been flipped over. The first part of the task is to determine how many different positions on the grid each piece has (Walter, 1970). Call positions "different" if a reflection or a turn is required to make them match. Therefore, the cross-shaped piece has only one position. The strip of five squares has two positions. Some pieces have as many as eight positions. The second part of the task is to find a relationship between the line symmetries and rotational symmetries for each piece and the number of positions it can have on the grid. Students may need to make a table of what they know.

Learning about Location

The location standard in *Principles and Standards* says that students should "specify locations and describe spatial relationships using coordinate geometry and other representational systems" (NCTM, 2000, p. 42). After early development of terms for how objects are located with respect to other objects (e.g., the ball is *under* the table), location activities involve analysis of paths from point to point as on a map and the use of coordinate systems.

Location for Level-0 Thinkers

In pre-K and kindergarten, children learn about everyday positional descriptions—*over, under, near, far, between, left,* and *right.* These are the beginnings of the *Standards* goal of specifying locations. However, helping students refine the way they answer questions of direction, distance, and location enhances spatial understandings. Geometry, measurement, and algebra are all supported by the use of a grid system with numbers or coordinates attached that can specify location on a grid. As students become more sophisticated, their use of coordinates progresses along with them. Importantly, students at the primary level can begin to think in terms of a grid system to identify location.

The next activity can serve as a readiness task for coordinates and help students see the value of having a way to specify location without pointing.

Activity 20.21

Hidden Positions

For the game boards, draw an 8-inch square on tagboard. Subdivide the squares into a 3 × 3 grid. Two students sit with a "screen" separating their desktop space so that neither student can see the other's grid (see Figure 20.34). Each student has four different pattern blocks. The first player places a block on four different sections of the grid. He then tells the other player where to put blocks on her grid to match his own. When all four pieces are positioned, the two

grids are checked to see if they are alike. Then the players switch roles. Model the game once by taking the part of the first student. Use words such as *top row, middle, left,* and *right.* Students can play in pairs as a station activity.

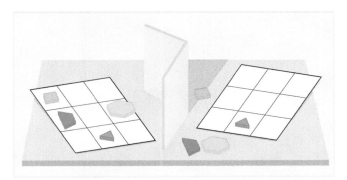

Figure 20.34 The "Hidden Positions" game.

The "Hidden Positions" game can easily be extended to grids up to 6 × 6. As the grid size increases, the need for a system of labeling positions increases. Students can begin to use a simple coordinate system as early as the first grade. Use a coordinate grid like the one shown in Figure 20.35 (see Blackline Master 48). Explain how to use two numbers to designate an intersection point on the grid. The first number tells how far to move to the right. The second number tells how far to move up. For younger children use the words along with the numbers: 3 right and 0 up. Be sure to include 0 in your introduction. Select a point on the grid and have students decide what two numbers name that point. If your point is at (2,4) and students incorrectly

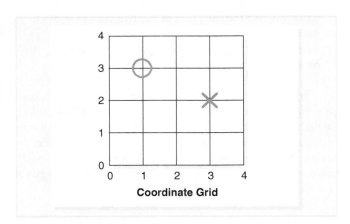

Figure 20.35 A simple coordinate grid. The X is at (3, 2) and the O is at (1, 3). Use the grid to play Three in a Row (like Tic-Tac-Toe). Put marks on intersections, not spaces (see Blackline Master 48).

say "four, two," then simply indicate where the point is that they named. Another way for students to visualize the difference is to compare students in the second row fourth seat to the fourth row second seat.

The next activity explores the notion of different paths on a grid.

Activity 20.22

Paths

On a sheet of 2-cm grid paper (see Blackline Master 34), mark two different points A and B as shown in Figure 20.36. Using the overhead, whiteboard, or floor tiles, demonstrate how to describe a path from A to B. For the points in the figure, one path is "up 5 and right 6." Another path might be "right 2, up 2, right 2, up 3, right 2." Count the length of each path. As long as you always move toward the target point (in this case either right or up), the path lengths will always be the same. Here they are 11 units long. Students draw three paths on their papers from A to B using different-colored crayons. For each path they write directions that describe their paths. Ask, "What is the greatest number of turns that you can make in your path?" "What is the smallest number?" "Where would A and B have to be in order to get there with no turns?"

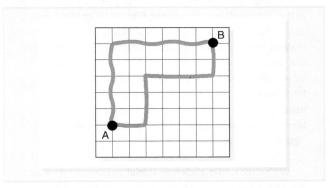

Figure 20.36 Different paths from A to B on a grid.

If you add a coordinate system on the grid in "Paths," students can describe their paths with coordinates: For example: (1, 2) ⟶ (3, 2) ⟶ (3, 5) ⟶ (7, 5) ⟶ (7, 7).

The e-Examples found at the NCTM website under "Standards & Focal Points" contains a nice applet (Applet 4.3) that is similar to the previous activity but offers some additional challenges. Students move a ladybug by issuing directions.

The task is to make a list of directions to hide the ladybug beneath a leaf. When the directions are complete, the ladybug is set in motion to follow them. The ladybug is also used to draw shapes such as a rectangle in a tilted position or to travel through mazes. This applet is a very basic version of the powerful computer programming language Logo. ◆

Location for Level-1 Thinkers

At level 1, one use of the coordinate grid is to examine transformations in a more analytic manner. There is not a lot of new knowledge about coordinates to learn except for the extension to four quadrants with the use of negative numbers. Even fourth- and fifth-grade students can use negative integers so that the full plane can be represented. The activities here suggest how coordinates can be used to examine transformations.

Activity 20.23

Coordinate Slides

Students will need a sheet of centimeter grid paper on which to draw two coordinate axes near the left and bottom edges. Have them plot and connect about five or six points on the grid to form a small shape (see Figure 20.37.) If you direct them to use only coordinates between 5 and 12, the figure will be reasonably small and near the center of the paper. Next, students make a new shape by adding 6 to each of the first coordinates (called the *x*-coordinates) of their shape, leaving the second coordinates the same. That is, for the point (5, 10) a new point, (11, 10) is plotted. When new points for each point in the figure have been plotted, these are connected as before. This new figure should be congruent to the original and translated to the right. Students then create a third figure by adding 9 to each second coordinate of the original.

With these two slides as initial guidance, stop and discuss what should be done to the coordinates to move the figure along a diagonal line up and to the right. Have students make and test their conjectures. Figure 20.37 shows a slide that was created by adding 6 to all of the first coordinates and adding 9 to all of the second coordinates. As long as all first coordinates are changed by the same amount and all second coordinates by the same amount, the figure will be translated without distortion. Challenge students to figure out how to change the coordinates to make the figure slide down and to the left. (Subtract from the coordinates instead of add.) Students' papers should show their original shape and four copies, each in a different location on the grid.

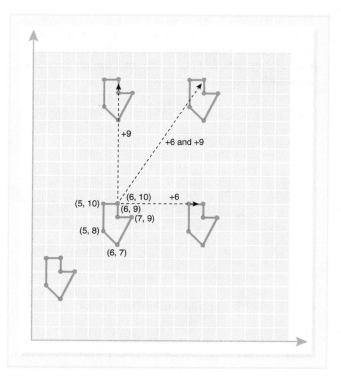

Figure 20.37 Begin with a simple shape and record the coordinates. By adding or subtracting from the coordinates, new shapes are found that are translations (slides) of the original.

Help students summarize what they've learned: What does adding (or subtracting) a number from the first coordinates cause? What if the number is added or subtracted from the second coordinates? From both coordinates? Have students draw lines connecting corresponding points in the original figure with one of those where both coordinates were changed. What do they notice? (The lines are parallel and the same length.) Pick any two of the five shapes in the final drawing. How can you begin with one of the shapes and change the coordinates to get to the other?

In "Coordinate Slides" the figure did not twist, turn, flip over, or change size or shape. The shape "slid" along a path that matched the lines between the corresponding points. Reflections can be explored on a coordinate grid just as easily as translations. At this beginning level, it is advisable to restrict the lines of reflection to the *x*- or *y*-axis as in the following activity.

Activity 20.24

Coordinate Reflections

Have students draw a five-sided shape in the first quadrant on coordinate grid paper using grid points

for vertices. Label the Figure ABCDE and call it Figure 1. Use the *y*-axis as a line of symmetry and draw the reflection of the shape in the second quadrant. Call it Figure 2 (for second quadrant) and label the reflected points A′B′C′D′E′. Now use the *x*-axis as the line of symmetry. Reflect both Figure 2 and Figure 1 into the third and fourth quadrants, respectively, and call these Figures 3 and 4. Label the points of these figures with double and triple primes (A″ and A‴, and so on). Write in the coordinates for each vertex of all four figures.

- How is Figure 3 related to Figure 4? How else could you have gotten Figure 3? How else could you have found Figure 4?
- How are the coordinates of Figure 1 related to its image in the *y*-axis, Figure 2? What can you say about the coordinates of Figure 4?
- Make a conjecture about the coordinates of a shape reflected in the *y*-axis and a different conjecture about the coordinates of a shape reflected in the *x*-axis.
- Draw lines from the vertices of Figure 1 to the corresponding vertices of Figure 2. What can you say about these lines? How is the *y*-axis related to each of these lines?

Refer to Figure 20.38 to answer these questions.

Students who have done the preceding activities should have a general way to describe translations and reflections across an axis, all in terms of coordinates. Rotations can also be explored with the use of coordinates. In the following activity, multiplying a constant times

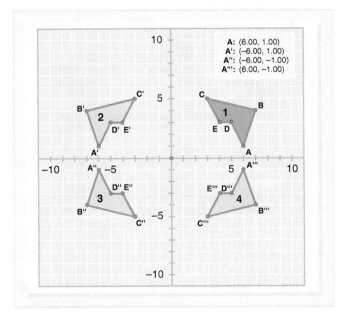

Figure 20.38 Exploring reflections on a coordinate grid.

the coordinates is a transformation that is not a rigid motion.

Activity 20.25
Coordinate Dilations

Students begin with a four-sided shape in the first quadrant. They then make a list of the coordinates and make a new set of coordinates by multiplying each of the original coordinates by 2. They plot the resulting shape. What is the result? Now have students multiply each of the original coordinates by $\frac{1}{2}$ and plot that shape. What is the result? Next, students draw a line from the origin to a vertex of the largest shape on their paper. Repeat for one or two additional vertices and ask for observations. (An example is shown in Figure 20.39.)

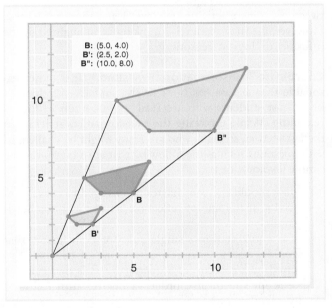

Figure 20.39 Dilations with coordinates.

Pause and Reflect

How do the lengths of sides and the areas of the shapes compare when the coordinates are multiplied by 2? What if they are multiplied by 3 or by $\frac{1}{2}$?

When the coordinates of a shape are multiplied as in the last activity, each by the same factor, the shape either gets larger or smaller. The size is changed but not the shape. The new shape is similar to the old shape. This is called a *dilation*, a transformation that is *not* rigid because the shape changes.

Your students may enjoy exploring this phenomenon a bit further. If they start with a line drawing of a simple face, boat, or some other shape drawn with straight lines connecting vertices, they will create an interesting effect by multiplying just the first coordinates, just the second coordinates, or using a different factor for each. When only the second coordinate is multiplied, the vertical dimensions alone are dilated, so the figure is proportionately stretched (or shrunk) in a vertical manner. Students can explore this process to distort shapes in various ways.

It is impressive to see how an arithmetic operation can control a figure. Imagine being able to control slides, flips, turns, and dilations, not just in the plane but also for three-dimensional figures. The process is identical to computer animation techniques.

Location for Level-2 Thinkers

On the surface, there may not be a clear distinction between coordinate activities for level 1 and those for level 2. However, the move to level-2 thinking is highlighted by the infusion of logical reasoning.

Coordinate Transformations Revisited. It is quite reasonable that a class has both level-1 and level-2 thinkers or at least students who are ready to move on to logical reasoning. While exploring the transformation activities in the last section, students who are ready might be challenged with questions such as the following that are a bit more than simple explorations:

- How should the coordinates be changed to cause a reflection if the line of reflection is not the *y*-axis but is parallel to it?
- Can you discover a single rule for coordinates that would cause a reflection across one of the axes followed by a rotation of a quarter turn? Is that rule the same for the reverse order—a quarter turn followed by a reflection?
- If two successive slides are made with coordinates and you know what numbers were added or subtracted, what number should be added or subtracted to get the figure there in only one move?
- What do you think will happen if, in a dilation, different factors are used for different coordinates?

Once students begin to explore questions of this type, they may well come up with their own questions and explorations. Dynamic geometry software includes an optional coordinate grid. If drawings are made with the points "snapped" to the grid, coordinate transformations can be explored much more easily. ◆

Applying the Pythagorean Relationship. The geometric version of the Pythagorean relationship is about areas. The following activity has students use the coordinate grid and the Pythagorean relationship to develop a formula for the distance between points.

Activity 20.26

The Distance Formula

Have students draw a line between two points in the first quadrant that are not on the same horizontal or vertical line. The task is to use only the coordinates of the endpoints to find the distance between them in terms of the units on the grid. To this end, suggest that they draw a right triangle using the line as the hypotenuse. The vertex at the right angle will share one coordinate from each endpoint. Students compute the areas of the squares on the legs and add to find the area of the square on the hypotenuse. Now the length of the original line segment (the distance between the points) is the number whose square is the area of the square on the hypotenuse. (This last sentence is a geometric interpretation of square root.) Have students follow these directions to compute the length of the line.

Next, have them look through all of their calculations and see how the coordinates of the two endpoints were used. Challenge students to use the same type of calculations to get the distance between two new points without drawing any pictures.

Level-2 students do not necessarily construct proofs but should be able to follow the rationale if shown proofs. By leading students through the procedure of finding the length of one line (or the distance between the endpoints), you give them sufficient information to compute the lengths of other lines. Students will see that all they need are the coordinates of the two endpoints to compute the areas of all three squares and, hence, the length of the hypotenuse. If you then help them substitute letters for specific coordinates, a general distance formula results.

Slope. The topic of slope is another important connection between geometry and algebra and need not wait for the study of linear equations. To begin a discussion of slope, draw several different slanted lines. Discuss how they are different. Some are steeper than others. Some go up, others go down. If you agree that "up" means sloping upward from left to right, then you can agree which ones go up and which go down. This "steepness" of a line is an attribute that can be measured like other measurable attributes. To give slope a number requires a reference line. The coordinate grid provides a reference (the *x*-axis) and the numbers

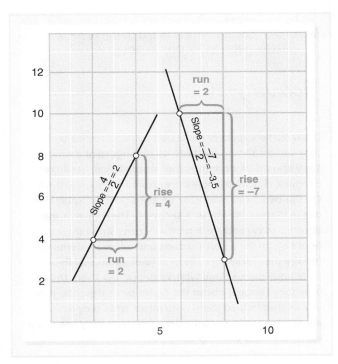

Figure 20.40 The slope of a line is equal to rise ÷ run.

to use in the measurement. Spend some time having students invent their own methods for attaching a number to the concept of steepness.

The convention for measuring the steepness of a line or the *slope* is based on the ideas of the *rise* and *run* between any two points on the line. The *rise* is the vertical change from the left point to the right point—positive if up, negative if down. The *run* is the horizontal distance from the left point to the right point. Slope is then defined as *rise ÷ run* or the ratio of the vertical change to the horizontal change (see Figure 20.40). By agreement, vertical lines have no slope or the slope is said to be "undefined." Horizontal lines have a slope of 0 as a result of the definition.

Once students are given the definition, they should be able to compute the slopes of any nonvertical line drawn on a coordinate grid without further assistance and *without formulas*. A good problem-based task is to figure out what can be said about the slopes of parallel lines and perpendicular lines.

Learning about Visualization

Visualization might be called "geometry done with the mind's eye." It involves being able to create mental images of shapes and then turn them around mentally,

thinking about how they look from different perspectives—predicting the results of various transformations. It includes the mental coordination of two and three dimensions—predicting the unfolding of a box (or net) or understanding a two-dimensional drawing of a three-dimensional shape. Any activity that requires students to think about a shape mentally, to manipulate or transform a shape mentally, or to represent a shape as it is seen visually will contribute to the development of students' visualization skills.

Visualization for Level-0 Thinkers

At level 0, students are quite bound to thinking about shapes in terms of the way they look. Visualization activities at this level will have students using a variety of physical shapes and drawings and will challenge them to think about these shapes in different orientations.

Finding out how many different shapes can be made with a given number of simple tiles demands that students mentally flip and turn shapes in their minds and find ways to decide if they have found them all. That is the focus of the next activity.

Activity 20.27

Pentominoes

A pentomino is a shape formed by joining five squares as if cut from a square grid. Each square must have at least one side in common with another. Provide students with five square tiles and a sheet of square grid paper for recording. Challenge them to see how many different pentomino shapes they can find. Shapes that are flips or turns of other shapes are not considered different. Do not tell students how many pentomino shapes there are. Good discussions will come from deciding if some shapes are really different and if all shapes have been found.

Once students have decided that there are just 12 pentominoes (revisit Figure 20.33), the 12 pieces can then be used in a variety of activities. Glue the grids with the children's pentominoes onto tagboard, and let them cut out the 12 shapes.

It is also fun to explore the number of shapes that can be made from six equilateral triangles or from four 45-degree right triangles (halves of squares), as shown in Figure 20.41. With the right triangles, sides that touch must be the same length. How many of each of these "ominoes" do you think there are?

Lots of activities can be done with pentominoes. For example, try to fit all 12 pieces into a 6 × 10 or 5 × 12 rectangle. Also, each of the 12 shapes can be used as a tessellation tile. Another task is to examine each of the 12 pentominoes

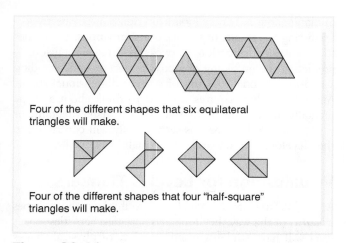

Four of the different shapes that six equilateral triangles will make.

Four of the different shapes that four "half-square" triangles will make.

Figure 20.41 Finding possible shapes with triangles.

and decide which will fold up to make an open box, also called a *net*. For those that are "box makers," which square is the bottom?

Another aspect of visualization for young children is to be able to think about solid shapes in terms of their faces or sides. For these activities you will need to make "face cards" by tracing around the different faces of a shape, making either all faces on one card or a set of separate cards with one face per card (see Figure 20.42).

Activity 20.28

Face Matching

There are two versions of the task: Given a face card, find the corresponding solid, or given a solid, find the face card. With a collection of single-face cards, students can select the cards that go with a particular block. For another variation, stack all of the single-face cards for one block face down. Turn them up one at a time as clues to finding the block.

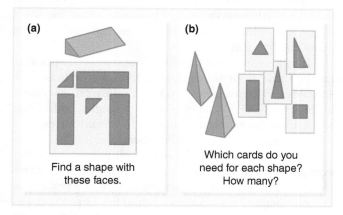

(a)

Find a shape with these faces.

(b)

Which cards do you need for each shape? How many?

Figure 20.42 Matching face cards with solid shapes.

The following activity has been adapted from NCTM's *Principles and Standards* and is found in the pre-K–2 section on geometry (NCTM, 2000, p. 101).

Activity 20.29

Quick Images

Draw some simple sketches on transparencies so that they can be shown to students one figure at a time. They should be drawings that students can easily reproduce. Some examples are shown in Figure 20.43. On the overhead projector or whiteboard display one of the figures for about 5 seconds. Then have students attempt to reproduce it on their own. Show the same figure again for a few seconds and allow students to modify their drawings. Repeat with additional figures.

In your discussions with students, ask them to tell how they thought about the figure or to describe it in words that helped them remember what they saw. As students learn to verbally describe what they see, their visual memory will improve.

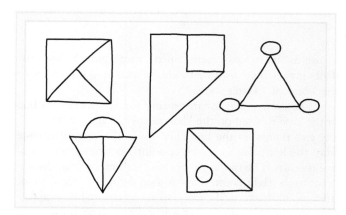

Figure 20.43 Examples of designs to use in the "Quick Images" activity.

In the last activity, visual memory as well as the ability to think about positions of lines and features of the figure are important.

Visualization for Level-1 Thinkers

In identifying a visualization task as either level 0 or level 1, one consideration is the degree of attention that must be given to the particular properties of shapes. The activities in this section are almost certainly too difficult for students at level 0.

One of the main goals of the visualization strand of the Geometry Standard is to be able to identify and draw two-dimensional images of three-dimensional figures and to build three-dimensional figures from two-dimensional images. Activities aimed at this goal often involve drawings of small "buildings" made of one-inch cubes.

Activity 20.30

Viewpoints

- In the first version, students begin with a building and draw the left, right, front, and back direct views. In Figure 20.44, the building plan shows a top view of the building and the number of blocks in each position. After students build a building from a plan like this, their task is to draw the front, right, left, and back direct views as shown in the figure.
- In the reverse version of the task, students are given a right and front view. The task is to build the building that has those views. To record their solution, they draw a building plan (top view with numbers).

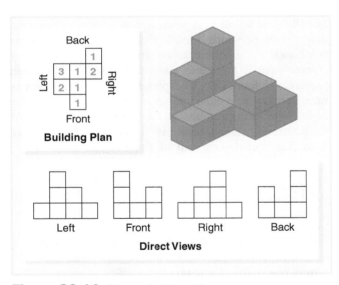

Figure 20.44 "Viewpoints" task.

Activity 20.31

Perspective Drawings

- In the first version, students begin with a perspective drawing of a building. The assumption is that there are no hidden blocks. From the drawing the students build the actual building with their blocks. To record the result, they draw a building plan indicating the number of blocks in each position.
- In the second version, students are given either a block plan or the five direct views (see Figure 20.45). They build the building accordingly and draw two or more of the perspective views. There are four possible perspectives from above the table: the front left and right, and the back left and right. It is useful to build the building on a sheet of paper with the words "front," "back," "left," and "right" written on the edges to keep from getting different viewpoints confused.

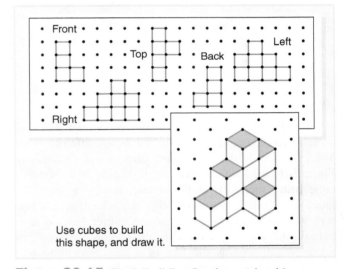

Figure 20.45 Block "buildings" on isometric grids.

Notice that front and back direct views are symmetric, as are the left and right views. That is why only one of each is given in the second part of the activity.

In "Viewpoints," students made "buildings" out of 1-inch cubes and coordinated these with direct views of the sides and top. A significantly more challenging activity is to draw perspective views of these block buildings or to match perspective drawings with a building. Isometric dot grids (Blackline Masters 38 and 39) are used for the drawings. The next activity provides a glimpse at this form of visualization activity.

 An amazing computer tool for drawing two- and three-dimensional views of block buildings is the Isometric Drawing Tool, available on the Illuminations website (http://illuminations.nctm.org/ActivityDetail.aspx?ID=125). This applet requires only mouse clicks to draw either whole cubes, any single face of a cube, or just lines. The drawings, however, are actually "buildings" and can be viewed as three-dimensional objects. They can be rotated in space so that they can be seen from any vantage. Prepared investigations are informative and also lead students through the features of the tool. ◆

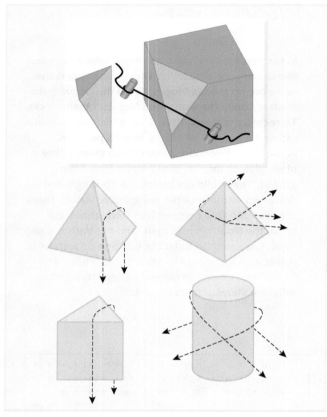

Figure 20.46 Cutting a clay model with a potter's wire.

Another interesting connection between two and three dimensions is found in slicing solids in different ways. When a solid is sliced into two parts, a two-dimensional figure is formed on the slice faces. Figure 20.46 shows a cube being sliced off at the corner, leaving a triangular face. Slices can be explored with clay sliced with a potter's wire as shown in the figure. A niftier method is to partially fill a plastic solid with water. The surface of the water is the same as the face of a slice coinciding with the surface of the water. By tilting the shape in different ways, every possible "slice" can be observed. Small plastic solids such as Power Solids are excellent for this.

Visualization for Level-2 Thinkers

Once again, we see that logical reasoning is what distinguishes activities for level-2 thinkers from those for level 1. It is important to note, however, that visualization is an area of geometry where the distinction is not particularly sharp. The activities described for level 1 can easily be modified to challenge level-2 thinkers. Likewise, the activities in this section will help to push level-1 students forward in their thinking.

Connecting Earlier Activities to Level-2 Visualization. Students who are ready can be challenged to make predictions about the types of slices that are possible. For example, given a particular solid, prior to testing with water as described previously they might go through a list of types of triangles and quadrilaterals and decide which can be made and which are impossible. For those they think are impossible, they should offer a reason for that hypothesis.

The following are extensions of pentomino activities that are appropriate visualization tasks for level 2:

- How many *hexominoes* are there? A hexomino is made of six squares following the same rule as for pentominoes. Since there are quite a few hexominoes (35), devising a good logical scheme for categorizing the shapes is one of the few ways there are of knowing they have all been found.
- Instead of putting together five squares, students can find all of the arrangements of five cubes. These shapes are called *pentominoids*. In general, shapes made of cubes in which adjoining cubes share a complete face are called *polyominoids*.

The Platonic Solids. A *polyhedron* is a three-dimensional shape with polygons for all faces. Among the various polyhedra, the Platonic solids are especially interesting. *Platonic solids* is the name given to the set of completely regular polyhedrons. "Completely regular" means that each face is a regular polygon and every vertex has exactly the same number of faces joining at that point. An interesting visualization task appropriate for this level is to find and describe all of the Platonic solids.

Activity 20.32
Search for the Platonic Solids

Provide students with a supply of equilateral triangles, squares, regular pentagons, and regular hexagons from one of the plastic sets for building solids (e.g., *Polydron* or *Geofix*). Explain what a completely regular solid is. The task is to find as many different completely regular solids as possible.

Some students, particularly those with special needs, may need additional structure. Therefore, you might suggest a systematic approach as follows. Since the smallest number of sides a face can have is three, begin with triangles, then squares, then pentagons, and so on. Furthermore, since every vertex must have the same number of faces, try three faces at a point, then four, and so on. (It is clearly impossible to have only two faces at a point.)

With this plan, students will find that for triangles they can have three, four, or five triangles coming to a point. For each of these, they can begin with a "tent" of triangles and then add more triangles so that each vertex has the same number. With three at a point you get a four-sided solid called a *tetrahedron* (in Greek *tetra* = four). With four at each point you get an eight-sided solid called an *octahedron* (*octa* = eight). It is really exciting to build the solid with five triangles at each point. It will have 20 sides and is called an *icosahedron* (*icosa* = twenty).

In a similar manner, students will find that there is only one solid made of squares—three at each point and six in all—a *hexahedron* (*hex* = six), also called a cube. And there is only one solid with pentagons, three at each point, 12 in all. This is called a *dodecahedron* (*dodeca* = twelve).

Pause and Reflect

Why are there no regular polyhedra with six or more triangles or four or more squares? Why are there no regular polyhedra made with hexagons or with polygons with more than six sides? The best way to answer these questions is to experiment with the polygons and explain the answers in your own words. Students should do the same.

A fantastic skeletal icosahedron can be built out of the newspaper rods described earlier (see Figure 20.11.) Since five triangles converge at each point, there are also five edges at each point. Simply work at bringing five rods to each vertex and remember that each face is a triangle. This icosahedron will be about 4 feet across and will be amazingly sturdy.

Reflections

Writing to Learn

1. Describe in your own words the first three van Hiele levels of geometric thought (levels 0, 1, and 2). Note in your description the object of thought and the product of thought. How would activities aimed at levels 0, 1, and 2 differ?
2. Briefly describe the nature of the content in each of the four geometric strands featured in this chapter and in the *Standards*: Shapes and Properties, Location, Transformations, and Visualization.
3. What can you do when the students in your classroom are at different van Hiele levels of thought?
4. Find one of the suggested applets for geometry or explore *Wingeom* and explain how it can be used. What are the advantages of using the computer in geometry instead of the corresponding hands-on materials or drawings?
5. How can a teacher assess students in terms of general geometric growth or spatial sense? Assuming that the van Hiele theory is correct, why is it important to understand where your students are in terms of that theory?

For Discussion and Exploration

1. Examine the teacher's edition of a textbook at any grade level. Select any lesson on geometry. What evidence do you find that the lesson responds to the van Hiele levels? How might the lesson be adapted for your students who may be at several different levels?
2. At the elementary and middle school levels, technology should be an important component of your instructional tools. If you are not familiar with the types of technology discussed in this chapter, play around to learn what each suggested digital tool or program can do. (Learning about a dynamic geometry program is highly recommended.)

Resources

Literature Connections

The Greedy Triangle *Burns, 1995*

This delightful book starts off with the story of a triangle that is very busy being a sail or musical instrument, or fitting into the crook of someone's arm when standing with hand on hip. It isn't long before he becomes bored and travels to the local shapeshifter for a change. Adding a new side and angle and becoming a quadrilateral gives the triangle new things to try as he fits into different four-sided figures in the environment. The greedy triangle goes through several other shape-shifts. This book links well with activities at level 0 and level 1. Using a meter-long loop of yarn for every pair of students (or three ace bandages in a loop for a class demonstration), have students follow and discuss events in the book by creating appropriate shapes with the loop (holding it in the air between their hands). First they can explore the different triangles that were made and eventually they can investigate properties as they shift from one shape to the next.

Snowflake Bentley *Martin, 1998*

This amazing true story describes the life of a persistent young scientist in Vermont who wanted to learn more about snowflakes. Living in an area averaging 120 inches of snow a year, Wilson Bentley established a lifelong dedication to this work. Using a photographic innovation he created, Bentley was able to produce beautiful and detailed images of these short-lived wonders. This book is a natural to use with symmetry and hexagonal shapes.

Color Farm, 1990

Color Zoo, 1989 *Ehlert*

These visually motivating books can engage young children in thinking about shapes. Using cut-out overlays of circles, rectangles, ovals, triangles, and other familiar shapes, images of either farm or zoo animals are created. The reader turns the page to remove a shape, transforming the image into a new animal. Because this book reinforces shapes, animals, and colors, it is a good vocabulary development book to engage English language learners and their families.

Cubes, Cones, Cylinders and Spheres, 2000

Shapes, Shapes, Shapes, 1996

So Many Circles, So Many Squares, 1998 *Hoban*

These books without words are a collection of vivid photographs on a geometric theme. Each one can engage students of all ages in thinking about and locating shapes in the environment. It is easy to see how students can use digital cameras to create their own Hoban-like books that invite readers to seek and identify two- and three-dimensional shapes in the world around them. Student-made books are great for children to take home to their families, for students in upper grades to make for younger children, or to add to the collection in the school or classroom library.

Recommended Readings

Articles

Glass, B. (2004). Transformations and technology: What path to follow? *Mathematics Teaching in the Middle School,* 9(7), 393–397.

Glass explores compositions of transformations with his middle school students. Part of their discourse revolve around this question: Is a composition of two or more transformations the same as the single transformation that will accomplish the same thing? For those exploring transformations at the upper grades, this is a useful article.

Koester, B. A. (2003). Prisms and pyramids: Constructing three-dimensional models to build understanding. *Teaching Children Mathematics,* 9(8), 436–442.
Koester's activities and explorations with third to fifth graders involves building models using straws and pipe cleaners. The activities involve classification and definitions of shapes and also Euler's formula relating faces, vertices, and edges.

Renne, C. G. (2004). Is a rectangle a square? Developing mathematical vocabulary and conceptual understanding. *Teaching Children Mathematics,* 10(5), 258–263.
The voices of children in this article are clear examples of the difficulty that students at level-1 reasoning have in attempting to make logical conclusions about geometric properties and relationships.

Books

Findell, C. R., Small, M., Cavanagh, M., Dacey, L., Greenes, C. E., & Sheffield, L. J. (2001). *Navigating through geometry in prekindergarten–grade 2.* Reston, VA: NCTM.
Gavin, M. K., Sinelli, A. M., & St. Marie, J. (2001). *Navigating through geometry in grades 3–5.* Reston, VA: NCTM.
Pugalee, D. K., Frykholm, J., Johnson, A., Slovin, H., Malloy, C., & Preston, R. (2002). *Navigating through geometry in grades 6–8.* Reston, VA: NCTM.
Each of these three excellent books from the Navigations Series provides both a perspective on the geometry standard and also a collection of excellent activities appropriate for the grade band of the book.

Online Resources

Cutting Corners
http://illuminations.nctm.org/tools/CutTool/CutTool.asp
A cutting tool allows any one of three simple shapes to be sliced into parts along any straight line. Shapes can be rearranged, rotated, and flipped.

Geoboards
http://nlvm.usu.edu/en/nav/category_g_2_t_3.html
The NLVM library has four geoboards. The first measures areas and perimeters. The circular board has pins in a circular arrangement. The isometric board has pins in a triangular arrangement (like isometric dot paper). The coordinate board shows coordinates for each peg when the cursor is on it. It measures the slope and distance between two points joined by a band and then the perimeter and area of banded shapes.

GeoGebra
www.geogebra.org/cms
This is a free downloadable dynamic geometry software that emphasizes geometry and algebra. Like *Geometer's Sketchpad,* you can construct with points, segments, and lines.

Maze Game

www.shodor.org/interactivate/activities/coords/index.html

The maze game provides practice with coordinates. The user plots points to guide a robot through a mine field.

Mirror Tool

http://illuminations.nctm.org/ActivityDetail.aspx?ID=24

A nice tool for early investigations of mirror or line symmetry.

Space Blocks

**http://nlvm.usu.edu/en/nav/frames_asid_195_g_3_t_3
.html?open=activities**

This applet allows the user to create "buildings" made of cubic blocks rather easily. Use it to explore surface area.

Tangrams

**http://nlvm.usu.edu/en/nav/frames_asid_268_g_1_t_3
.html**

These virtual tangrams can be manipulated freely. Plus, there are 14 puzzle shapes to fill in with all 7 tangrams.

Visualizing Transformations

**http://standards.nctm.org/document/eexamples/chap6/
6.4/index.htm**

This four-part applet provides an excellent exploration of the three rigid-motion transformations including composition of two transformations.

Field Experience Guide Connections

This chapter includes many literature links; see Field Experience 2.6 for designing and teaching a lesson using children's literature. What van Hiele developmental level have students achieved within an area such as shapes and properties? Use Field Experience 7.2 to prepare an interview to find out! The FEG Expanded Lessons 9.17, 9.18, and 9.19 target geometric concepts for grades K–3, 5–7, and 7–8, respectively. These explorations are engaging opportunities to explore concepts of shapes and their properties.

Developing Concepts of Data Analysis

From Chapter 21 of *Elementary and Middle School Mathematics: Teaching Developmentally*, 7/e. John A. Van de Walle. Karen S. Karp. Jennifer M. Bay-Williams. Copyright © 2010 by Pearson Allyn and Bacon. All rights reserved.

Developing Concepts of Data Analysis

Graphs and statistics bombard the public in areas such as advertising, opinion polls, reliability estimates, population trends, health risks, and progress of students in schools. We hear that the average amount of rainfall this summer is more than it was last summer or that the average American household consists of 1.86 people. We read on the U.S. Census website (www.census.gov) that the median home price in 2000 was $119,600, and in May 2008 it was $281,000. The mean home price in May 2008 was $311,300. Knowing these statistics should raise a range of questions: How were these data gathered? What was the purpose? What does it mean to have an average of 1.86 people? Why are the median and the mean for home sales so different? Which statistic makes more sense for communicating about home sales?

Statistical literacy is critical to understanding the world around us. Misuse of statistics occurs even in trustworthy sources like newspapers, where graphs are often designed to exaggerate a finding. Students in pre-K through grade 8 should have meaningful experiences with basic concepts of statistics throughout their school years. At the pre-K–grade 2 level, students can begin this understanding by learning how data can be categorized and displayed in various graphical forms. In grades 3–5, students should have many experiences collecting and organizing sets of data as well as representing data in frequency tables, bar graphs, line plots, and picture graphs. As they mature in understanding, they should be introduced to new data representations such as box-and-whisker plots, scatter plots, and stem-and-leaf plots. Students should also study measures of center—for example, median and mean (NCTM, 2006; Schrelack & Seeley, 2007).

Big Ideas

1. Statistics is its own field different from mathematics; one key difference is focus on variability of data in statistical reasoning.

2. Doing statistics involves a four-step process: formulating questions, collecting data, analyzing data, and interpreting results.

3. Data are gathered and organized in order to answer questions about the populations from which the data come. With data from only a sample of the population, inferences are made about the population.

4. Different types of graphs and other data frameworks provide different information about the data and, hence, the population from which the data were taken. The choice of graphical representation can impact how well the data are understood.

5. Measures that describe data with numbers are called *statistics*. Data can be organized in various graphical forms to visually convey information. The use of a particular graph or statistic can mediate what the data tell about the population.

6. Both graphs and statistics can provide a sense of the shape of the data, including how spread out or how clustered they are. Having a sense of the shape of data is having a big picture of the data rather than a collection of numbers.

Mathematics Content Connections

Statistics involves using data in the form of numbers and graphs to describe our world. Certainly, there are connections to the numeric areas of the curriculum. However, the connection to algebra is perhaps one of the most important mathematical connections.

- **Number Sense:** Young children create graphs of class data (such as "What color socks?" or "How many buttons?") and use the graphs to talk about quantity.

- **Algebra:** Algebra is used to analyze and describe relationships. Whenever data are gathered on two related variables (e.g., height and arm span, age and growth), algebra can be used to describe the relationship between the variables. The resulting relationship can then be used to predict outcomes for which no data have yet been gathered. The better that the data are approximated by the algebraic relationship or function, the more predictive value the function has.

- **Fractions, Decimals, and Percents:** Fractions, decimals, and percents are used to describe data.

- **Proportional Reasoning:** Statistical reasoning *is* proportional reasoning. When a population is sampled (a subset selected), that sample is assumed to be proportional to the larger population.

- **Measurement:** Much of the real-world data that are gathered consist of measurements. Pedagogically, measurement can be interwoven with data analysis as students make measurements to answer questions and create data to be analyzed.

What Does It Mean to Do Statistics?

Doing statistics is a different process from doing mathematics, a notion that has recently received much attention by standards documents and research (Burrill & Elliott, 2006; Franklin et al., 2005; Shaugnessy, 2003). As Richard Scheaffer, past president of the American Statistics Association notes,

> Mathematics is about numbers and their operations, generalizations and abstractions; it is about spatial configurations and their measurement, transformations, and abstractions. . . . Statistics is also about numbers—but numbers in context: these are called data. Statistics is about variables and cases, distribution and variation, purposeful design or studies, and the role of randomness in the design of studies, and the interpretation of results. (Scheaffer, 2006, pp. 310–311)

This section describes some of the big ideas regarding statistics and explains a general process for doing statistics. Each of the four steps in the process is used as a major section in the organization of this chapter.

Is It Statistics or Is It Mathematics?

Statistics and mathematics are two different fields; however, statistical questions are often asked in assessments with questions that are mathematical in nature rather than statistical. The harm in this is that students are not focusing on statistical reasoning, as shown by the following excellent exemplars from Scheaffer (2006).

II ———————— *Pause and Reflect*

Read the questions below and code each as "doing mathematics" or "doing statistics."

1. The average weight of 50 prize-winning tomatoes is 2.36 pounds. What is the combined weight, in pounds, of these 50 tomatoes? (NAEP sample question)
   a. 0.0472   **b.** 11.8   **c.** 52.36   **d.** 59   **e.** 118

2. Joe had three test scores of 78, 76, and 74, whereas Mary had scores of 72, 82, and 74. How did Joe's average (mean) compare to Mary's average (mean) score? (TIMSS eighth-grade released item)
   a. Joe's was one point higher.
   b. Joe's was one point lower.
   c. Both averages were the same.
   d. Joe's was 2 points higher.
   e. Joe's was 2 points lower.

3. Table 21.1 gives the times each girl has recorded for seven runnings of the 100-meter dash this year. Only one girl may compete in the upcoming tournament. Which girl would you select for the tournament and why?

Table 21.1

Race Times for Three Runners							
	Race						
Runner	**1**	**2**	**3**	**4**	**5**	**6**	**7**
Suzie	15.2	14.8	15.0	14.7	14.3	14.5	14.5
Tanisha	15.8	15.7	15.4	15.0	14.8	14.6	14.5
Dara	15.6	15.5	14.8	15.1	14.5	14.7	14.5

Which of these involves statistical reasoning? All of them? None of them? As explained by Schaeffer, only the last is statistical in nature. The first requires knowing the formula for averages, but the task required is to work backwards through a formula—mathematical thinking, not statistical thinking. Similarly in the second problem, one must know the formula for the mean, but the question is about the computational process of using the formula. In both of these, you might notice that the context is irrelevant to the problem. The final question is statistical in nature because the situation requires analysis—graphs or averages might be used to determine a solution. The mathematics here is basic; the focus is on statistics. Notice the context is central to the question.

In statistics the context is essential to analyzing and interpreting the data (Franklin & Garfield, 2006; Franklin et al., 2005; Rossman, Chance, & Medina, 2006; Schaeffer, 2006). Looking at the spread, or shape, of data and considering the meaning of unusual data points (outliers) are determined based on the context.

Variability

The second concept that is critical and unique in statistics is variability. Statisticians must deal with variability in the data (Franklin & Garfield, 2006; Franklin et al., 2005; Rossman, Chance, & Medina, 2006; Schaeffer, 2006). Students do not have a clear understanding of variability, perhaps because the mathematical process of analyzing data dominates the data analysis phase. Shaughnessy (2006), a noted researcher on statistics education, summarized the findings on what students know about variability in the following list, starting with basic notions and progressing to more sophisticated ideas:

1. Focusing only on outliers or extremes (but not on the full distribution of the data).
2. Considering change over time (can lead into discussions of other types of variation).
3. Examining variability as the full range of data. Range is everything that occurs but doesn't reveal the frequency of different events within the range.
4. Considering variability as the likely range or expected value.
5. Looking at how far data points are from the center (e.g., the mean).
6. Looking at how far off a set of data is from some fixed value.

All of these are accessible to students in elementary and middle school, when students are engaged in doing experiments to answer questions (Shaughnessy, 2006). In order to be prepared to teach students variability beyond outliers and extremes, it is important to know about the way that variability occurs in statistics.

Variability can occur in numerous ways. The *Guidelines for Assessment and Instruction in Statistics Education* (GAISE) report (Franklin et al., 2005) discusses three levels of statistical thinking, which although developmental in nature can be roughly mapped to elementary, middle, and secondary level curriculum. The report states that the variability that should be the focus at the elementary level includes variability within a group—for example, the varying lengths of students' names, varying family sizes, and so on. When students create a bar graph of class data and compare the data collected, they are discussing the variability within a group.

At the next level, variability within a group continues, but groups of data are also considered. Students might compare the variability of fifth-graders' favorite music choices with eighth-graders' music choices, an example of variability between groups. In addition, middle school students study how the change in one variable relates to change in another variable—yes, algebra! Students analyze two variables to see whether there is a relationship (discussed in more depth in the section on scatter plots).

Another type of relevant variability in pre-K–8 is sampling variability (Franklin et al., 2005). When students flip a coin 10 times, as a sample, they may get 5 heads and 5 tails, but they also may get many other results (even 0 heads and 10 tails). This is

sampling variability. The larger the sample, the more the data reflect the expected values (50 percent heads, 50 percent tails).

Finally, at the third level, students can examine natural and induced variability. For example, plants grow at different rates. When one flower naturally grows taller than the one right next to it in the garden, that is natural variability. If the two plants were in two different gardens, then other variables come into play: fertilization, amount of sunlight, amount of water, and so on, which can "induce" different growth rates. Knowing these variability terms is less important than knowing that in designing an experiment to look at one factor (e.g., sunlight), all other factors should be kept the same. This is at the heart of doing statistics (Franklin & Garfield, 2006).

Students need to understand variability. One way to help students do this is including questions on variability in the discussion of data. Friel, O'Conner, and Mamer (2006), using the context of heart rates, suggest the following questions as an example of how to get students to focus on data and variability:

- If the average heart rate for 9- to 11-year-olds is 88 beats per minute, does this mean every student this age has a heart rate of 88 beats per minute? (Note the range is actually quite large—from 60 to 110 beats per minute.)
- If we found the heart rate for everyone in the class (of 30), what might the distribution of data look like?
- If another class (of 30) was measured, would their distribution look like our class?
- Would the distribution of data from 200 students look like the data from the two classes?

The Shape of Data

A big conceptual idea in data analysis can be referred to as the *shape of data:* a sense of how data are spread out or grouped, what characteristics about the data set as a whole can be described, and what the data tell us in a global way about the population from which they are taken.

There is no single technique that can tell us what the shape of the data is. Across the pre-K–8 curriculum, students begin looking at the shape of data by examining various graphs. Different graphing techniques or types of graphs can provide a different snapshot of the data as a whole. For example, bar graphs and circle graphs (percentage graphs) each show how the data cluster in different categories. The circle graph focuses more on the relative values of this clustering whereas the bar graph adds a dimension of quantity. The choice of which and how many categories to use in these graphs will cause different pictures of the shape of the data.

Part of understanding the shape of data is being aware of how spread out or clustered the data are. In the early grades this can be discussed informally by looking at almost any graph.

For numeric data, there are statistics that tell us how data are spread. The simplest of these is the *range*. Averages (the *mean* and the *median*) tell us where the "center" of the data is. In high school students will learn about the standard deviation statistic, which is also a measure of spread. At the middle school level, a simple graphical technique called the *box-and-whisker plot* is designed to give us visual information about the spread of data.

Process of Doing Statistics

Just as learning addition involves much more than the procedure for combining, doing statistics is much more than the computational procedures for finding the mean or the process of creating a circle graph. To engage students *meaningfully* in learning and doing statistics, they should be involved in the full process, from asking and defining questions to interpreting results. This broad approach provides a framework and purpose under which students learn how to create graphs, compute the mean, and analyze data in other ways. This chapter is organized around this process, which is presented in Figure 21.1.

I. Formulate Questions
- Clarify the problem at hand
- Formulate one (or more) questions that can be answered with data

II. Collect Data
- Design a plan to collect appropriate data
- Employ the plan to collect the data

III. Analyze Data
- Select appropriate graphical and numerical methods
- Use these methods to analyze the data

IV. Interpret Results
- Interpret the analysis
- Relate the interpretation to the original question

Figure 21.1 Process of doing statistics.
Source: Franklin, C., Kader, G., Mewborn, D., Moreno, J., Peck, R., Perry, M., & Scheaffer, R. (2005, August). *Guidelines for Assessment and Instruction in Statistics Education (GAISE) Report: A Pre-K–12 Curriculum Framework,* p. 11. Reprinted with permission. Copyright 2005 by the American Statistical Association. All rights reserved.

Formulating Questions

Statistics is about more than making graphs and analyzing data. It includes both asking and answering questions about our world. The first goal in the Data Analysis and Probability standard of *Principles and Standards* says that students should "formulate questions that can be addressed with data and collect, organize, and display relevant data to answer them" (NCTM, 2000, p. 48). Notice that data collection should be for a purpose, to answer a question, just as in the real world. Then the analysis of data actually adds information about some aspect of our world, just as political pollsters, advertising agencies, market researchers, census takers, wildlife managers, medical researchers, and hosts of others gather data to answer questions.

Students should be given opportunities to generate their own questions, decide on appropriate data to help answer these questions, and determine methods of collecting the data. For example, in a second-grade class studied by Susan Jo Russell (lead author of *Investigations*), a student wanted to know how many houses were on her street (Russell, 2006). Or a teacher may ask, "How many sisters and brothers do you have?" Whether the question is teacher initiated or student initiated, students should engage in conversations about how well defined the question is. In the house example, students wondered whether they should include houses that weren't finished yet or whether apartments counted. In the second case, there is a need to discuss half-siblings, for example.

When students formulate the questions they want to ask, the data they gather become more meaningful. How they organize the data and the techniques for analyzing them have a purpose.

Ideas for Questions

Often the need to gather data will come from the class naturally in the course of discussion or from questions arising in other content areas. Science, of course, is full of measurements and, thus, abounds in data requiring analysis. Social studies is also full of opportunities to pose questions requiring data collection. The next few sections suggest some additional ideas.

Classroom Questions. Students want to learn about themselves, their families and pets, measures such as arm span or time to get to school, their likes and dislikes, and so on. The easiest questions to deal with are those that can be answered by each class member contributing one piece of data. Here are a few ideas:

- *Favorites:* TV shows, games, movies, ice cream, video games, sports teams, music CDs. (When there are lots of possibilities, suggest that students restrict the number of choices.)
- *Numbers:* Number of pets, sisters, or brothers; hours watching TV or hours of sleep; bedtime; time spent on the computer.
- *Measures:* Height, arm span, area of foot, long-jump distance, shadow length, seconds to run around the track, minutes spent on the bus.

Beyond One Classroom. The questions in the previous section are designed for students to contribute data about themselves. These questions can be expanded by asking,

"How would this compare to another class?" Comparison questions are a good way to help students focus on the data they have collected and the variability within that data (Russell, 2006). As children get older, they can begin to think about various populations and differences between them. For example, how are fifth graders similar or different from middle school students? Students might examine questions concerning boys versus girls, adults or teachers versus students, or categories of workers or college graduates. These situations involve issues of sampling and making generalizations and comparisons. In addition, students can ask questions about things beyond the classroom. Discussions about communities provide a good way to integrate social studies and mathematics.

The newspaper suggests all sorts of data-related questions. For example, how many full-page ads occur on different days of the week? What types of stories are on the front page? Which comics are really for kids and which are not?

Science is another area where questions can be asked and data gathered. For example, what is the width of oak leaves that fall to the ground. How many times do different types of balls bounce when each is dropped from the same height? How many days does it take for different types of bean, squash, and pea seeds to germinate when kept in moist paper towels?

Data Collection

Gathering data is not easy for students, especially young students. In a first-grade class, a teacher asked students to gather data on "Are you 6?" Upon receiving the prompt, 18 eager students began asking others in the class if they were 6 and tallying the yes and no responses. The problem? They had no idea whom they had asked more than once or whom they had not asked at all. This provided an excellent entry into a discussion about how statisticians must gather data. Carolyn Cook, a kindergarten teacher, asked her students to help think of an organized manner to gather the data from their classmates on favorite ice cream flavors. These students decided a class list (see Figure 21.2) would allow them to keep track (Cook, 2008).

Gathering data also must take into consideration variability. Young children can understand that asking a group of first graders their favorite TV show will produce different answers than asking a group of fifth graders. Answers also may vary based on the day the question is asked or whether a particular show has been recently discussed.

For older students (GAISE recommends this at the second level of statistical thinking), planning data collection includes gathering data from more than

myeducationlab

Go to the Building Teaching Skills and Dispositions section of Chapter 21 of MyEducationLab. Click on Videos and watch the video entitled "**Food Survey Lesson**" to see a class collect, display, and analyze data.

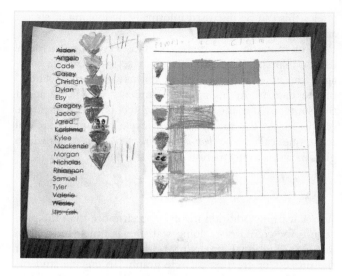

Figure 21.2 Kindergartners collect data on ice cream flavor choices, keeping track of who they have surveyed, tallying the data, and then creating a horizontal bar graph.

Source: Cook, C. D. (2008). "I Scream, You Scream: Data Analysis with Kindergartners." *Teaching Children Mathematics, 14*(9), p. 539. Reprinted with permission. Copyright © 2008 by the National Council of Teachers of Mathematics, Inc. www.nctm.org. All rights reserved.

one classroom to seek a more representative sample, or even using random sampling. In fact, for middle school students, it is important that they engage in the whole process of doing statistics, including designing an experiment in which most variables (induced) are kept the same so that one variable can be analyzed.

Using Existing Data Sources

Data do not have to be collected by survey; data abound in various places, such as the following sources of print and Web data.

Print Resources. Newspapers, almanacs, sports record books, maps, and various government publications are possible sources of data that may be used to answer student questions.

Children's literature is an excellent and engaging resource. Young students can tally words in a repeating verse like "Hickory, Dickory, Dock" (Niezgoda & Moyer-Packenham, 2005). Similarly, books like *Good Night Moon* (Brown, 1947) or *Green Eggs and Ham* (Dr. Seuss, 1960) have many repeated words or phrases. Nonfiction literature can be a source of data, especially for older students. For example, the *Book of Lists: Fun Facts, Weird Trivia, and Amazing Lists on Nearly Everything You Need to Know!* (Buckley & Stremme, 2006) reports on various statistics and includes surveys at the end of every section. Books on sports, such as *A Negro League Scrapbook* (Weatherform, 2005), can have very interesting statistics about historic periods that students can explore and compare.

Websites. Students may be interested in facts about another country as a result of a social studies unit or a country in the news. Olympic records in various events over the years or data related to space flight are other examples of topics around which student questions may be formulated. For these and hundreds of other questions, data can be found on the World Wide Web. Here are four websites with a lot of interesting data.

- U.S. Census Bureau (www.census.gov): This website contains copious statistical information by state, county, or voting district.
- Economic Research Service, USDA (www.ers.usda.gov/data/foodconsumption): Here you can find wonderful data sets on the availability and consumption of hundreds of foods. Per capita estimates on a yearly basis often go back as far as 1909.
- The World Fact Book (https://www.cia.gov/library/publications/the-world-factbook/index.html): This website provides demographic information for every nation in the world, including population; age distributions; death and birth rates; and information on the economy, government, transportation, and geography. Maps are included as well.
- Internet Movie Database (www.imdb.com): This website offers information about movies of all genres.

Data Analysis: Classification

Classification involves making decisions about how to categorize things, a basic activity that is fundamental to data analysis. In order to formulate questions and decide how to represent data that have been gathered, decisions must be made about how things might be categorized. Young children might group farm animals, for example, by number of legs; by type of product they provide; by those that work, provide food, or are pets; by size or color; by the type of food they eat; and so on. Each of these groupings is based on a different attribute of the animals.

Young children need experiences with categorizing things in different ways in order to learn to make sense of real-world data. Attribute activities are explicitly designed to develop this flexible reasoning about the characteristics of data.

Attribute Materials

Attribute materials can be any set of objects that lend themselves to being sorted and classified in different ways—for example, seashells, leaves, the children themselves, or the set of the children's shoes. The *attributes* are the ways that the materials can be sorted. For example, hair color, height, and gender are attributes of children. Each attribute has

a number of different *values:* for example, blond, brown, black, or red (for the attribute of hair color); tall or short (for height); male or female (for gender). An example of a teacher-made attribute set is displayed in Figure 21.3. These cards are available in Blackline Master 59.

Commercially available attribute blocks are sets of 60 plastic attribute materials, with each piece having four attributes: color (red, yellow, blue), shape (circle, triangle, rectangle, square, hexagon), size (big, little), and thickness (thick, thin). The specific values, number of values, or number of attributes that a set may have is not important.

"Organizing data into categories should begin with informal sorting experiences, such as helping to put away groceries. . . . Young children should continue activities that focus on attributes of objects and data so that by the second grade, they can sort and classify simultaneously, using more than one attribute" (pp. 109–110). ◆

Activities with Attribute Materials. Most attribute activities are best done with young children sitting on the floor in a large circle where all can see and have access to the materials. Kindergarten classes can have fun with simple Venn diagram activities. With the use of words such as *and,*

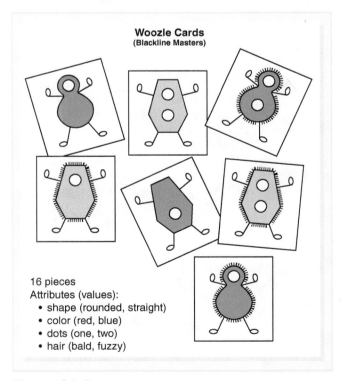

Woozle Cards
(Blackline Masters)

16 pieces
Attributes (values):
- shape (rounded, straight)
- color (red, blue)
- dots (one, two)
- hair (bald, fuzzy)

Figure 21.3 Woozle Cards can be duplicated on card stock colored with red and blue bodies, and then laminated and cut into individual cards (see Blackline Master 59).

or; and *not,* the loop activities become quite challenging, even for fifth graders.

Activity 21.1

What about "Both"

Give children two large loops of yarn or string and attribute blocks. Direct them to put all the red pieces inside one string and all triangles inside the other. Let the children try to resolve the difficulty of what to do with the red triangles. When the notion of over-lapping the strings to create an area common to both loops is clear, more challenging activities can be explored.

Affix or draw labels on each loop and have students take turns placing pieces in the appropriate regions. As shown in Figure 21.4, the labels need not be restricted to single attributes. If a piece does not fit in any region, it is placed outside all of the loops.

It is important to introduce labels for negative attributes such as "not red" or "not small." Also important is the eventual use of *and* and *or* connectives, as in "red and square" or "big or happy." This use of *and, or;* and *not* significantly widens children's classification schemes.

An engaging and challenging activity is to infer how things have been classified when the loops are not labeled.

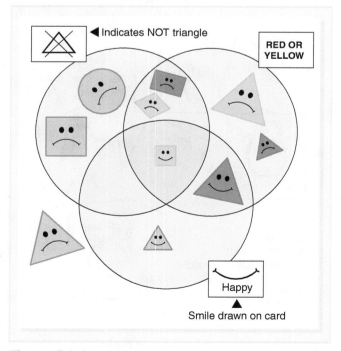

Figure 21.4 A Venn Diagram activity with attribute pieces. A rule is written on each card.

The following activities require students to make and test conjectures about how things are being classified.

Activity 21.2

Guess My Rule

For this activity, try using students instead of shapes as attribute "pieces." Decide on an attribute of your students such as "blue jeans" or "stripes on clothing," but do not tell your rule to the class. Silently look at one child at a time and move the child to the left or right according to this attribute rule. After a number of students have been sorted, have the next child come up and ask students to predict which group he or she belongs in. Before the rule is articulated, continue the activity for a while so that others in the class will have an opportunity to determine the rule. This same activity can be done with virtually any materials that can be sorted, such as students' shoes, shells, or buttons.

Activity 21.3

Hidden Labels

Select label cards for the loops of string, and place the cards face down. Ask students to select a piece for you to place. Begin to sort pieces according to the turned-down labels. As you sort, have students try to determine what the labels are for each of the loops. Let students who think they have guessed the labels try to place a piece in the proper loop, but avoid having them guess the labels aloud. Students who think they know the labels can be asked to "play teacher" and respond to the guesses of the others. Point out that one way to test an idea about the labels is to select pieces that you think might go in a particular section. Do not turn the cards up until most students have figured out the rule. With simple one-value labels and only two loops, this activity can easily be played in kindergarten.

"Guess My Rule" can and should be repeated with real-world materials connected to students' current explorations. For example, if you were doing a unit on animals in the backyard, you can use pictures of animals (see Figure 21.5). The loops used with the attribute materials provide a first form of data presentation. The class can "graph" data about themselves by placing information in loops with labels. A graph of "Our Pets" might consist of a picture of each student's pet or favorite stuffed animal (in lieu of a pet) and be affixed to a wall display showing how the pets were classified.

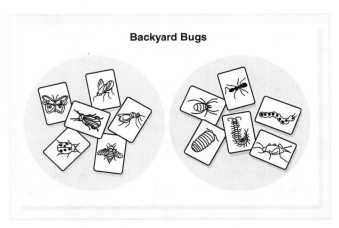

Backyard Bugs

Figure 21.5 Can you guess the rule that was used to sort these bugs?

Data Analysis: Graphical Representations

How data are organized should be directly related to the question that caused you to collect the data in the first place. For example, suppose that students want to know how many pockets they have on their clothing (Burns, 1996; Russell et al., 2007). Each student in the room counts his or her pockets and the data are collected.

Pause and Reflect

If your second-grade class had collected these data, what methods might you suggest they use for organizing and graphing them? Is one of your ideas better than others for answering the question about how many pockets?

If a large bar graph is made with a bar for every student, that will certainly tell how many pockets each student has. However, is it the best way to answer the question? If the data were categorized by number of pockets, then a graph showing the number of students with two pockets, three pockets, and so on will easily show which number of pockets is most common and how the number of pockets varies across the class.

Students should be involved in deciding how they want to represent their data. However, for children lacking experience with the various methods of picturing data, you can suggest alternatives.

Once students have made the display, they can discuss its value. Analyzing data that are numerical (number of pockets) versus categorical (color of socks) is an added challenge for students as they struggle to make sense of the graphs (Russell, 2006). If for example, the graph has seven stickers above the five, students may think that five people have seven pockets or seven people have five pockets.

The emphasis or goal of this instruction should be to help children see that graphs and charts tell about information and that different types of representations tell different things about the same data. The value of having students actually construct their own graphs is not so much that they learn the techniques but that they are personally invested in the data and that they learn how a graph conveys information. Once a graph is constructed, the most important activity is discussing what it tells the people who see it, especially those who were not involved in making the graph. Discussions about graphs of real data that the children have themselves been involved in gathering will help them analyze and interpret other graphs and charts that they see in newspapers and on TV.

What we should *not* do is get overly anxious about the tedious details of graph construction. The issues of analysis and communication are your agendas and are much more important than the technique! In the real world, technology will take care of details.

Students should construct graphs or charts by hand and with technology. First, you can encourage students to make charts and graphs that make sense to them and that they feel communicate the information they wish to convey. Young students may feel more personally invested in their work when creating by hand and not distracted by the techniques of technology. The intent is to get the students involved in accurately communicating a message about their data.

Technology use is very common in graphical representations. Computer programs and graphing calculators can provide various graphical displays with very little effort. Discussion can then focus on the information that each display provides. Students can make their own selections among different graphs and justify their choice based on their own intended purposes. ◆

Bar Graphs and Tally Charts

Bar graphs and tally charts are some of the first ways to group and present data and are especially useful in grades pre-K–3. At this early level, bar graphs should be made so that each bar consists of countable parts such as squares, objects, tallies, or pictures of objects. Figure 21.6 illustrates a few techniques that can be used to make a graph quickly with the whole class.

A "real graph" uses the actual objects being graphed. Examples include types of shoes, seashells, and books. Each item can be placed in a square or on a floor tile so that comparisons and counts are easily made.

Picture graphs use a drawing of some sort that represents what is being graphed. Students can make their own drawings, or you can duplicate drawings to be colored or cut out to suit particular needs.

Symbolic graphs use something like squares, blocks, tallies, or Xs to represent the items being counted in the graph. An easy idea is to use sticky notes as elements of a graph. These can be stuck directly to the chalkboard or other chart and rearranged if needed.

Recall that analyzing data in this way is step 3 of the process of doing statistics. A question is posed and data are collected based on the categories that will be graphed. Figure 21.6 illustrates two quick ways to gather information so that it is already displayed in a bar, combining steps 2 and 3 of doing statistics. A class of 25 to 30 students can make a graph in less than 10 minutes, leaving ample time to use it for questions and observations.

Once a graph has been constructed, engage the class in a discussion of what information the graph tells or conveys. "What can you tell about our class by looking at this shoe graph?" Graphs convey factual information (more people wear sneakers than any other kind of shoe) and also provide opportunities to make inferences that are not directly observable in the graph (kids in this class do not like to wear leather shoes). The difference between actual facts and inferences is an important idea in graph construction and is also an important idea in science. Older students can examine graphs found in newspapers or magazines and discuss the *facts* in the graphs and the *message* that may have been intended by the person who made the graph.

Circle Graphs

Typically, we think of circle graphs as showing percentages and, as such, these would probably not be appropriate for primary students. However, notice in Figure 21.7 that the circle graph could be set up to only indicate the number of data points (in that case, students) in each of five categories. Many computer graphing programs will create a similar graph. An understanding of percentages is not required when the computer creates the graph.

Notice also that the circle graph shows information that is not as easily available from the other graphs. For example, when comparisons are made between two populations of very different size, the circle graph offers visual ratios that allow for these comparisons. In Figure 21.7, the two graphs shows the percentages of students with different numbers of siblings. One graph is based on classroom data and the other on schoolwide data. Because circle graphs display ratios rather than quantities, the small set of class data can be compared to the large set of school data, which could not be done with bar graphs.

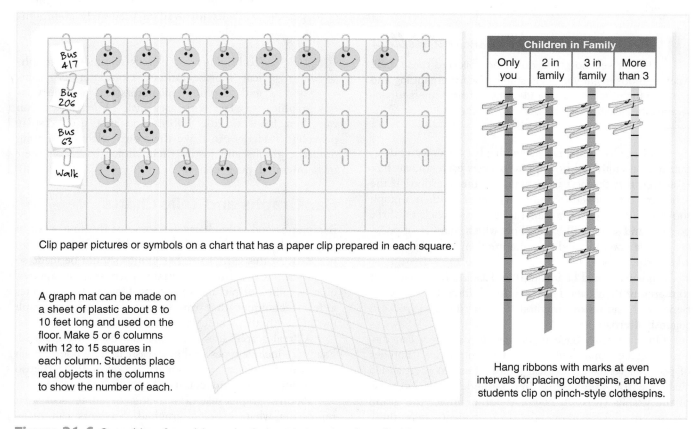

Clip paper pictures or symbols on a chart that has a paper clip prepared in each square.

A graph mat can be made on a sheet of plastic about 8 to 10 feet long and used on the floor. Make 5 or 6 columns with 12 to 15 squares in each column. Students place real objects in the columns to show the number of each.

Hang ribbons with marks at even intervals for placing clothespins, and have students clip on pinch-style clothespins.

Figure 21.6 Some ideas for quick graphs that can be used again and again.

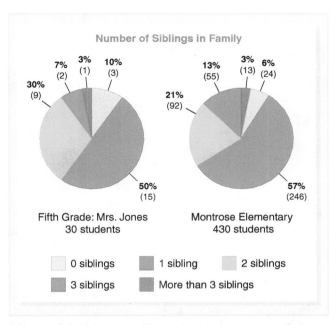

Number of Siblings in Family

7% (2) 3% (1) 10% (3)

30% (9)

50% (15)

Fifth Grade: Mrs. Jones
30 students

13% (55) 3% (13) 6% (24)

21% (92)

57% (246)

Montrose Elementary
430 students

- 0 siblings
- 1 sibling
- 2 siblings
- 3 siblings
- More than 3 siblings

Figure 21.7 Circle graphs show ratios of part to whole and can be used to compare ratios.

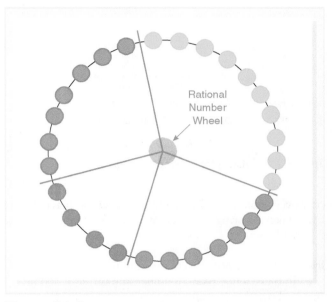

Rational Number Wheel

Figure 21.8 A human circle graph: Students are arranged in a circle, with string stretched between them to show the divisions.

Easily Made Circle Graphs. Circle graphs of the students in your room can be made quickly and quite dramatically. Suppose, for example, that each student picked his or her favorite basketball team in the NCAA tournament's "Final Four." Line up all of the students in the room so that students favoring the same team are together. Now form the entire group into a circle of students. Tape the ends of four long strings to the floor in the center of the circle, and extend them to the circle at each point where the teams change. Voilà! A very nice circle graph with no measuring and no percentages. If you copy and cut out a rational number wheel (see Blackline Master 28) and place it on the center of the circle, the strings will show approximate percentages for each part of your graph (see Figure 21.8). Percent necklaces or a loop with 100 pieces of colored cereal, like Froot Loops, can be used in a similar fashion.

Another easy approach to circle graphs is similar to the human circle graph. Begin by having students make a bar graph of the data. Once complete, cut out the bars themselves, and tape them together end to end. Next, tape the two ends together to form a circle. Estimate where the center of the circle is, draw lines to the points where different bars meet, and trace around the full loop. You can estimate percentages using the rational number wheel or percent necklace as before.

Determining Percentages. If students have experienced either of the two methods just described, using their own calculations to make circle graphs will make more sense. The numbers in each category are added to form the total or whole. (That's the same as taping all of the strips together or lining up the students.) By dividing each of the parts by the whole with a calculator, students will find the decimals and convert to percents. It is an interesting proportional problem for students to convert between percents and degrees, since one is out of 100 and the other out of 360. It is helpful to start students with obvious values, like 50 percent, 25 percent, and 10 percent before moving to more difficult values.

 As you evaluate students in the area of graphing, it is important not to focus undue attention on the skills of constructing a graph. It is more important to think about the choice of graphs that the students make to help answer their questions or complete their projects. Your goal is for students to understand that a graph helps answer a question and provides a picture of the data. Different graphs tell us different things about the data.

Students should write about their graphs, explaining what the graph tells and why they selected that type of graph to illustrate the data. Use this information for your assessment. ◆

Continuous Data Graphs

Bar graphs or picture graphs are useful for illustrating categories of data that have no numeric ordering—for example, colors or TV shows. When data are grouped along a continuous scale, they should be ordered along a number line. Examples of such information include temperatures that

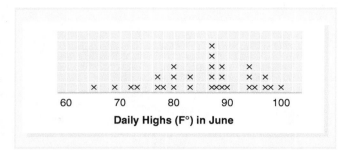

Figure 21.9 Line plot of temperatures.

occur over time, height or weight over age, and percentages of test takers scoring in different intervals along the scale of possible scores.

Line Plots. *Line plots* are counts of things along a numeric scale. To make a line plot, a number line is drawn and an X is made above the corresponding value on the line for every corresponding data element. One advantage of a line plot is that every piece of data is shown on the graph. It is also a very easy type of graph for students to make. It is essentially a bar graph with a potential bar for every possible value. A simple example is shown in Figure 21.9.

Stem-and-Leaf Plots. *Stem-and-leaf plots* are a form of bar graph in which numeric data are graphed and displayed as a list. By way of example, suppose that the American League baseball teams had posted the following record of wins over the past season:

Baltimore	45	Tampa Bay	91
Boston	94	Minnesota	98
Los Angeles	85	New York	100
Chicago	72	Oakland	101
Cleveland	91	Seattle	48
Detroit	102	Toronto	64
Kansas City	96	Texas	65

If the data are to be grouped by tens, list the tens digits in order and draw a line to the right, as shown in Figure 21.10(a). These form the "stem" of the graph. Next, go through the list of scores, and write the ones digits next to the appropriate tens digit, as shown in Figure 21.10(b). These are the "leaves." The process of making the graph groups the data for you. Furthermore, every piece of data can be retrieved from the graph. (Notice that stem-and-leaf plots are best made on graph paper so that each digit takes up the same amount of space.) The graph can be quickly rewritten, ordering each leaf from least to most, as shown in Figure 21.10(c).

Stem-and-leaf graphs are not limited to two-digit data. For example, if the data ranged from 600 to 1300, the stem could be the numerals from 6 to 13 and the leaves made of two-digit numbers separated by commas.

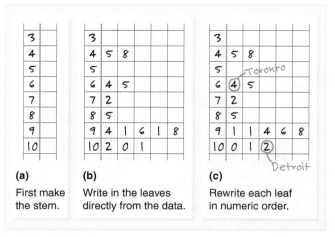

(a)
First make the stem.

(b)
Write in the leaves directly from the data.

(c)
Rewrite each leaf in numeric order.

Figure 21.10 Making a stem-and-leaf plot.

Figure 21.11 illustrates two additional variations. When two sets of data are to be compared, the leaves can extend in opposite directions from the same stem. In the same example, notice that the data are grouped by fives instead of tens. When plotting 62, the 2 is written next to the 6; for 67, the 7 is written next to the dot below the 6.

Notice that the stem-and-leaf plot in Figure 21.11 clearly shows the shape of the data. You can observe how the data spread and how they cluster. From observation, students can find the range, median, mode, and any outliers. In Figure 21.11, again using rows grouped by fives instead of by tens illustrates the spread of the

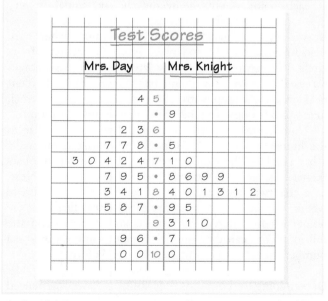

Figure 21.11 Stem-and-leaf plots can be used to compare two sets of data.

data, perhaps to illustrate particular grades (e.g., B from B+). Determining how to set up the stem-and-leaf plot depends on the context and on the question being asked.

Histograms. A *histogram* is a form of bar graph in which the categories are consecutive equal intervals along a numeric scale. The height or length of each bar is determined by the number of data elements falling into that particular interval. Histograms are not difficult in concept but can cause problems for the students constructing them. What is the appropriate interval to use for the bar width? What is a good scale to use for the length of the bars? That all of the data must be grouped and counted within each interval causes further difficulty. Figure 21.12 shows a histogram for the same temperature data used in Figure 21.9. Notice how similar the two displays are in illustrating the spread and clustering of data. Histograms can be created with graphing calculators or by computer software, making the process of creation immediate.

Line Graphs. A *line graph* is used when there is a numeric value associated with equally spaced points along a continuous number scale. Points are plotted to represent two related pieces of data, and a line is drawn to connect the points. For example, a line graph might be used to show how the length of a flagpole shadow changed from one hour to the next during the day. The horizontal scale would be time, and the vertical scale would be the length of the shadow. Discrete points can be plotted and straight lines drawn connecting them. In the previous example, a shadow was present at all times, but its length did not jump or drop from one plotted value to the other. It changed continuously as suggested by the graph. See the example in Figure 21.13 for a line graph on temperature change.

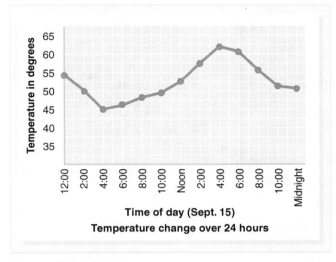

Figure 21.13 Line graph of one day's temperatures.

Scatter Plots

Data are often analyzed to search for or demonstrate relationships between two sets of data or phenomena. For example, what are the relationships, if any, between time spent watching television and overall grades?

All sorts of real situations exist in which we are interested in relationships between two variables or two numeric phenomena. How far does a toy car roll beyond an inclined plane as the angle of the plane varies? Is there a relationship between the air in a balloon and the time it takes to deflate? Such data are generally gathered from some sort of experiment that is set up and observed, with measurements taken.

Data that may be related are gathered in pairs. For example, if you were going to examine the possible relationship between hours of TV watched and grades, each person in the survey or sample would produce a pair of numbers, one for TV time and one for grade point average.

Data involving two variables can be plotted on a *scatter plot*, a graph of points on a coordinate grid with each axis representing one of the two variables. Each pair of numbers from the two sets of data, when plotted, produces a visual image of the data as well as a hint concerning any possible relationships. Suppose that the following information was gathered from 25 eighth-grade boys: height in inches, weight in pounds, and number of letters in their last name. The two graphs in Figure 21.14 show two possibilities. Graph (a) is a scatter plot of height to weight, and graph (b) is a plot of name length to weight.

As you would expect, the boys' weights seem to increase as their heights increase. However, the relationship is far from perfect. There is no reason to expect any relationship between name length and weight, and indeed the dots appear to be almost randomly distributed.

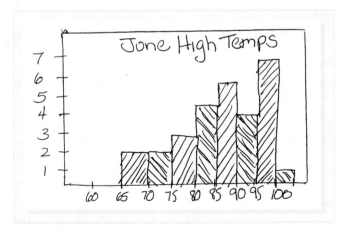

Figure 21.12 Histogram of June high temperatures.

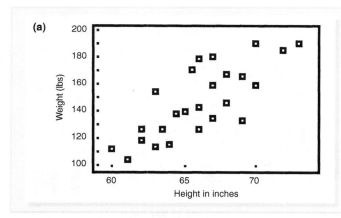

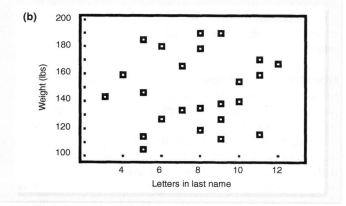

Figure 21.14 Scatter plots show potential relationships or lack of relationships.

 "Teachers should encourage students to plot many data sets and look for relationships in the [scatter] plots; computer graphing software and graphing calculators can be very helpful in this work. Students should see a range of examples in which plotting data sets suggests linear relationships, and no apparent relationships at all" (p. 253). ◆

Best-Fit Lines. If your scatter plot indicates a relationship, it can be simply described in words. "As boys get taller, they tend to get heavier." This is correct but not particularly useful. What exactly is the relationship? If I knew the height of a boy, could I predict what his weight might be based on this information? Like much of statistical analysis, the value of a statistic is to predict what has not yet been observed. We poll a small sample of voters before an election to predict how the full population will vote. Here, can a sample of 30 students predict the weights of other students? The line of best fit helps students develop conjectures.

The relationship in these cases is not a number like a mean or a standard deviation but rather a line or curve. Is there a line that can be drawn through the scatter plot that represents the "best" approximation of all of the dots and reflects the observed trend? If the scatter plot seems to indicate a steadily increasing or steadily decreasing relationship (as in the height–weight graph), you would probably try to find a straight line that approximates the dots. Sometimes the plot will indicate a curved relationship, in which case you might try to draw a smooth curve like a parabola to approximate the dots.

What Determines Best Fit? From a strictly visual standpoint, the line you select defines the observed relationship and could be used to predict other values not in the data set. The more closely the dots in the scatter plot hug the line you select, the greater the confidence you would have in the predictive value of the line. Certainly you could try to

draw a straight line somewhere in the name length–weight graph, but you would not have much faith in its predictive capability because the dots would be quite dispersed from any line you might draw.

Activity 21.4

Best-Fit Line

Once students have collected related data and prepared a scatter plot, duplicate an accurate version of the plot for each group of students. Provide the groups with an uncooked piece of spaghetti to use as a line. The task is to tape the line on the plot so that it is the "best" line to represent the relationship in the dots. Furthermore, the students are to develop a rationale for why they positioned the line as they did.

Using an overhead transparency of the plot, compare the lines chosen by various groups and their rationales.

⏸ ———————— *Pause and Reflect*

Before reading further, return to the height–weight plot in Figure 21.14(a) and draw a straight line that you think would make a good line of best fit. (You may want to make a photo enlargement of that figure to use with your class.) What reason would you offer for why you drew the line where you did?

Encourage students to use a "mathematical" reason for why a line might be best. Since a good line is one around which most dots cluster, a good-fitting line is one where the distances from all of the dots to the line are minimal. This general notion of least distance to the line for all points can lead to an algorithm that will always produce a unique line for a given set of points. Two such algorithms are well known and used in statistics. The more complicated approach is called the *least squares regression* line. It is an algebraic procedure that is not accessible to middle grade students and is also rather tedious to compute. The second algorithm produces what is called the *median-median* line, which is easier to determine. It basically involves dividing the data into three sets and finding the medians of each. The medians are plotted and further manipulated to find a best-fit line. More specific information can be found by online searching.

The connection among the real world, statistics, and algebraic ideas is a valuable one to make.

 Data analysis is an area of the curriculum in which technology really changes the way we teach. In the past, the emphasis was on *how* to create the graph and *how* to compute the statistic. Students had to labor over graph paper, drawing scales, labeling axes, coloring the graphs, and so on. Today, every graphical technique and every statistic mentioned in this chapter is readily available in a variety of technologies, with the possible exception of stem-and-leaf plots. With the help of technology, the focus of instruction in data analysis can and should shift to the big ideas of using graphs and statistics: to describe data, to get a sense of the shape of data, to answer questions with data, and to communicate this information to others.

Spreadsheets will compute any statistic for columns or rows of data. If the data are changed, the statistics change instantly. Spreadsheets also make very nice bar graphs, line graphs, and circle graphs. Teachers should also check to see if the publisher of their textbook offers graphing software.

The graphing calculator puts data analysis technology in the hands of every student. The TI-73 calculator is designed for middle grade students. It will produce eight different kinds of plots or graphs, including circle graphs, bar graphs, and picture graphs and will compute and graph best-fit lines.

An argument can be made for having students do some graphing and computing of statistics without technology. Appropriate methods have been suggested in this chapter. However, the intent of by-hand methods should always be to analyze the question posed and interpret results. ◆

Data Analysis:
Measures of Center

Although graphs provide visual images of data, measures of the data are a different and important way to describe data. The most common numerical descriptions of a set of data relate to the spread (the *range*) and the center (a *mean*, *median*, or *mode*), and dispersion within the range (the *variance* or *dispersion*). Students can get an idea of the importance of these statistics by exploring the ideas informally.

Averages

The term *average* is heard quite frequently in everyday usage. Sometimes it refers to an exact arithmetic average, as in "the average daily rainfall." Sometimes it is used quite loosely, as in "She is about average height." In either situation, an average is a single number or measure that is descriptive of a larger collection of numbers. If your test average is 92, it is assumed that somehow all of your test scores are reflected by this number.

The *mean*, *median*, and *mode* are specific types of averages, also called *measures of center* or *measures of central tendency*. The *mode* is the value that occurs most frequently in the data set.

The *mean* is computed by adding all of the numbers in the set and dividing the sum by the number of elements added.

The *median* is the middle value in an ordered set of data. Half of all values lie at or above the median and half at or below. The median is easier to understand and to compute and is not affected, as the mean is, by one or two extremely large or extremely small values outside the range of the rest of the data. Median is also more accessible to elementary age students. Many researchers and curriculum developers find median is appropriate for upper elementary, but that mean should be delayed until middle school (Russell, 2006). *Curriculum Focal Points* places descriptive statistics as a focus in eighth grade, integrated with number and algebra (NCTM, 2006).

As mentioned earlier, the context in statistics is important. The context of a situation will determine whether the mode, mean, or median is the measure you want to use. For example, in reporting home prices, the median is quite different from the mean, with the mean being higher. Which better portrays the cost of housing? Very expensive homes can drive the mean up, so typically the median is a more common measure for describing the center of housing costs. If a travel agent gathered data on the number of days that families usually travel as part of planning a promotional vacation package, the agent would be more interested in the mode, because the other measures would not be as helpful in answering the question.

Understanding the Mean:
Two Interpretations

There are actually two different ways to think about the mean. First, it is a number that represents what all of the data items would be if they were leveled out. In this sense, the mean represents all of the data items. Statisticians prefer to think of the mean as a central balance point. This concept of the mean is more in keeping with the notion of a measure of the "center" of the data or a measure of central tendency. Both concepts are discussed in the following sections.

Leveling Interpretation. Suppose that the average number of family members for the students in your class is 5. One way to interpret this is to think about distributing the entire collection of moms, dads, sisters, and brothers to each of the students so that each would have a "family" of the same size. To say that you have an average score of 93 for the four tests in your class is like spreading the total of all of your points evenly across the four tests. It is as if each student had the same family size and each test score were the same, but the totals matched the actual distributions. This concept of the mean has the added benefit that it connects to the algorithm for computing the mean.

Activity 21.5

Leveling the Bars

Have students make a bar graph of some data using plastic connecting cubes. Choose a situation with 5 or 6 values. For example, the graph in Figure 21.15 shows prices for six toys. The task for students is to use the graph itself to determine what the price would be if all of the toys were the same price, assuming that the total for all the toys remained the same. Students will use various techniques to rearrange the cubes in the graph but will eventually create six equal bars, possibly with some leftovers that could mentally be distributed in fractional amounts.

Explain to students that the size of the leveled bars is the *mean* of the data—the amount that each item would cost if all items cost the same amount but the total of the prices remained fixed.

Follow "Leveling the Bars" with the next activity to help students develop an algorithm for finding the mean.

Activity 21.6

The Mean Foot

Pose the following question: What is the mean length of our feet in inches? Have each student cut a strip of adding machine tape that matches the length of his or her foot. Students record their names and the length of their feet in inches on the strips. Suggest that before finding a mean for the class, you will first get means for smaller groups. Put students into groups of four, six, or eight students. (Groups of five or seven

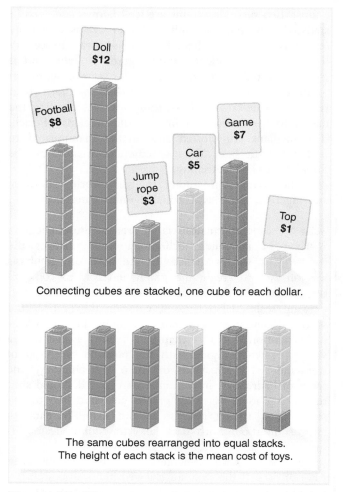

Connecting cubes are stacked, one cube for each dollar.

The same cubes rearranged into equal stacks. The height of each stack is the mean cost of toys.

Figure 21.15 Understanding the mean as a leveling of the data.

will prove to be problematic.) In each group, have the students tape their foot strips end to end. The task for each group is to come up with a method of finding the mean without using any of the lengths written on the strips. They can only use the combined strip. Each group will share their method with the class. From this work, they will devise a method for determining the mean for the whole class.

⏸ ——————————— *Pause and Reflect*

Before reading on, what is a method that the students could use in "The Mean Foot"?

To evenly distribute the inches for each student's foot among the members of the group, they can fold the strip into equal parts so that there are as many sections as students in the group. Then they can measure the length of any one part.

How can you find the mean for the whole class? Suppose there are 23 students in the class. Using the strips already taped together, make one very long strip for the whole class. It is not reasonable to fold this long strip into 23 equal sections. But if you wanted to know how long the resulting strip would be, how could that be done? The total length of the strip is the sum of the lengths of the 23 individual foot strips. To find the length of one section if the strip were actually folded in 23 parts, simply divide by 23. In fact, students can mark off "mean feet" along the strip. There should be very close to 23 equal-length "feet." This dramatically illustrates the algorithm for finding the mean.

Balance Point Interpretation. Statisticians think about the mean as a point on a number line where the data on either side of the point are balanced. To help think about the mean in this way, it is useful to think about the data placed on a line plot. What is important is not how many pieces of data are on either side of the mean or balance point but the distances of data from the mean.

To illustrate, draw a number line on the board, and arrange eight sticky notes above the number 3 as shown in Figure 21.16(a). Each sticky note represents one family. The notes are positioned on the line to indicate how many pets are owned by the family. Stacked up like this would indicate that all families have the same number of pets. The mean is three pets. But different families are likely to have different numbers of pets. So we could think of eight families with a range of numbers of pets. Some may have zero pets, and some may have as many as ten or even more. How could you change the number of pets for these eight families so that the mean remains at 3? Students will suggest moving the sticky notes in opposite directions, probably in pairs. This will result in a symmetrical arrangement. But what if one of the families has eight pets, a move of five spaces from the 3? This might be balanced by moving two families to the left, one three spaces to the 0 and one two spaces to the 1. Figure 21.16(b) shows one way the families could be rearranged to maintain a mean of 3. You should stop here and find at least two other distributions of the families, each having a mean of 3.

Use the next activity to find the mean or balance point given the data.

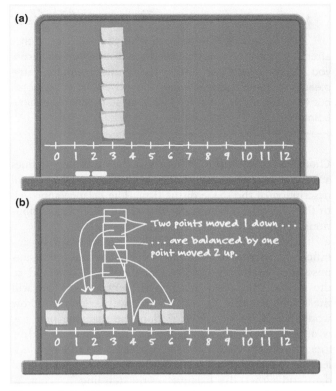

Figure 21.16 (a) If all data points are the same, the mean is that value. (b) By moving data points away from the mean in a balanced manner, different distributions can be found that have the same mean.

computation. The task is to determine the actual mean by moving the sticky notes in toward the "center." That is, the students are finding out what price or point on the number line balances out the six prices on the line. For each move of a sticky one space to the left (a toy with a lower price), a different sticky must be moved one space to the right (a toy with a higher price). Eventually, all stickies should be stacked above the same number, the balance point or mean.

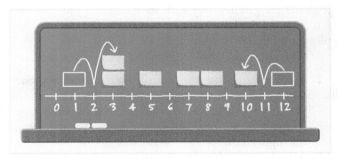

Figure 21.17 Move data points in toward the center or balance point without changing the balance around that point. When you have all points at the same value, that is the balance or the mean.

Activity **21.7**

Finding the Balance Point

Have students draw a number line from 0 to 12 with about an inch between the numbers. Use six small sticky notes to represent the prices of six toys as shown in Figure 21.17. Have them place a light pencil mark on the line where they think the mean might be. For the moment, avoid the add-up-and-divide

Pause and Reflect

Stop now and try this exercise yourself. Notice that after any pair of moves that keep the distribution balanced, you actually have a new distribution of prices with the same mean. The same was true when you moved the sticky notes out from the mean when they were all stacked on the same point.

Changes in the Mean.   Notice that the mean only defines a "center" of a set of data and so by itself is not a very useful description of the shape of the data. The balance approach to the mean clearly illustrates that many different distributions can have the same mean.

Especially for small sets of data, the mean is significantly affected by extreme values. For example, suppose that another toy with a price of $20 is added to the six we have been using in the examples. How will the mean change? If the $1 toy were removed, how would the mean be affected? Suppose that one new toy is added that increases the mean from $6 to $7. How much does the new toy cost? Students should be challenged with questions such as these using small sets of data and either the balance or the leveling concept.

In the e-Examples found at the NCTM website under Standards & Focal Points, Applet 6.6, "Comparing Properties of the Mean and the Median," shows seven data points that can be dragged back and forth along a number line with the mean and median updated instantly. The applet allows students to see how stable the median is and how changing one point can affect the mean. ◆

Box-and-Whisker Plots

Box-and-whisker plots (or just *box plots*) are a method for visually displaying not only the center (median) but also information about the range and distribution or variance of data. In Figure 21.18, the ages in months for 27 sixth-grade students are given, along with stem-and-leaf plots for the full class and the boys and girls separately. Box-and-whisker plots are shown in Figure 21.19.

Each box-and-whisker plot has these three features:

1. A box that contains the "middle half" of the data, one-fourth to the left and right of the median. The ends of the box are at the *lower quartile*, the median of the lower half of the data, and the *upper quartile*, the median of the upper half of the data.
2. A line inside the box at the median of the data.
3. A line extending from the end of each box to the *lower extreme* and *upper extreme* of the data. Each line, therefore, covers the upper and lower fourths of the data.

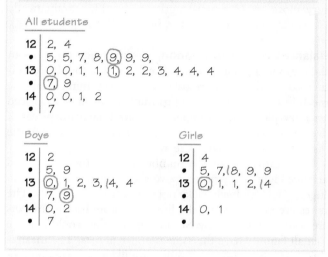

Figure 21.18 Ordered stem-and-leaf plots grouped by fives. Medians and quartiles are circled or are represented by a bar (I) if they fall between two elements.

Look at the information these box plots provide at a glance! The box and the lengths of the lines provide a quick indication of how the data are spread out or bunched

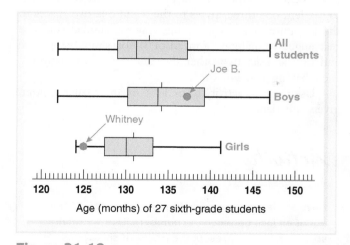

Figure 21.19 Box-and-whisker plots show a lot of information. In addition to showing how data are distributed, data points of particular interest can be shown.

together. Since the median is shown, this spreading or bunching can be determined for each quarter of the data. The entire class in this example is much more spread out in the upper half than the lower half. The girls are much more closely grouped in age than either the boys or the class as a whole. It is immediately obvious that at least three-fourths of the girls are younger than the median age of the boys. The *range* of the data (difference between upper and lower extremes) is represented by the length of the plot, and the extreme values can be read directly. The mean is indicated by the small marks above and below each box. A box plot provides useful visual information to help understand the shape of a data set.

To make a box-and-whisker plot, put the data in order. Next, find the median. Simply count the number of values and determine the middle one. This can be done on stem-and-leaf plots as in Figure 21.18. To find the two quartiles, ignore the median itself, and find the medians of the upper and lower halves of the data. Mark the two extremes, the two quartiles, and the median above an appropriate number line. Draw the box and the lines. Box plots can also be drawn vertically.

Note that the means for the data in our example are each just slightly higher than the medians (class = 132.4; boys = 133.9; girls = 130.8). For this example, the means themselves do not provide nearly as much information as the box plots.

Tech NOTES Graphing calculators and several computer programs draw box-and-whisker plots, making this process even more accessible. The TI-73, TI-84, and TI Nspire calculators can draw box plots for up to three sets of data on the same axis. Remember that a box-and-whisker plot, like any graph, is a tool for learning about the question posed, not an end in itself (McClain, Leckman, Schmitt, & Regis, 2006). Because a box-and-whisker plot offers so much information on the spread and center of the data, much can be learned from careful examination, and particularly from comparing two box-and-whisker plots with related data. ◆

❚❚ ———————— *Pause and Reflect*

Notice that in Figure 21.19 the box for the boys is actually a bit longer than the box for the whole class. How can that be when there are clearly more students in the full class than there are boys? How would you explain this apparent discrepancy to a class of seventh graders?

Interpreting Results

Interpretation is the fourth step in the process of doing statistics. As seen in the sample test items shown earlier, sometimes questions focus on mathematical ideas rather than statistical ideas. Although it is helpful to ask mathematical questions, it is essential to ask questions that are statistical in nature. That means the questions focus on the context of the situation and seeing what can be learned or inferred from the data. In addition, they should focus on the key ideas of statistics, such as variability, center of the data, and the shape of the data. During interpretation, students might want to loop back and create a different data display to get a different look at the data, or might want to gather data from a different population to see if their results are representative.

Different researchers have recommended questions that focus on statistical thinking (Franklin et al., 2005; Friel, O'Conner, & Mamer, 2006; Russell, 2006; Shaughnessy, 2006). Here are some ideas from their lists to get you started on having meaningful discussions interpreting data:

- What do the numbers (symbols) tell us about our class (or other population)?
- If we asked another class (population), how would our data look? What if we asked a larger group, how would the data look?
- How do the numbers in this graph (population) *compare* to this graph (population)?
- Where are the data "clustering"? How much of the data are in the cluster? How much are *not* in the cluster? About what percent is or is not in the cluster?
- What kinds of variability might need to be considered in interpreting these data?
- Would the results be different if . . . [change of sample/population or setting]? (Example: Would gathered data on word length in a third-grade book be different for a fifth-grade book? Would a science book give different results than a reading book?)
- How strong is the association between two variables (scatter plot)? How do you know? What does that mean if you know *x*? If you know *y*?
- What does the graph *not* tell us? What might we infer?
- What new questions arise from these data?

This section is shorter than the sections on data analysis, but only because these prompts apply across many data displays. It certainly should be a major focus of your instruction. Consider it the *after* phase of your lesson, though some of these questions will be integrated in the *during* phase as well.

Our world is inundated with data, from descriptive statistics to different graphs. It is essential that we prepare students to be literate about what can be interpreted from data and what cannot be interpreted from data, what is important to pay attention to and what can be discarded as misleading or poorly designed statistics. This is important for success in school, as well as for being a mathematically literate citizen.

Reflections

Writing to Learn

1. How is statistics different from mathematics? In a lesson on the mean, what mathematical questions and what statistical questions might you ask?
2. What is meant by the "shape of data"?
3. Explain why attribute activities are important in the development of data analysis skills.
4. Data should be collected to answer questions. What are some examples of questions that students might explore with data at the K–2 level and what are some for the upper grades?
5. What kinds of graphs can be used for data that can be put into categories?
6. What is the difference between a bar graph and a histogram? What kinds of data are required for a histogram?
7. What are three ways to make a circle graph? What does a circle graph tell you that a bar graph does not? What does it not tell?
8. Give an example of a context in which you would you choose to use median over mean and when would you choose mean over median (not the ones given in the text).
9. Describe two different concepts of the mean. How can each be developed? Which idea leads to the method of computing the mean?
10. Pick one of the contexts from this chapter and give three questions that you would ask students that focus on statistical thinking.

For Discussion and Exploration

1. Select a popular news weekly such as *Time* or *Newsweek*. Look through at least one issue carefully to see graphs and statistical information a typical reader would be expected to understand. Note that you will not be able to do this by simply looking for graphs. Statistics are frequently used without any corresponding graphs.
2. The process of doing statistics must be clear to students, even when they are working on a piece (e.g., circle graphs) within the process. Pick a grade band (pre-K–2, 3–5, 6–8), and consider possibilities for authentic and engaging (and researchable) questions. Then discuss how you would plan instruction in order to include the four-step process and engage students in statistical thinking.

Resources

Literature Connections

Literature is full of situations in which things must be sorted, compared, or measured. Each of these can be the springboard for a data-collection and representation activity. As noted earlier in this chapter, books of lists also are fruitful beginnings for data explorations. Students can use the data in the books and/or compare similar data collected themselves.

The Best Vacation Ever *Murphy, 1997*

This is in the MathStart series, designed as a collection of single-concept books to generate simple activities in mathematics. In this book, appropriate for first or second grade, a little girl gathers data from her family on what is important to them to decide where the family would have the best vacation.

This book nicely introduces the concept of gathering data to answer a question. Use the book as an introduction to this important topic.

Frog and Toad Are Friends *Lobel, 1970*

When Frog and Toad go walking, Frog loses a button. As they search to find the button, they find many buttons. Whenever one of Frog's friends asks, "Is this your button?" Frog responds (with a touch of frustration), "No, that is not my button! That button is _____, but my button was _____."

This classic story is a perfect lead-in to sorting activities as described in this chapter. Young students can model the story directly with sets of buttons, shells, attribute blocks, Woozle Cards (Blackline Master 59), or other objects with a variety of attributes.

200% of Nothing: An Eye-Opening Tour Through the Twists and Turns of Math Abuse and Innumeracy *Dewdney, 1993*

This middle school–friendly chapter book has explanations of the many ways that "statistics are turned" to mislead the common person. Because the examples are *real*, provided by readers of *Scientific American*, this book is an excellent tool for showing the power of statistics and how important it is to be statistically literate in today's society. Reading the examples can launch a mathematics project into looking for error in advertisements and at how overlapping groups (as in a Venn Diagram) can be reported separately to mislead readers. (See Bay-Williams and Martinie, 2009, for more ideas connected with this book.)

If the World Were a Village: A Book about the World's People *Smith, 2002*

This is a favorite as well as important book about how wealth, culture, language, and other influences play out in the world. Each beautiful two-page spread shares the statistics for the topic (e.g., language). This book can give rise to other questions about the world, which can be researched and interpreted into the village metaphor. The data can also be compared to other populations (e.g., within the school).

The Inch Boy *Morimoto, 1991*
Swamp Angel *Isaacs and Zelinsky, 2000*

Both of these are examples of books with a character who is *not* average. The Inch Boy is very small and the Swamp Angel is very large. These books create interest in gathering descriptive statistics and seeing the impact of outliers on the mean and median. Beyond height, many things can be measured—weight of backpacks, shoulder width, shoe length, and so on. For an engaging investigation with *The Inch Boy*, see Foss (2008).

Recommended Readings

Articles

Harper, S. R. (2004). Students' interpretations of misleading graphs. *Mathematics Teaching in the Middle Grades, 9*(6), 340–343.
Harper explores some of the types of misleading graphing techniques that are often seen in the popular press and discusses how she explored these graphs with students. This is a very short version of a few of the ideas found in the classic book How to Lie with Statistics *(Huff, 1954/1993).*

Manchester, P. (2002). The lunchroom project: A long-term investigative study. *Teaching Children Mathematics, 9*(1), 43–47.
A third-grade teacher describes how her class decided to do something about their dislike of the cafeteria food. She explains the difficulty of designing appropriate questions and gathering the data. Student work shows how the students dealt with the data collected.

Books

Burrill, G. F., & Elliott, P. C. (Eds.). (2006). *Thinking and reasoning about data and chance: Sixty-eighth yearbook.* Reston, VA: NCTM.
This NCTM Yearbook is full of excellent articles that can inform and improve your understanding and teaching of statistics. Many of the articles are cited in this chapter.

Franklin, C., Kader, G., Mewborn, D., Moreno, J., Peck, R., Perry, M., & Scheaffer, R. (2005). *Guidelines for assessment and instruction in statistics education* (GAISE Report). Alexandria, VA: American Statistical Association.
The examples provided in this excellent framework for teaching statistics, prepared by statistics educators, are great tasks to use with students in pre-K–8.

Sheffield, L. J., Cavanagh, M., Dacey, L., Findell, C. R., Greenes, C. E., & Small, M. (2002). *Navigating through data analysis and probability in prekindergarten–grade 2.* Reston, VA: NCTM.

Chapin, S., Koziol, A., MacPherson, J., & Rezba, C. (2002). *Navigating through data analysis and probability in grades 3–5.* Reston, VA: NCTM.

Bright, G. W., Brewer, W., McClain, K., & Mooney, E. S. (2003). *Navigating through data analysis in grades 6–8.* Reston, VA: NCTM.
Each of these books is strongly suggested as a reference for excellent activities and explorations with students.

Online Resources

Bar Graph
www.shodor.org/interactivate/activities/BarGraph
The user of this applet can enter data as well as manipulate the *y*-axis values to create a bar graph. The ability to manipulate the *y*-axis values allows the creation of potentially misleading graphs, a good source of discussion.

Box Plotter
http://illuminations.nctm.org/ActivityDetail.aspx?ID=77
The user can enter data and create box-and-whisker plots.

Circle Grapher
http://illuminations.nctm.org/ActivityDetail.aspx?ID=60
Make your own circle graph with your own data, or display a circle graph from a given set of data.

Collecting, Representing, and Interpreting Data Using Spreadsheets and Graphing Software
http://standards.nctm.org/document/eexamples/chap5/5.5/index.htm
Data are provided in a spreadsheet. The data can be changed and/or ordered in different ways with simple buttons. Scatter plots and bar graphs are also easily made with various combinations of data. Lesson suggestions are provided.

Histograms
http://illuminations.nctm.org/ActivityDetail.aspx?ID=78
Each of these sites offers an interactive applet allowing the user to create and manipulate histograms. User data can be entered or data are supplied.

Stem-and-Leaf Plot
www.shodor.org/interactivate/activities/StemAndLeafPlotter
Enter data and calculate mean, median, and mode.

Field Experience Guide Connections

Field Experiences 1.2, 1.3, and 1.5 focus on an environment for learning and can be used to explore the extent to which lessons incorporate the process of *doing* statistics. FEG Expanded Lesson 9.20 is a lesson on using the four-step process of doing statistics; it can be used by itself, or with Field Experiences 1.5 ("Establishing Your Environment") or 2.5 ("Planning a Problem-Based Lesson"). FEG Expanded Lesson 9.22 engages students in comparing different ways to graph data, analyzing the differences in the two. FEG Expanded Lesson 9.24 explores the impact of outliers in data sets.

Exploring
Concepts of Probability

From Chapter 22 of *Elementary and Middle School Mathematics: Teaching Developmentally*, 7/e. John A. Van de Walle.
Karen S. Karp. Jennifer M. Bay-Williams. Copyright © 2010 by Pearson Allyn and Bacon. All rights reserved.

Exploring
Concepts of Probability

References to probability are all around us: The weather forecaster predicts a 60 percent chance of snow; medical researchers predict people with certain diets have a high chance of heart disease; investors calculate risks of specific stocks; and so on. Simulations of complex situations are frequently based on probabilities and are then used in the design process of such undertakings as spacecraft, highways and storm sewers, or plans for responding to disasters. Because the ideas and methods of probability are so prevalent in today's world, this strand of mathematics has risen in visibility in the school curriculum.

Realistic concepts of chance require considerable development before children are ready to construct formal ideas about the probability of a future event. This development occurs most optimally as children consider and discuss with their peers the outcomes of a wide variety of probabilistic situations. The emphasis should be on exploration rather than rules and formal definitions. If done well, these informal experiences will provide a useful background from which more formal ideas can be developed in middle and high school. In *Curriculum Focal Points* (NCTM, 2006) probability is a connection to content in seventh grade.

Big Ideas

1. Chance has no memory. For repeated trials of a simple experiment, the outcomes of prior trials have no impact on the next. The chance occurrence of six heads in a row has no effect on getting a head on the next toss of the coin. That chance remains 50–50.

2. The probability that a future event will occur can be characterized along a continuum from impossible to certain.

3. The *probability* of an event is a number between 0 and 1 that is a measure of the chance that a given event will occur. A probability of 0 indicates impossibility and that of 1 indicates

certainty. A probability of $\frac{1}{2}$ indicates an even chance of the event occurring.

4. The relative frequency of outcomes (from *experiments*) can be used as an estimate of the probability of an event. The larger the number of trials, the better the estimate will be. The results for a small number of trials may be quite different from those experienced in the long run.

5. For some events, the exact probability can be determined by an analysis of the event itself. A probability determined in this manner is called a *theoretical probability*.

6. *Simulation* is a technique used for answering real-world questions or making decisions in complex situations in which an element of chance is involved. To see what is likely to happen in the real event, a model must be designed that has the same probabilities as the real situation.

Mathematics Content Connections

Probability and data analysis have long been joined when talking about the mathematics curriculum and there is a real mathematical connection as students reach the upper grades.

- **Fractions and Percents:** Students can see fractional parts of spinners or sets of counters in a bag and use these fractions to determine probabilities. Percents provide useful common denominators for comparing ratios (e.g., rolling a 7 three times in the first 20 rolls, or 15%, and 16 times in 80 rolls, or 20%).

- **Ratio and Proportion:** Comparing probabilities means relating part-to-whole ratios. To understand these comparisons requires proportional reasoning.

- **Data Analysis:** The purpose of probability is to answer statistics-related questions. When performing a probability experiment, the results are data—a sample of the theoretically infinite experiments that could be done.

Introducing Probability

Young children's concept of the likelihood of a future event is often surprising. Children can be absolutely convinced that the next roll of the die will be a 3 "because I just know it's going to happen" or "because 3 is my lucky number."

Likely or Not Likely

To change these early misconceptions, a good place to begin is with a focus on possible and not possible (Activity 22.1) and later impossible, possible, and certain (Activity 22.2). In preparation for these activities, discuss the words *impossible* and *certain*. *Certain* is the more difficult of these words for children.

Activity 22.1
Nursery Rhyme Possibilities

Create a table, labeling one column "Impossible" and the other "Possible." Take a nursery rhyme verse, such as "Hey, Diddle, Diddle" (or a picture book) and for each line, ask students if it goes in the impossible or possible column. Record each statement in the appropriate column.

Activity 22.2
Is It Likely?

Ask students to judge various events as *certain, impossible,* or *possible* ("might happen"). Consider these examples:

- It will rain tomorrow.
- Drop a rock in water and it will sink.
- Trees will talk to us in the afternoon.
- The sun will rise tomorrow morning.
- Three students will be absent tomorrow.
- George will go to bed before 8:30 tonight.
- You will have two birthdays this year.

Have children describe or make up events that are certain, impossible, or possible. For each event, they should justify their choice of likelihood.

The key idea to developing chance or probability on a continuum is to help children see that some of these possible events are more likely or less likely than others. For instance, if a group of students has a running race, the chance that Gregg, a really fast runner, will be first is not certain but is very likely. It is more likely that Gregg will be near the front of the group than near the back of the pack.

The use of random devices that can be analyzed (e.g., spinners, number cubes, coins to toss, colored cubes drawn from a bag) can help students make predictions about the likelihood of an event. The process of exploring the likeliness of an event maps to the *before, during, after* lesson plan model. In the *before* phase, students make predictions of what they think will be likely; in the *during* phase, students experiment to explore the likeliness of the event; and in the *after* phase, students analyze the experimental results to determine the likeliness of the event.

The following activity or variations of it should be repeated often either using the same random devices or with a variety of devices.

Activity 22.3
Race to the Top

Show students the spinner in Figure 22.1 and ask: "If we count spins that land on red and ones that land on blue, which one will reach the top first." Two players take turns spinning the spinner. Each game requires a simple recording sheet with ten rows or spaces. Figure 22.1 shows a sheet for the two-color spinner. In the simplest version of the game, use only one spinner: one-fourth red and three-fourths blue. Before playing, each student predicts which color will win, red or blue. (Note that it is *color* that wins, not a player!) After each spin, an X is drawn in the appropriate column. Play continues until one color reaches the top of the chart.

Students should play "Race to the Top" several times. After all students have played, ask "Which color is likely to win? Why do you think so?"

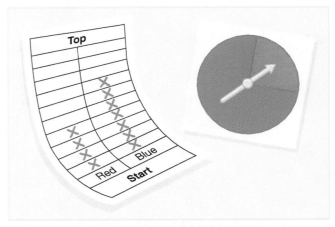

Figure 22.1 Students take turns spinning a spinner and recording the result. The first color to reach the top is the winner.

In activities such as "Race to the Top," use a variety of spinners. Use spinners that have two colors with the same area—and colors covering different areas, as shown here.

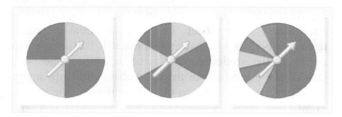

As a random device, spinners have the advantage that students can see the relative portion of the whole given to each color or outcome. Students do not always see that the first two spinners, or a spinner divided into just two sections, have the same likelihood of getting blue (Cohen, 2006; Jones, Langrall, Thornton, & Magill, 1997; Nicolson, 2005). Therefore, it is important to use spinners that are partitioned in different ways. Spinner faces can easily be made to adjust the chances of different outcomes. An effective way to connect the idea that the larger region on the spinner is more likely to have a spin land there is to have

students use frequency charts to record data. In Figure 22.2 a student explains how she knows which frequency table goes with which circle graph.

Devices other than spinners should also be used for "Race to the Top" and similar activities. Colored dots can be stuck on the sides of a wooden cube to create different color probabilities. Similarly, opaque bags with eight red and two blue tiles, or some other ratio of red to blue, can be used. Students draw a tile from the bag and then return it after each draw. In the *after* phase of each experience, focus on what is likely/unlikely and certain/impossible.

The following activity is a game of chance with unequal outcomes. However, students will not readily be able to predict which result is most likely, so it provides a good opportunity for discussion.

Activity 22.4

Add, Then Tally

Make number cubes with sides as follows: 1, 1, 2, 3, 3, 3. Each game requires two cubes. Students take turns rolling the two cubes and recording the sum of

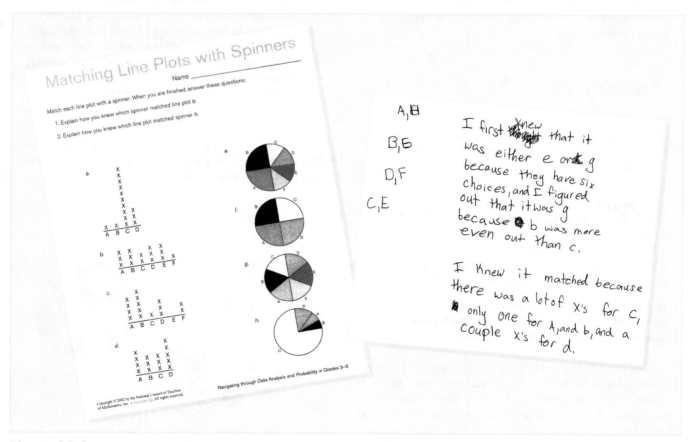

Figure 22.2 Student explanations connecting frequency charts to spinners.

Source: Adapted from Chapin, S., Kozial, A., MacPherson, J., & Rezba, C. (2002). *Navigating Through Data Analysis and Probability in Grades 3–5*. Reston, VA: NCTM, p. 116. Reprinted with permission. Copyright © 2002 by the National Council of Teachers of Mathematics, Inc. www.nctm.org. All rights reserved.

the two numbers. To record the results, run off tally sheets with six rows of ten squares, labeled 1 through 6 (see Figure 22.3). Students continue to roll the cubes until one of the rows is full. They can repeat the game on a new tally sheet as long as time permits. Before play begins ask students to predict which row will fill the fastest.

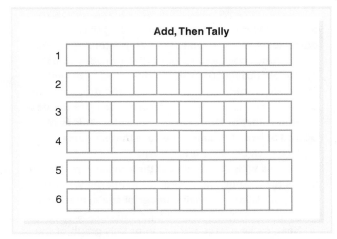

Add, Then Tally

1
2
3
4
5
6

Figure 22.3 A recording sheet for "Add, Then Tally."

It is important to talk with students after they have played "Add, Then Tally." Which numbers "won" the most and the least often? If they were to play again, which number would they pick to win and why? Furthermore, although an outcome of 1 is impossible, all of the other outcomes, 2 through 6, are possible. A sum of 4 is the most likely. Sums of 2 or 3 are the least likely.

Students' ideas about chance must develop from experience. Students' experiences with likely events can lead to misconceptions about chance.

For example, some students think a 1 is not as likely as rolling a 5 on a dice, perhaps because they play a game where 1 is desirable. The 1 is not likely compared to the other 5 choices, but it is as likely as any other number (Nicolson, 2005; Watson & Moritz, 2003). During discussions, your task is to elicit their ideas. The main idea is that the sum rolled is not necessarily just pure luck, but that some results are clearly more or less likely because of the design of the spinner or dice. ◆

The Probability Continuum

To begin refining the concept that some events are more or less likely to occur than others, introduce the idea of a continuum of likelihood between impossible and certain. Draw a long line on the board, as in Figure 22.4. Label the left end "Impossible" and the right end "Certain." Write "Chances of Spinning Blue" above the line. Discuss various positions on the line and what the corresponding spinner would look like. To review these ideas, show the spinners one at a time and ask which marks represent the chance of getting blue for that spinner. Also name events (e.g., having a snow day) and ask where they would go (or have students think of events for selected points on the line).

In the next activity students design random devices that they think will create chances for various designated positions on the probability line.

Activity 22.5

Design a Bag

(Note that students must be introduced to the idea of a probability continuum as just described.)

Use the worksheet shown in Figure 22.5 (see Blackline Master 60) and provide students with a copy. On the board mark a place on a probability line

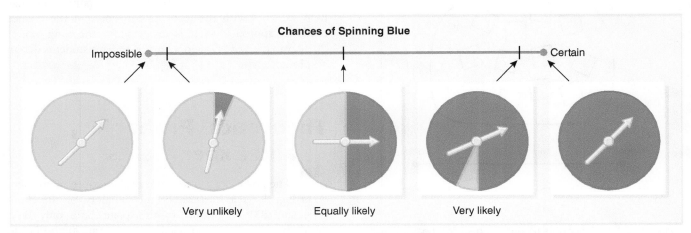

Chances of Spinning Blue

Impossible ●————|——————————|——————————|——● Certain

Very unlikely   Equally likely   Very likely

Figure 22.4 The probability continuum. Use these spinner faces to help students see how chance can be at different places on a continuum between impossible and certain.

at roughly the 20 percent position. At this time do not use percent or fraction language with the children. Students are to mark this position on their worksheet probability lines. Students should color the square indicated by "Color" at the top of the page. Explain that they are going to decide what color tiles should be put in bags of 12 total tiles so that the chance of drawing this designated color is about the same as the chance indicated on the probability line. Before students begin to design their bags, ask for ideas about which colors of tiles might be put in the bag if the mark were very close to the middle of the line. Show how the real bags will be filled based on the design on the page. Emphasize that the tiles will be shaken up so that which particular squares on the bag design are colored will not reflect the actual position in the bag.

At the bottom of each sheet (and on the reverse if needed), students explain why they chose their tiles. Give them an example: *We put in 8 red and 4 of other colors because _____.*

Collect and display the designs made by the students in "Design a Bag." Discuss the ideas that students had for the number of designated colors to put in the bag. (Expect some variation.)

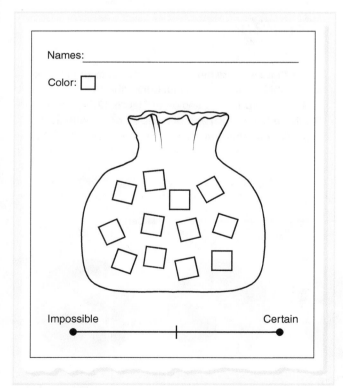

Figure 22.5 A possible recording sheet for the "Design a Bag" activity (see Blackline Master 60).

The "Design a Bag" activity provides useful information about how your students conceive of chance as appearing on a continuum. The next follow-up activity focuses on doing an experiment to see if the design predicted was reasonable.

Activity 22.6

Testing Bag Designs

Select a bag design (from Activity 22.5) that most students seem to agree on for the 20 percent mark. Distribute lunch bags and colored tiles or cubes to pairs of students to fill according to the selected design. Once filled, students shake the bag and draw out one tile. Tally marks are used to record a Yes (for the designated color) or No for any other color. This is repeated at least ten times. Be sure that students replace each tile after it is drawn.

Discuss with the class how their respective experiments turned out. Did it turn out about the way they expected? With the small number of trials, there will be groups that get rather unexpected results.

Next, make a large bar graph or tally graph of the data from all of the groups together. This should show many more No's than Yes's. Here the discussion can help students see that if the experiment is repeated a lot of times, the results are closer to what was predicted.

The dual activities of "Design a Bag" and "Testing Bag Designs" can and should be repeated for two or three other marks on the probability line. Try marks at about $\frac{1}{3}$, $\frac{1}{2}$, and $\frac{3}{4}$.

"Design a Bag" and "Testing Bag Designs" are important activities. Because no numbers are used for the probabilities, there are no "right" answers. The small-group testing of a design shows students that chance is not an absolute predictor in the short run. The group graphs may help students with the difficult concept that the chance tends to approach what is expected in the long run.

A variation of "Design a Bag" is to have students design a spinner.

Theoretical Probability and Experiments

The *probability* is a measure of the chance of an event occurring. It is a measure of the certainty of the event (Franklin, 2005). Students to this point have only been asked to place events on a continuum from impossible to certain or to compare the likelihood of one event with another. So how do you measure a chance? In many situations, there are actually two ways to determine this measure.

Probability has two distinct types. The first type involves any specific event whose likelihood of occurrence is known (e.g., that a fair die has a $\frac{1}{6}$ chance of producing each number). When the likeliness of an event is known, probability can be established theoretically by examining all the possibilities.

The second case involves any event whose likeliness of occurrence isn't observable—but can be established through *empirical data*, or evidence from past experiments or data collection (Colgan, 2006; Nicolson, 2005). Examples include a basketball player's likelihood of making free throws in a game (based on the player's previous record), the chance that a telecommunicator will be successful (based on prior rates of success), or the chance of rain (based on how often it rained under equivalent conditions). Although this latter type of probability is less common in the school curriculum, it is the most applicable to most fields that use probability and therefore important to include in your teaching (Franklin et al., 2005).

In both cases, *experiments* or *simulations* can be designed to explore the phenomena being examined (sometimes in the K–12 curriculum this is referred to as *experimental probability* although this terminology is not employed by statisticians).

Coin flips have a known likelihood of occurrence. Logically, we can argue that if it is a fair coin, obtaining a head is just as likely as obtaining a tail. Since there are two possible outcomes that are equally likely, each has a probability of $\frac{1}{2}$. Hence, the theoretical probability of obtaining a head is $\frac{1}{2}$. When all possible outcomes of a simple experiment are equally likely, the *theoretical probability* of an event is

$$\frac{\text{Number of outcomes in the event}}{\text{Number of possible outcomes}}$$

Instead, consider the question, "Is this coin fair?" This is a statistics problem that can only be answered by doing an experiment and establishing the frequency of heads and tails over the long run (Franklin et al., 2005). The answer requires empirical data and the probability will be:

$$\frac{\text{Number of observed occurrences of the event}}{\text{Total number of trials}}$$

Because it is impossible to conduct an infinite number of trials, we can only consider the relative frequency for a very large number of trials as an approximation of the theoretical probability. This emphasizes the notion that probability is more about predictions over the long term than predictions of individual events.

myeducationlab

Go to the Activities and Application section of Chapter 22 of MyEducationLab. Click on Videos and watch the video entitled "**Probability Lesson: Flipping a Coin**" to see students predict and experiment with how many times a coin will land on heads.

Theoretical Probability

A problem-based way to introduce theoretical probability is to engage students in an activity with an unfair game and have students later examine the possibilities within the game to determine theoretically if it is fair. In the following activity, the results of the game will likely be contrary to students' intuitive ideas. This in turn will provide a real reason to analyze the game in a logical manner and find out why things happened as they did—theoretical probability.

Activity 22.7
Fair or Unfair?

Three students toss 2 like coins (e.g., 2 pennies or 2 nickels) and are assigned points according to the following rules: Player A gets 1 point if the coin toss results in "two heads"; player B gets 1 point if the toss results in "two tails"; and player C gets 1 point if the toss results are "mixed" (one head, one tail). The game is over after 20 tosses. The player who has the most points wins. Have students play the game at least two or three times. After each game, the players are to stop and discuss if they think the game is fair and make predictions about who will win the next game.

When the full class has played the game several times, conduct a discussion on the fairness of the game. Challenge students to make an argument *not* based on the data as to whether the game is fair or not and why.

A common analysis of the game in Activity 22.7 goes something like this: There are three outcomes: two tails, one head and one tail, or two heads. Each has an equal chance. The game should be fair. However, after playing "Fair or Unfair?" students will find that player C (gets points for a mixed result) appears to have an unfair advantage (especially if they have played several games or the class has pooled its data). This observation seems to contradict the notion that the outcomes are equally likely.

Rubel (2006, 2007) used a similar two-coin task with students from fifth to eleventh grades, asking for the probability of getting a head and a tail with two coins. She found that about half (54 percent) answered this problem correctly (across grades), but that many of the fifth and seventh graders used faulty reasoning, having picked that answer believing there is a 50–50 chance in any experiment. About 25 percent of the students said the probability was $\frac{1}{3}$—because three things could happen (two heads, one of each, two tails).

Encourage students to analyze the situation and generate all the possible outcomes. A student explanation may be as follows:

There is only one way for two heads to occur and one way for two tails to occur, but there are two ways for a head and a tail to occur: Either the first coin is heads and the second tails, or vice versa. That makes a total of four possible outcomes, not three. [See Figure 22.6.] Getting a head and a tail happens in two out of the four possible outcomes. Since each outcome is equally likely, getting a head and a tail has a probability of $\frac{2}{4}$ or $\frac{1}{2}$.

First Coin	Second Coin
Head	Head
Head	Tail
Tail	Head
Tail	Tail

Figure 22.6 Four possible outcomes of flipping two coins.

This theoretical probability is based on a logical analysis of the experiment, not on experimental results.

Another great context is the game of "rock, paper, scissors," which can be played in the normal way, or adapted so "same" scores 1 point and "different" scores 1 point for the other player. Decide whether this is a fair game (Ellis, Yeh, & Stump, 2007).

Experiments

As noted earlier, some probabilities cannot be analyzed by the theoretical likeliness of an event or the theoretical probability. The probability of these events can be determined only through empirical data, which may be preexisting or may be established through experimentation, conducting a sufficiently large number of trials to become confident that the resulting relative frequency is an approximation of the theoretical probability. The following activity provides students with such a situation.

Activity 22.8

Cup Toss

Provide a small plastic cup to pairs of students. Ask them to list the possible ways that the cup could land if they tossed it in the air and let it land on the floor. Which of the possibilities (upside down, right side up, or on its side) do they think is most and least likely? Why? Have students toss the cup 20 times, each time recording how it lands. Students should agree on a uniform method of tossing the cups to ensure unbiased data (e.g., dropping the cups from the same height). Record each pair's data in a class chart. Discuss the differences and generate reasons for them. Have students predict what will happen if they pool their data. Pool the data and compute the three ratios (upside down, right side up, and on the side) to the total number of tosses. The relative frequency of the combined data should approximate the actual probability.

In the cup-tossing experiment there is no practical way to determine the results before you start. However, once you have results for 200 tosses (empirical data), you would undoubtedly feel more confident in predicting the results of the next 100 tosses. After gathering data for 1000 trials, you would feel even more confident. The more tosses that are made, the more confident you become. You have determined a probability of $\frac{4}{5}$ or 80 percent for the cup to land on its side. It is empirical data because it is based on the results of an experiment rather than a theoretical analysis of the cup.

The Law of Large Numbers. The phenomenon that the relative frequency becomes a closer approximation of the actual probability or the theoretical probability as the size of the data set (sample) increases is referred to as *the law of large numbers.* The larger the size of the data set, the more representative the sample is of the population. Thinking about statistics, a survey of 1000 people provides more reliable and convincing data about the larger population than a survey of 5 people. The larger the number of trials (people surveyed), the more confident you can be that the data reflect the larger population. The same is true when you are attempting to determine the probability of an event through data collection.

Although critical to understanding probability, this concept is difficult for students to grasp. Students commonly think that a probability should play out in the short term, a misconception sometimes referred to as "the law of small numbers" (Flores, 2006; Tarr, Lee, & Rider, 2006). Therefore, students think that if a coin, for example, has had a series of heads, it is more likely to have several tails. But a coin has no memory, and the likelihood of heads and tails is still 50–50. The next activity emphasizes the large variability of data in the short run (only a small number of trials).

Activity 22.9

Get All 6!

Ask students to list the numbers 1 through 6 at the bottom of a frequency table. Ask students to roll a die and to mark an X over each number until they have rolled each number at least once. Repeat five or six times. Discuss how the frequency charts compare in each case. Students will see that in some cases there are many 4s, for example, and it took 25 rolls before getting all numbers, while in other cases, they got all the numbers in only 10 rolls. Focus discussion on the fact that in the short run, data varies a lot—it is over the long run that the data "evens out." This activity can also be done on a graphing calculator (Flores, 2006).

Truly random events often occur in unexpected groups; a fair coin may turn up heads five times in a row. A 100-year flood may hit a town twice in ten years. Hands-on random devices such as spinners, dice, or cubes drawn from a bag give students an intuitive feel for the imperfect distribution of randomness. Students believe in the unbiased outcomes of these devices. The downside is that hands-on devices require a lot of time to produce a large number of trials. This is where technology can help enormously.

The next activity is designed to help students with this difficult idea without resorting to comparing ratios expressed as fractions.

Activity 22.10

What Are the Chances?

Make a transparency of Blackline Master 61 shown in Figure 22.7. Provide pairs of students with a spinner face that is half red and half blue. Discuss the chances of spinning blue. Mark the $\frac{1}{2}$ point on the Impossible–Certain continuum and draw a vertical line down through all of the lines below this point. Then have each pair of students spin their spinner 20 times, tallying the number of red and blue spins. Mark the number of blue spins on the second line. For example, if there are 13 blue and 7 red, place a mark at about 13 on the 0-to-20 number line. If the result of these 20 spins was not exactly 10 and 10, discuss possible reasons why this may be so.

Now have student pairs each spin their spinners 20 more times. Collect these results and add them to the tallies for the first 20 spins. Mark the total in the right-hand box of the third line and indicate the number of blue spins on the line as before. Repeat this at least

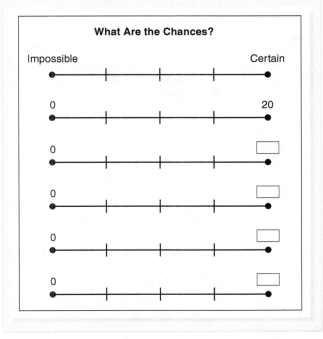

Figure 22.7 This activity is used to explore probability in the short run and the long run (see Blackline Master 61).

two more times, continuing to add the results of new spins to the previous results. Each time, enter the total in the right-hand box to create a new number line but with the same length as before. If possible, try to get the total number of spins to be at least 200. Using a graphing calculator, even 1000 trials is possible in a short amount of time.

The successive number lines used in "What Are the Chances" each have the same length and each represent the total number of trials. When the results are plotted on any one number line, the position shows the fraction of the total spins as a visual portion of the whole line. With more trials, the marks will get closer and closer to the $\frac{1}{2}$ mark you drew at the top of the page. Note that 240 blue spins out of 500 is 48 percent, or very close to one-half. This is so even though there are 20 more red spins (260) than blue. To be that close with only 100 spins, the results would need to be 48 and 52.

The same Blackline Master and the same process of accumulating data in stages can and should be used for other experiments as well. For example, try using this approach with the "Cup Toss" experiment. Rather than draw a vertical line before collecting data, decide on the best guess at the actual probability after the numbers have gotten large. Then draw the vertical line at that time to observe how more and more trials brought the results closer to the line. For students who have an understanding of percentages, the probabilities at each stage can be expressed as percents.

 Pose the following situation to students to assess their ideas about long-run results versus short-run results. Have students write about their ideas.

Margaret spun the spinner ten times. Blue turned up on three spins. Red turned up on seven spins. Margaret says that there is a 3-in-10 chance of spinning blue. Carla then spun the same spinner 100 times. Carla recorded 53 spins of blue and 47 spins of red. Carla says that the chance of spinning blue on this spinner is about even.

Who do you think is more likely to be correct: Margaret or Carla? Explain. Draw a spinner that you think they may have been using.

Look for evidence that students understand that even 10 spins is not very good evidence of the probability and that 100 spins tells us more about the chances. Also, to assess whether students understand the big idea that chance has no memory, have students either write about or discuss the following:

Duane has a lucky coin that he has tossed many, many times. He is sure that it is a fair coin—that there is an even chance of heads or tails. Duane tosses his coin six times and heads come up six times in a row. Duane is sure that the next toss will be tails because he has never been able to toss heads seven times in a row. What do you think the chances are of Duane tossing heads on the next toss? Explain your answer.

In this case you are looking for the idea that each toss of the coin is independent of prior tosses. ◆

Implications for Instruction

There are many reasons why an experimental approach to probability, actually conducting experiments and examining outcomes, is important in the middle grades classroom.

- It develops an appreciation for a simulation approach to solving problems. Many real-world problems are actually solved by conducting experiments or doing simulations.
- It is significantly more intuitive. Results begin to make sense and do not come from some abstract rule.
- It eliminates guessing at probabilities and wondering, "Did I get it right?" Counting or trying to determine the number of elements in a sample space can be very difficult without some intuitive background information.
- It provides an experiential background for examining the theoretical model. When you begin to sense that the probability of two heads is $\frac{1}{4}$ instead of $\frac{1}{3}$, the analysis in Figure 22.6 seems more reasonable.

- It helps students see how the ratio of a particular outcome to the total number of trials begins to converge to a fixed number. For an infinite number of trials, the relative frequency and theoretical probability would be the same.
- It is a lot more fun and interesting! Even searching for a correct explanation in the theoretical model is more interesting.

Try to use an experimental approach in the classroom whenever possible, posing interesting problems to investigate. If a theoretical analysis (such as with the two-coin experiment in "Fair or Unfair?") is possible, it should also be examined, and the results compared to the expected outcome.

The experimental approach is much like the inquiry approach that is the basis of the *before, during,* and *after* lesson format. In an experiment, you start with a problem (*before*), design and implement a way to explore it (*during*), and analyze the results of the experiment (*after*).

Use of Technology in Experiments

Electronic devices, including some relatively simple calculators and graphing calculators, are designed to produce random outcomes at the press of a button. Computer software is available that flips coins, spins spinners, or draws numbers from a hat. Calculators produce random numbers that can then be interpreted in terms of the desired device. As long as students accept the results generated by the technology as truly random or equivalent to the hands-on device, they offer significant advantages for performing experiments.

Technology makes some content more accessible, and this is certainly the case with probability experiments. Using software or a graphing calculator has the advantage of enabling many more trials in much less time. These devices can also explore across a variety of tools (virtual dice, coins, cards, etc.) and show graphical displays of the trials. For teachers, technology means that dice can be "loaded" and that spinners can easily be created with different partitions (Beck & Huse, 2007; Phillips-Bey, 2004). One particular website to explore is the National Library of Virtual Manipulatives. This site has been recommended in many chapters, but it is worth emphasizing here, as it is an outstanding site for doing virtual experiments.

Software for exploring probability concepts can generally be described as computer-animated random devices. Graphics show students the coins being flipped or the spinner being spun. Most allow different speeds. In a slow version, students may watch each spin of a spinner or coin flip. Faster speeds show the recording of each trial but omit the graphics. An even quicker mode simply shows the cumulative results. The number of trials can be set by the user.

Sample Spaces and Probability of Two Events

Understanding the concepts of outcome and sample space is central to understanding probability. The *sample space* for an experiment or chance situation is the set of all possible outcomes for that experiment. For example, if a bag contains two red, three yellow, and five blue tiles, the sample space consists of all ten tiles. An *event* is a subset of the sample space. The event of drawing a yellow tile has three elements or outcomes in the sample space and the event of drawing a blue tile has five elements in the sample space. For rolling a single number cube, the sample space always consists of the numbers 1 to 6.

Rolling a single die, drawing one colored chip from a bag, or the occurrence of rain tomorrow are all examples of one-event experiments. A two-event experiment is an experiment that requires two (or more) activities to determine an outcome. Examples include rolling two dice, drawing two cubes from a bag, or the occurrence of rain and forgetting your umbrella.

When exploring two-event experiments, there is another factor to consider: Does the occurrence of the event in one stage have an effect on the occurrence of the event in the other? In the following sections we will consider two-event experiments of both types—those with *independent* events and those with *dependent* events.

Independent Events

Recall that in Activity 22.7, "Fair or Unfair?," students explored the results of tossing two coins. The toss of one coin had no effect on the other. These were examples of *independent events*; the occurrence or nonoccurrence of one event has no effect on the other. The same is true of rolling two dice—the result on one die does not affect the other. The common error for both tossing two coins or rolling two dice is a failure to distinguish between the two events, especially when the outcomes are combined, as in "a head and a tail" or adding the numbers on two dice.

We've already solved the problem of tossing two coins. Let's explore rolling two dice and adding the results. Suppose that your students tally the sums that they get for two dice. The results might look like Figure 22.8. Clearly, these events are not equally likely and in fact the sum of 7 appears to have the best chance of occurring. To explain this, students might look for the combinations that make 7: 1 and 6, 2 and 5, and 3 and 4. But there are also three combinations for 6 and for 8. It seems as though 6 and 8 should be just as likely as 7, and yet they are not.

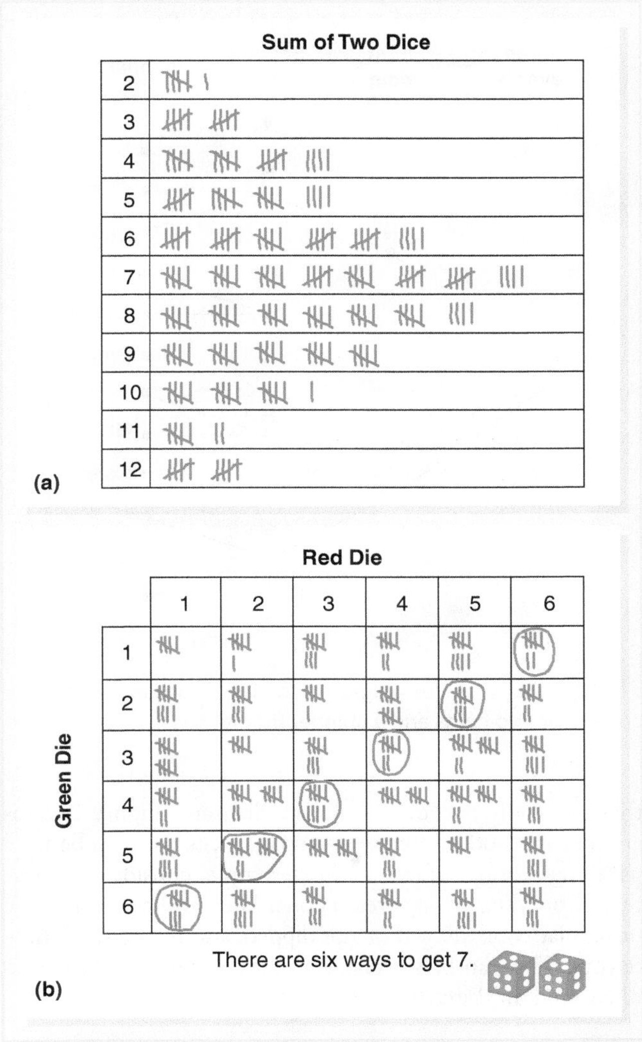

Figure 22.8 Tallies can account only for the total (a) or keep track of each die (b).

Now suppose that the experiment is repeated. This time, for the sake of clarity, suggest that students roll two different-colored dice and that they keep the tallies in a chart like the one in part (b) of Figure 22.8.

The results of a large number of dice rolls indicate what one would expect, namely, that all 36 cells of this chart are equally likely. But there are more cells with a sum of 7 than any other number. Therefore, students were really looking for the event consisting of any of the six ways, not three ways, that two dice can add to 7. There are six outcomes in the desired event out of a total of 36, for a probability of $\frac{6}{36}$, or $\frac{1}{6}$.

To create the sample space for two independent events, it is helpful to use a chart or diagram that keeps the two events separate and illustrates all possible combinations. The matrix in Figure 22.8(b) is one good suggestion when

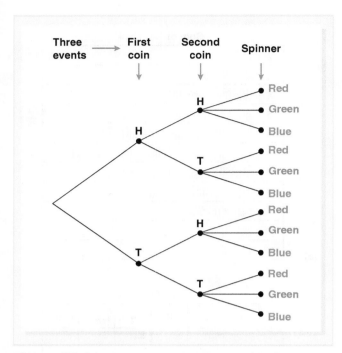

Figure 22.9 A tree diagram showing all possible outcomes for two coins and a spinner that is $\frac{2}{3}$ red.

there are only two events. A tree diagram (Figure 22.9) is another method of creating sample spaces that can be used with any number of events. For example, consider the context of building an ice cream cone. You can choose a waffle or regular cone, dipped or not dipped, and then any of three flavors. This can be simulated using coins and a spinner, as illustrated in Figure 22.9.

❚❚ ─────────── Pause and Reflect

Use a chart and/or tree diagram to analyze the sum of two number cubes each with sides 1, 1, 2, 3, 3, and 3. (These were the cubes used in "Add, Then Tally," Activity 22.4.) What is the probability of each sum, 1 through 6?

Activity 22.11

Exploring Multistage Events

The following are examples of multistage events composed of independent events.

- **Rolling an even sum with two dice**
- **Spinning blue twice on a spinner**
- **Having a tack or a cup land up if each is tossed once**
- **Getting at *least* two heads from tossing four coins**

Have students first make and defend a prediction of the probability of the event. Then they should

conduct an experiment with a large number of trials, comparing their results to their predicted probabilities. Finally, they should reconcile differences. Where appropriate, students can try to determine the theoretical probability as part of their final analysis of the experiment.

Words and phrases such as *and, or, at least*, and *no more than* can also cause students some trouble. Of special note is the word *or*, since its everyday usage is generally not the same as its strict logical use in mathematics. In mathematics, *or* includes the case of *both*. So in the tack-and-cup example, the event includes tack up, cup up, and *both* tack *and* cup up.

Two-Event Probabilities with an Area Model

One way to determine the theoretical probability of a multistage event is to list all possible outcomes and count the number of outcomes that make up the event. This is effective, but has some limitations. First, what if the events are not all equally likely? For example, the spinner may be only $\frac{1}{4}$ blue. Second, it can get tedious when there are many possibilities. An area model approach has been used successfully with students as young as fifth grade and is quite helpful for some reasonably difficult problems.

Students like to explore data about themselves. Consider the context of birthdays of the entire seventh-grade class. Asking students which animal represents their Chinese birth year and which season they were born represents two independent events. Figure 22.10 illustrates how to model this using an area model, with 64 percent of the class born in the year of the tiger and 36 percent born in the year of the rabbit. Seasons are assumed to be equally likely.

In Figure 22.10(b) you can visually see that students in the tiger and spring groups make up $\frac{1}{4}$ of 64 percent or 16 percent of the population. This should look very familiar, as the same process is used for multiplying fractions. In Figure 22.10(c), the situation is more complex because it is an OR situation. Half of the students are born in summer or fall and 36 percent are born in the year of the rabbit. But some students are both, and they have been double counted. The diagram shows this case as the overlap of the shaded columns with the shaded rows. In the situation under consideration that amount is $\frac{1}{2}$ of 36, or 18 percent. Therefore, the population that is summer or fall or born in the year of the rabbit is 50 + 36 − 18 = 68 percent of the population.

The area approach is accessible to a range of learners, as it is less abstract than equations or tree diagrams. For more than two independent events, further subdivision of each region is required but is still quite reasonable. The use

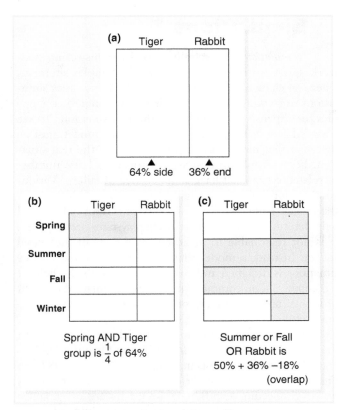

Figure 22.10 An area model for determining probabilities.

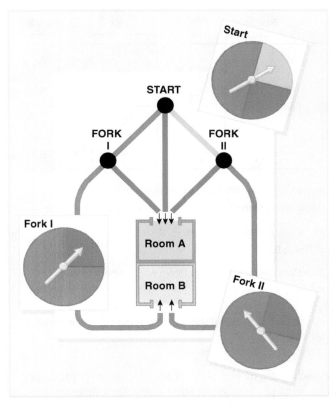

Figure 22.11 Should you place your key to freedom in Room A or Room B? At each fork, the spinner determines your path.

of *and* and *or* connectives can be modeled effectively. It is clear to students, without memorization of formulas, how to find probabilities of independent events.

Dependent Events

Dependent events occur when the second event depends on the result of the first. For example, suppose that there are two identical boxes. In one box is a dollar bill and two counterfeit bills. In the other box is one of each. You may choose one box and from that box select one bill without looking. What are your chances of getting a genuine dollar? Here there are two events: selecting a box and selecting a bill. The probability of getting a dollar in the second event depends on which box is chosen in the first event. These events are *dependent*, not independent.

As a whimsical but engaging context, suppose that you are a prisoner in a faraway land. The king has pity on you and gives you a chance to leave. He shows you the maze in Figure 22.11. At the start and at each fork in the path, you must spin the spinner and follow the path that it points to. You may request that the key to freedom be placed in one of the two rooms. In which room should you place the key to have the best chance of freedom? Notice that the prob-

ability of ending the maze in any one room is dependent on the result of the first spin.

Either of these two problems could be explored with an experimental approach, a simulation. Remember that experiments are a good lead-in to theoretical probability. You can use the area model to determine the theoretical probabilities. An area model solution to the prisoner problem is shown in Figure 22.12. How would the area model for the prisoner problem be different if the spinner at Forks I and II were $\frac{1}{3}$ A and $\frac{2}{3}$ B spinners?

❚❚ ──────── *Pause and Reflect*

Try the area approach for the problem of the counterfeit bills. The chance of getting a dollar is $\frac{5}{12}$. Can you get this result?

───────────────────

The area model will not solve all probability problems. However, it fits very well into a developmental approach to the subject because it is conceptual, it is based on existing knowledge of fractions, and more symbolic approaches can be derived from it. Figure 22.13 shows a tree diagram for the same problem, with the probability

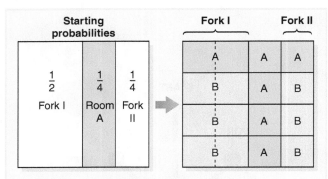

At Fork I, $\frac{3}{4}$ of the time you will go to Room B.

(Note: Not $\frac{3}{4}$ of the square but $\frac{3}{4}$ of the times you go to Fork I.)

At Fork II, $\frac{3}{4}$ of these times (or $\frac{3}{16}$ of total time) you will go to Room B.

Therefore, you will end up in Room A $\frac{7}{16}$ of the time and Room B $\frac{9}{16}$ of the time.

Figure 22.12 Using the area model to solve the maze problem.

of each path of the tree written in. After some experience with probability situations, the tree diagram model is probably easier to use and adapts to a wider range of situations. You should be able to match up each branch of the tree diagram in Figure 22.13 with a section of the square in Figure 22.12. Use the area model to explain why the probability for each complete branch of the tree is determined by multiplying the probabilities along the branch.

Simulations

Simulation is a technique used for answering real-world questions or making decisions in complex situations where an element of chance is involved. Many times simulations are conducted because it is too dangerous, complex, or expensive to manipulate the real situation. To see what is likely to happen in the real event, a model must be designed that has the same probabilities as the real situation. For example, in designing a rocket, a large number of related systems all have some chance of failure. Various combinations of failures might cause serious problems with the rocket. Knowing the probability of serious failures will help determine if redesign or backup systems are required. It is not reasonable to make repeated tests of the actual rocket. Instead, a model that simulates all of the chance situations is designed and run repeatedly with the help of a computer. The computer model can simulate thousands of flights, and an estimate of the chance of failure can be made.

The following problem and model are adapted from the excellent materials developed by the Quantitative Literacy Project (Gnanadesikan, Schaeffer, & Swift, 1987). In Figure 22.14, a diagram shows water pipes for a pumping system connecting A to B. The five pumps are aging, and it is estimated that at any given time, the probability of pump failure is $\frac{1}{2}$. If a pump fails, water cannot pass that station. For example, if pumps 1, 2, and 5 fail, water can flow only through 4 and 3. Consider the following questions that might well be asked about such a system:

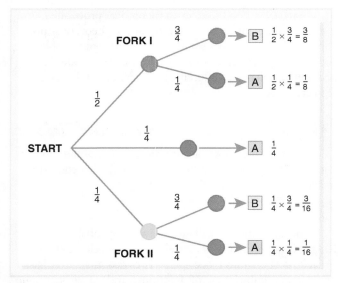

Figure 22.13 A tree diagram is another way to model the outcomes of two or more dependent events.

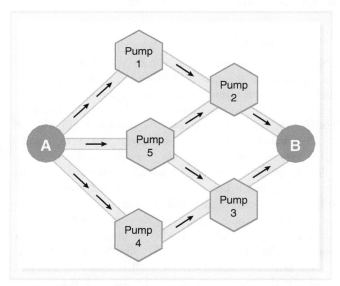

Figure 22.14 Each of these five pumps has a 50 percent chance of failure. What is the probability that some path from A to B is working?

- What is the probability that water will flow at any time?
- On the average, about how many stations need repair at any time?
- What is the probability that the 1–2 path is working at any time?

For any simulation, the following steps can serve as a useful guide.

1. *Identify key components and assumptions of the problem.* The key component in the water problem is the condition of a pump. Each pump is either working or not. The assumption is that the probability that a pump is working is $\frac{1}{2}$.

2. *Select a random device for the key components.* Any random device can be selected that has outcomes with the same probability as the key component—in this case, the pumps. Here a simple choice might be tossing a coin, with heads representing a working pump.

3. *Define a trial.* A *trial* consists of simulating a series of key components until the situation has been completely modeled one time. In this problem, a trial could consist of tossing a coin five times, each toss representing a different pump.

4. *Conduct a large number of trials and record the information.* For this problem, it would be good to keep the record of heads and tails in groups of five because each set of five is one trial and represents all of the pumps.

5. *Use the data to draw conclusions.* There are four possible paths for the water, each flowing through two of the five pumps. As they are numbered in the drawing, if any one of the pairs 1–2, 5–2, 5–3, and 4–3 is open, it makes no difference whether the other pumps are working. By counting the trials in which at least one of these four pairs of coins both came up heads, we can estimate the probability of water flowing. To answer the second question, the number of tails per trial can be averaged.

|| ——————— *Pause and Reflect*

How would you answer the third question concerning the 1–2 path's being open?

The interesting problem-solving aspects of simulation activities are in the first three steps, where the real-world situation is translated into a model. Steps 4 and 5 are the same as solving a probability problem by experimental means. Translation of real-world information into models is the essence of applied mathematics.

Here are a few more examples of problems for which a simulation can be used to gather empirical data.

In a true-or-false test, what is the probability of getting 7 out of 10 questions correct by guessing alone? (**Key component: answering a question. Assumption: Chance of getting it correct is $\frac{1}{2}$.**)
Simulation option: **Flip a coin 10 times for one trial.**

In a group of five people, what is the chance that two were born in the same month? (**Key component: month of birth. Assumption: All 12 months are equally likely.**)
Simulation option: **12-sided dice or 12 cards. Draw/roll one, replace, and draw/roll again.**

Casey's batting average is .350. What is the chance he will go hitless in a complete nine-inning game? (**Key component: getting a hit. Assumptions: Probability of a hit for each at-bat is .35. Casey will get to bat four times in the average game.**)
Simulation option: **Spinner with 35 percent shaded. Spin 4 times for one trial.**

Students often have trouble selecting an appropriate random device for their simulations. Spinners are an obvious choice since faces can be adjusted to match probabilities. Coins or two-colored chips are useful for probabilities of $\frac{1}{2}$. A standard die can be used for probabilities that are multiples of $\frac{1}{6}$. There are also dice available from educational distributors with 4, 8, 12, and 20 sides.

 Many relatively simple calculators include a key that will produce random numbers that can be used to simulate experiments (e.g., 1 means true, 2 means false). Usually, the random numbers generated are between 0 and 1. Students who are going to use these random number generators will need some direction in using them to their advantage. Each number generated will likely have eight or more decimal places. A list of five numbers might look like this:

0.8904433368
0.0232028877
0.1669322714
0.1841957303
0.5523714952

How could a list of decimals like this replace flipping a coin or spinning a spinner? Suppose each was multiplied by 2. The results would be between 0 and 2. If you ignore the decimal part, you would have a series of zeros and ones that could stand for heads and tails, boys and girls, true and false, or any other pair of equally likely outcomes. For three outcomes, the same as a $\frac{1}{4}$-$\frac{1}{4}$-$\frac{1}{2}$ spinner, you might decide to look at the first two digits of the number and assign values from 0 to 24 and 25 to 49 to the two quarter portions and values 50 to 99 for the one-half portion. Alternatively, each number could be multiplied by 4, the decimal part ignored, resulting in random numbers 0, 1, 2, and 3. These could then be assigned to the desired outcomes. In effect, random numbers can simulate any simple random device.

With graphing calculators, the random number generator can be used inside of a simple program that produces the numbers and stores them in a list. The list can then be displayed graphically. The program in Figure 22.15 is for a TI-83 calculator. It will "roll" as many dice as you request. At the end of the program, a histogram displays the totals for each sum. With the TRACE feature, the value for each bar in the graph is displayed. The figure shows the result of rolling two dice 1000 times. It took about $2\frac{1}{2}$ minutes to run the program and produce the graph. (Computer programs produce the result almost instantly.) The TI-73 calculator designed for middle school has a built-in coin and dice function. ◆

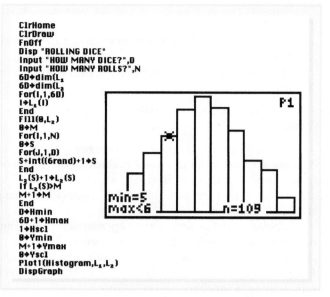

Figure 22.15 This TI-83 program can be used to simulate thousands of dice rolls and accumulate the results.

Reflections

Writing to Learn

1. What are the first ideas about probability that students should develop? How can you help students with these ideas?

2. Activities 22.3 and 22.4 ("Race to the Top" and "Add, Then Tally") are each designed to help students see that some outcomes are more likely than others. What is the difference between these two activities? Why might this difference be useful in helping students?

3. Explain what is meant by the statement "Chance has no memory."

4. Describe the difference between experimental probability and theoretical probability. Will these ever be the same? Which is the "correct" probability?

5. What are the advantages of having students conduct experiments even before they attempt to figure out a theoretical probability?

6. Explain the law of large numbers. Describe an activity that might help students to appreciate this idea.

7. Describe the difference between a single-stage and a multistage experiment. In multistage experiments, what are independent events and dependent events? Give an example of each.

8. Use an area model and a tree diagram to determine the probability for the following situation:

   Dad puts a $5 bill and three $1 bills in the first box. In a second box, he puts another $5 bill with just one $1 bill. For washing the car, Junior gets to take one bill from the first box without looking and put it in the second box. After these are well mixed, he then gets to take one bill from the second box. What is the probability that he will get $5?

   Design a simulation for the problem and try it out. Does your simulation agree with your theoretical probability?

9. The three outcomes of a sample space have probabilities of $\frac{1}{3}$, $\frac{1}{6}$, and $\frac{1}{2}$. Describe how you could use a random number generator on a calculator or computer to simulate these probabilities.

For Discussion and Exploration

1. The "Monty Hall Problem" has become a classic. In the game show, the contestant chooses from one of three doors. Behind one of the three doors is a big prize. Monty shows the contestant a goat behind one of the doors not selected and then offers the contestant the opportunity to switch doors. Does the contestant have a better chance of winning the big prize by switching, staying with the original choice, or is there no difference? There are numerous methods of answering this question. Make a convincing argument for your own answer based on the ideas and techniques in this chapter.

2. Go to the Illuminations website and find the activities related to probability. Explore the tasks for various trials. Discuss (a) the advantages and disadvantages of virtual experiments and (b) content within this chapter that could be discussed following student exploration on these applets.

Resources

Literature Connections

The books described here offer both fanciful and real-life data for investigating probability. Also, listed in Recommended Readings is an article with two more great literature links.

Go Figure! A Totally Cool Book about Numbers *Ball, 2005*

This wonderful book could be placed in every chapter of this book. About 40 different topics are covered, one of which is called "Take a Chance." This two-page spread is full of interesting contexts for probability, including a match-dropping experiment and genetics.

Harry Potter Books *Rowling, 1998, 1999a, 1999b, 2000, 2003, 2005, 2007*

The game of Qidditch can lend itself to creating a simulation to explore the likelihood of winning. Wagner and Lachance (2004) suggest that sums of two dice be linked to Qidditch actions. For example, a roll of 7 means a player scores a Quaffle, which is worth 10 points. Rolls of 2 or 12 mean the player catches the snitch and the game ends, 150 points; 3, 5, 9, 11 means hit by bludger—lose a turn; 4, 6, 8, 10 means dodge a bludger, no points.

Do You Wanna Bet? Your Chance to Find Out about Probability *Cushman, 1991*

The two characters in this book, Danny and Brian, become involved in everyday situations both in and out of school. Each situation has an element of probability involved. For example, two invitations to birthday parties are for the same day. What is the chance that two friends would have the same birthday? In another situation, Danny flips heads several times and readers are asked about Brian's chances on the next flip. An excellent opportunity to explore this possible misconception. These and other situations lead to a probability experiment or discussion. Students might create simulations to examine some of the ideas.

My Little Sister Ate One Hare *Grossman, 1996*

This counting book will appeal to the middle school set as well as to young children due to the somewhat gross thought of a little girl eating one rabbit, two snakes, three ants, and so on, including bats, mice, worms, and lizards. Upon eating ten peas, she throws up everything she ate.

Bay-Williams and Martinie (2004) used this tale with middle school students to create a wonderful introductory lesson in probability. If one of the things the little sister "spilled" on the floor is picked up at random in the process of cleaning up, what is the probability of getting a polliwog (or other animal or category of animal)? Students can use cards for the correct number of each thing eaten and approach the task experimentally and also compare the results to the theoretical probability.

Recommended Readings

Articles

Coffey, D. C., & Richardson, M. G. (2005). Rethinking fair games. *Mathematics Teaching in the Middle School, 10*(6), 298–303.

Students explore the fairness of a matching game both experimentally and using a theoretical model. They then set out to create a variation of the game that would be fair by assigning points to a match and to a mismatch. A TI-73 program is included that simulates the revised game.

Edwards, T. G., & Hensien, S. M. (2000). Using probability experiments to foster discourse. *Teaching Children Mathematics, 6*(8), 524–529.

Fifth-grade students experiment with outcomes of flipping a coin, spinning a spinner, and rolling a die. The discourse is directed to the disparity between the observed outcomes and the theoretical probabilities. For example, is it reasonable that there are 77 heads out of 150 tosses?

Lawrence, A. (1999). From *The Giver* to *The Twenty-One Balloons:* Explorations with probability. *Mathematics Teaching in the Middle School, 4*(8), 504–509.

Lawrence uses two award-winning books to motivate some nontrivial explorations for her middle school students. One task was to decide how often in a series of 50 births there will be 25 boys and 25 girls. In a related task, students tried to find out if it was more likely to have the same number of girls and boys in a small family or a large family. The ideas here are quite challenging and the results are interesting.

McMillen, S. (2008). Predictions and probability. *Teaching Children Mathematics, 14*(8), 454–463.

This article provides a series of high-quality probability lessons—various contexts and models are used, as well as calculators. The lessons include a number of key concepts discussed in this chapter and two handouts are provided.

Books

Shaughnessy, J. M. (2003). Research on students' understanding of probability. In J. Kilpatrick, W. G. Martin, & D. Schifter (Eds.), *A research companion to Principles and Standards for School Mathematics* (pp. 216–226). Reston, VA: NCTM.

Shaughnessy's chapter offers interesting insights from research and makes useful recommendations. Teachers serious about the teaching of probability will benefit from checking this out.

Online Resources

Adjustable Spinner (Shodor)
www.shodor.org/interactivate/activities/AdjustableSpinner

A virtual spinner can be adjusted to have any number of sections of any size. It can then be spun any number of times in increments of 100,000.

A Better Fire! (Shodor's Project Interactivate)
www.shodor.org/interactivate/activities/ABetterFire

This site offers a realistic simulation of actual forest fires, with controls for wind speed and direction to add more realism. The simulation uses a virtual "die" to see if a tree should be planted for each square. Then the fire is set and allowed to burn. An excellent authentic use of simulations.

Box Model (NLVM)
http://nlvm.usu.edu/en/nav/frames_asid_146_g_3_t_5 .html

The applet permits creating a box of up to 16 colored cubes, including the possibility of duplicates. Cubes can then be drawn at random (with replacement). A bar graph shows the results that can be compared to the theoretical results.

Coin Tossing (NLVM)
http://nlvm.usu.edu/en/nav/frames_asid_305_g_3_t_5 .html

A single coin can be "tossed" any number of times. The results are shown in order, which can help with the concept of randomness. A bar graph shows results.

Marble Mania
www.sciencenetlinks.com/interactives/marble/marble mania.html

This applet explores randomness and probability. You'll be able to control how many and what color marbles to place in a virtual marble bag. An advantage of this applet is that you can run a large number of different trials in a short amount of time.

Probability (Shodor)
www.shodor.org/interactivate/activities/ExpProbability/ index.html

A spinner can be created with up to four regions or two like dice can be made with each side adjustable from 1 to 6. The devices can then be used in experiments.

Spinners (NLVM)
http://nlvm.usu.edu/en/nav/frames_asid_186_g_1_t_1 .html

This site provides a spinner that can be customized and used for experiments.

Field Experience Guide Connections

Children have very interesting notions about probability. Use Diagnostic Interview 7.2 with activities from this chapter to find out what students think is likely or not likely and why they think so. Or adapt Student Interview 4.5 to focus on attitudes about probability. FEG Expanded Lesson 9.21 ("Create a Game") engages students in designing a fair game, and FEG Expanded Lesson 9.23 ("Testing Bag Designs") provides more details on using this activity.

Developing Concepts of Exponents, Integers, and Real Numbers

Students in the middle grades need to develop a more complete understanding of the number system, which includes extending whole numbers to integers and starting to think of fractions as rational numbers (both positive and negative). In these ways and others they can begin to appreciate the completeness of the real number system.

The ideas presented in this chapter build on ideas that have been developed throughout this book. Exponents are used in algebraic expressions and add to the operations. Scientific notation expands how large and small numbers are represented, building on place-value concepts. Integers open up the counting numbers less than 0 and therefore extend the number line (as well as operations) to include negative values. The *Curriculum Focal Points* (NCTM, 2006) states that seventh graders should be "developing an understanding of operations on all rational numbers and solving linear equations" (p. 19) and that in eighth grade, "Students use exponents and scientific notation to describe very large and very small numbers. They use square roots when they apply the Pythagorean theorem." (p. 20).

Big Ideas

1. Exponential notation is a way to express repeated products of the same number. Specifically, powers of 10 express very large and very small numbers in an economical manner.

2. Integers add to the number system the negative (and positive) counting numbers, so that every number has both size and a positive or negative relationship to other numbers. A negative number is the opposite of the positive number of the same size.

3. Whole numbers, fractions, and integers are rational numbers. Every rational number can be expressed as a fraction.

4. Many numbers are not rational; the irrationals can be expressed only symbolically or approximately using a close rational number. Examples include $\sqrt{2} \approx 1.41421\ldots$ and $\pi \approx 3.14159\ldots$

Mathematics Content Connections

The ideas in this chapter represent an expansion of the ways in which we represent numbers. These representations expand or enhance earlier ideas of whole numbers, fractions, and decimals.

- **Whole-Number Place Value, Fractions, and Decimals:** When exponential notation is combined with decimal notation, very small and very large numbers can be written efficiently. Decimals and fractions help to describe the difference between rational and irrational numbers. Negative numbers extend the number line in both directions.

- **Algebra:** The symbolic manipulation of numbers, including the rules for order of operations, is exactly the same as is used with variables. The study of integers helps with the notion of "opposite," represented by a negative sign: $^-6$ is the opposite of $^+6$ and ^-x is the opposite of ^+x, regardless of whether x is negative or positive. Exponents can also be variables, giving rise to exponential functions.

Exponents

As numbers in our technological world get very small or very large, expressing them in standard form is cumbersome. Exponential notation is much more efficient for conveying numeric or quantitative information.

Exponents in Expressions and Equations

In algebra classes, students get confused trying to remember the rules of exponents. For example, when you raise numbers to powers, do you add or multiply the exponents? This is an example of procedural knowledge that is often learned without supporting conceptual knowledge. Before algebra, students should have ample opportunity to explore exponents with whole numbers rather than with letters or variables. By doing so, they are able to deal directly with the concept and actually generate the rules themselves.

A *whole-number exponent* is simply shorthand for repeated multiplication of a number times itself; for example, $3^4 = 3 \times 3 \times 3 \times 3$.

Conventions of symbolism must also be learned. These are arbitrary rules with no conceptual basis. The first is that *an exponent applies to its immediate base.* For example, in the expression $2 + 5^3$, the exponent 3 applies only to the 5, so the expression is equal to $2 + (5 \times 5 \times 5)$. However, in the expression $(2 + 5)^3$, the 3 is an exponent of the quantity $2 + 5$ and is evaluated as $(2 + 5) \times (2 + 5) \times (2 + 5)$, or $7 \times 7 \times 7$.

Students' first encounter with exponents should be squares and cubes, numbers that can be represented geometrically. For example, consider the following problem:

Minia knows that square animal pens are the most economical for the amount of space they provide. Can you provide a table for Minia that shows the areas of square pens that have between 4 meters and 10 meters of fence on each side?

Students may set up a table similar to Figure 23.1, showing possible areas for the pen.

Students can also explore algebraic growing patterns involving squares and/or cubes. The Painted Cube Problem, which involves both squares and cubes, is a popular investigation that appears in many places, including the *Connected Mathematics* curriculum (see Figure 23.2). In this problem the faces of the cube are squares. Therefore, the

sides getting painted are also squares, and the growth pattern is a square. The cubes getting no sides painted are those hidden inside the painted cube. In a $2 \times 2 \times 2$, there are 0 inside cubes, but in a $3 \times 3 \times 3$ there is one hidden cube inside that will not get painted. This "hidden cube" grows at a cubic rate. In exploring the pattern, students get experience with squares and cubes.

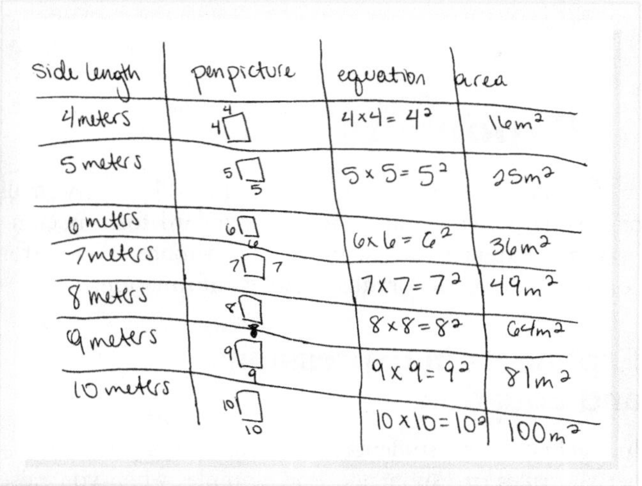

Order of Operations. The other convention involves the *order of operations:* Multiplication and division are always done before addition and subtraction. Since exponentiation is repeated multiplication, it also is done before addition and subtraction. In the expression $5 + 4^2 - 6 \div 3$, 4^2 and $6 \div 3$ are done first. Therefore, the expression is evaluated as $5 + 16 - 2 = 21 - 2 = 19$.

⏸ ——————————— *Pause and Reflect*

Try evaluating the same expression in left-to-right order. Do you get 4?

Parentheses are used to group operations that are to be done first. Therefore, in $(5 + 4) \times 2 - 6 \div 3$, the addition can be done inside the parentheses first, or the distributive property can be used, and the final result is 16. The phrase "*P*lease *e*xcuse *m*y *d*ear *A*unt *S*ally" is sometimes used to help students recall that operations inside *p*arentheses are done first, then *e*xponentiation, and then *m*ultiplication and *d*ivision before *a*ddition and *s*ubtraction.

Although this phrase is a good mnemonic, it can lead students to think that addition is done before subtraction and multiplication comes before division. An improvement might involve writing it as a verse in rows that show the last four words as pairs. Another option is to just use the acronym "PEMDAS," with the letters listed in rows to indicate order:

P = parenthesis
E = exponents
MD = multiplication and division (whichever is first from left to right)
AS = addition and subtraction (whichever is first from left to right)

Sometimes, students' only experience is to simplify expressions applying the order. You can both assess and strengthen their understanding of this process by having them write equations that indicate the proper order of operations, as in the activity below.

Figure 23.1 A student records possibilities for making a square pen.

Activity 23.1

Guess My Number

This algebraic activity involves the teacher giving hints about a number and students thinking backwards to

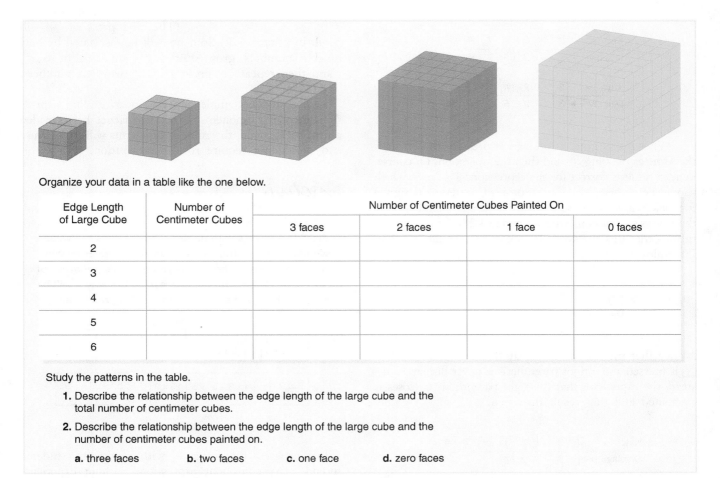

Organize your data in a table like the one below.

Edge Length of Large Cube	Number of Centimeter Cubes	Number of Centimeter Cubes Painted On			
		3 faces	2 faces	1 face	0 faces
2					
3					
4					
5					
6					

Study the patterns in the table.

1. Describe the relationship between the edge length of the large cube and the total number of centimeter cubes.

2. Describe the relationship between the edge length of the large cube and the number of centimeter cubes painted on.

a. three faces   **b.** two faces   **c.** one face   **d.** zero faces

Figure 23.2 The Painted Cube Problem provides a context for exploring squares and cubes.

Source: Adapted from *Connected Mathematics: Frogs, Fleas and Painted Cubes: Quadratic Relationships* by Glenda Lappan, James T. Fey, William M. Fitzgerald, Susan N. Friel, & Elizabeth Difanis Phillips. Copyright © 2006 by Michigan State University. Used by permission of Pearson Education, Inc. All rights reserved.

find it (using logical reasoning). **Students create equations, using parentheses appropriately to reflect the clues the teacher gives, as in the following three examples:**

- **I am thinking of a number; I add 5, double it, and get 22. [$(n + 5) \times 2 = 22$]**
- **I am thinking of a number; I subtract 2, square it, and get 36. [$(n - 2)^2 = 36$]**
- **I am thinking of a number; I double it, add 2, cube it, and get 1000. [$(2n + 2)^3 = 1000$]**

The writing stories activity is another excellent tool for learning and applying the order of operations. Students can be asked to write an expression using all the operations and parentheses—for example, $(4 + 2)^2 \times 2 \div 4$—and then write a story, using a context of their choice, to fit the expression they have created (Golembo, 2000).

Writing stories is an excellent assessment of students' understanding of the order of operations. Golembo (2006) includes a student page and assessment pages. As students write expressions or stories, determine whether they realize that multiplication and division (and addition and subtraction) are equal in order and should be solved left to right. Also, ask students questions to see whether they understand when parentheses are optional and when they are necessary. ◆

Exponent Notation on the Calculator. Most scientific calculators employ "algebraic logic" that evaluates expressions using the order of operations and also allows grouping with parentheses. However, with the exception of the TI-MathMate and other newer calculators designed specifically for school use, most simple four-function calculators do not use algebraic logic. Operations are processed as they are entered. On calculators without algebraic logic, the following two keying sequences produce the same results:

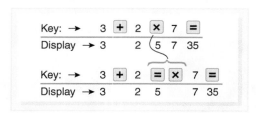

Whenever an operation sign is pressed, the effect is the same as pressing $=$ and then the operation. Of course, neither result is correct for the expressions $3 + 2 \times 7$, which should be evaluated as $3 + 14$, or 17. Calculators designed for middle grades do use algebraic logic and include parenthesis keys so that both $3 + 2 \times 7$ and $(3 + 2) \times 7$ can be keyed in the order that the symbols appear. See the difference in the following displays:

```
Key: →    3  +  2  ×  7  =
Display → 3    2      7  17
```

Notice that the following display does not change when $\times$ is pressed and a right parenthesis is never displayed. Instead, the expression that the right parenthesis encloses is calculated and that result displayed.

```
Key: →    (  3  +  2  )  ×  7  =
Display → [  3     2  5      7  35
```

Some basic calculators and graphing calculators show the expression $3 + 2 \times (6^2 - 4)$. Nothing is evaluated until you press Enter or EXE. Then the result appears on the next line to the right of the screen:

```
3 + 2 * (6² − 4)
                    67
```

Moreover, the last expression entered can be recalled and edited so that students can see how different expressions are evaluated. Only minimum key presses are required.

```
3 + 2 * (6² − 4)
                    67
(3 + 2) * (6² − 4)
                    160
(3 + 2) * 6² − 4
                    176
3 + 2 * 6² − 4
                    71
```

The simple four-function calculator remains a powerful tool for exploration. For example, to evaluate 3^8, press

3 ×$=$$=$$=$$=$$=$$=$$=$. (The first press of $=$ will result in 9, or 3×3.) Students will be fascinated by how quickly numbers grow. Enter any number, press $\times$, and then repeatedly press $=$. Try two-digit numbers. Try 0.1.

Give students ample opportunity to explore expressions involving exponents. When experience has provided a firm background, the rules of exponents will make sense and should not require rote memorization.

Activity 23.2
Entering Expressions

Provide students with numeric expressions to evaluate with simple four-function calculators. Ask: "How will you have to enter these to correctly apply the order of operations?" Rewrite the expression the way it will be entered. Here are some examples of expressions:

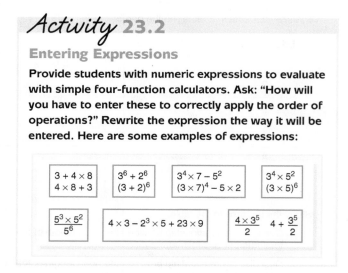

When experiencing difficulty with exponents, students should write equivalent expressions without exponents or include parentheses to indicate explicit groupings. For example:

$$
\begin{aligned}
(7 \times 2^3 - 5)^3 &= (7 \times (2 \times 2 \times 2) - 5) \times \\
&\quad (7 \times (2 \times 2 \times 2) - 5) \times \\
&\quad (7 \times (2 \times 2 \times 2) - 5) \\
&= ((7 \times 8) - 5) \times \\
&\quad ((7 \times 8) - 5) \times \\
&\quad ((7 \times 8) - 5) \\
&= (56 - 5) \times (56 - 5) \times (56 - 5) \\
&= 51 \times 51 \times 51
\end{aligned}
$$

For many expressions, there is more than one way to proceed, and sharing different ways is important.

Of course, calculators with algebraic logic will automatically produce correct results. Yet it remains important for students to know these rules, and the calculator should not replace an understanding of the order of operations. These rules apply to symbolic manipulation in algebra and must be understood for mental calculations or for using a basic calculator.

Negative Exponents

When students begin to explore exponents and have also experienced negative integers, it is interesting to consider what it might mean to raise a number to a negative power. For example, what does 2^{-4} mean? The following two related options can help students explore the possibilities of negative exponents. First, based on the importance of patterns in mathematics, examine a pattern of numbers, and see how it might best be expanded. The powers of 10 are good to explore because they are directly related to place value. Have students consider 10^N as follows:

$$10^4 = 10,000$$
$$10^3 = 1000$$
$$10^2 = 100$$
$$10^1 = 10$$
$$10^0 = ?$$
$$10^{-1} = ?$$

In this sequence, the most obvious entry for 10^0 is 1, which is the *definition* of 10^0. That is, it is a convention that 10 or any other nonzero number raised to the power 0 is 1. So what is 10^{-1}? If the pattern is to continue, the 1 should move to the right of the decimal:

$$10^0 = 1$$
$$10^{-1} = 0.1$$
$$10^{-2} = 0.01$$
$$10^{-3} = 0.001$$

and so on. Notice how each of these numbers is written as a fraction:

$$10^{-1} = 0.1 = \frac{1}{10}$$
$$10^{-2} = 0.01 = \frac{1}{100} = \frac{1}{10^2}$$
$$10^{-3} = 0.001 = \frac{1}{1000} = \frac{1}{10^3}$$

Second, students can explore negative exponents on a calculator. For example, tell students, "Use a calculator to see if you can figure out what 4^{-3} or 2^{-5} equal." The calculator should, of course, never be seen as the *reason* for anything in mathematics, but here you are exploring notation convention. If the calculator has decimal-to-fraction conversion, suggest that students use that feature to help develop the meaning of negative exponents. Figure 23.3 gives an example of how this might look on a graphing calculator.

Scientific Notation

The more common it becomes to find very large or very small numbers in our daily lives, the more important it is to have convenient ways to represent them. One option is to say and write numbers in their common form. However, this practice can at times be cumbersome. Another option is to use exponential notation and our base-ten place-value system—scientific notation. In scientific notation, a number is changed to be the product of a number greater than or equal to 1 and less than ten (meaning only one digit in front of the decimal) multiplied by a multiple of 10. For example,

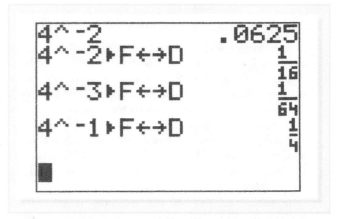

Figure 23.3 Graphing calculators evaluate expressions as decimals. However, they also convert decimals to fractions. This figure shows the screen of a TI-73 calculator. The $\boxed{\text{F↔D}}$ key converts fractions to decimals (and decimals to fractions) as shown here.

3,414,000,000 can be written as 3.414×10^9. Since you have moved the decimal back nine places (divided by 1 billion) to place the decimal, to keep the number equivalent, you must multiply by 1 billion (10^9).

Different notations have different purposes and values. Consider this fact: In 1990, the population of the world was more than 5,050,700,000 persons, about 1 billion fewer than in the year 2000. This can be expressed in various ways:

5 billion 50 million 700 thousand
5,050,700,000
5.0507×10^9
Less than 5.1 billion
A little more than 5 billion

Each way of stating the number has value and purpose in different contexts. Rather than spend time with exercises converting numbers from standard form to scientific notation, consider large numbers found in newspapers, magazines, and atlases. How are they written? How are they said aloud? When are they rounded? When not and why? What forms of the numbers seem best for the purposes?

 The *Standards* reminds us that large numbers and scientific notation are used in various contexts. "A newspaper headline may proclaim, 'Clean-Up Costs from Oil Spill Exceed \$2 Billion!' or a science textbook may indicate that the number of red blood cells in the human body is about 1.9×10^{13}" (p. 217). ◆

Contexts for Very Large Numbers. The real world is full of very large quantities and measures. We see references to huge numbers in the media all the time. Unfortunately, most of us have not developed an appreciation for extremely large numbers, such as the following examples:

- A state lottery with 44 numbers from which to pick 6 has over 7 million possible combinations of 6 numbers. There are $44 \times 43 \times 42 \times 41 \times 40 \times 39$ possible ways that the balls could come out of the hopper (5,082,517,440). But generally the order in which they are picked is not important. Since there are $6 \times 5 \times 4 \times 3 \times 2 \times 1 = 720$ different arrangements of 6 numbers, each collection appears 720 times. Therefore, there are *only* 5,082,517,440 ÷ 720 possible lottery numbers, or in other words, 1 out of 7,059,052 chances to win.
- The estimated size of the universe is 40 billion light-years. One light-year is the number of miles light travels in *one year*. The speed of light is 186,281.7 miles per *second*, or 16,094,738,880 miles in a single day.
- The human body has about 100 billion cells.
- The distance to the sun is about 150 million kilometers.
- The population of the world in 2008 was about 6.71 billion.

Connecting these large numbers to meaningful points of reference can help students get a handle on their true magnitude. For example, suppose students determine the population in their city or town is about 500,000 people. They can then figure that it would take about 12,500 cities of the same population size to generate the population of the world. Or suppose students determine that it is about 4600 km between San Francisco, California, and Washington, DC. This would mean that it would take over 32,000 trips back and forth between these two cities to equal the distance between the earth and the sun. Building from such familiar or meaningful reference points can help students develop benchmarks to work with and make sense of large numbers.

The following activity uses real data and asks students to use scientific notation and create a scale drawing.

Activity 23.3
How Far Away from the Sun?

A problem-based way to explore scientific notation is to have students research planetary distances from the sun (in km), record the data in scientific notation, and create a scaled illustration of the distances. Alternatively, the following figures can be provided:

Mercury	57,909,000	Jupiter	778,400,000
Venus	108,200,000	Saturn	1,423,600,000
Earth	149,600,000	Uranus	2,867,000,000
Mars	227,940,000	Neptune	4,488,400,000

Contexts for Very Small Numbers. It is extremely important to use real examples of very small numbers. Without real contexts, you may be tempted to resort to drill exercises that have little meaning for students. As with large numbers, connecting these small numbers to points of reference can help students conceptualize how very tiny these numbers really are, as shown by the following real-world examples:

- The length of a DNA strand in a cell is about 10^{-7} m. This is also measured as 1000 *angstroms*. (Based on this information, how long is an angstrom?) For perspective, the diameter of a human hair is about 2.54×10^{-5} m.
- Human hair grows at the rate of 10^{-8} miles per hour. Garden snails have been clocked at about 3×10^{-2} mph.
- The chances of winning the Virginia lottery, based on selecting six numbers from 1 to 44, is 1 in 7.059 million. That is a probability of less than 1.4×10^{-10}.
- The mass of one atom of hydrogen is 0.000 000 000 000 000 000 000 001 675 g compared to the mass of one paper clip at about 1 g.
- It takes sound 0.28 second (2.8×10^{-1}) to travel the length of a football field. In contrast, a TV signal travels a full mile in about 0.000005368 second, or 5.3×10^{-6} second. A TV viewer at home hears the football being kicked before the receiver on the field does.

Scientific Notation on the Calculator. Students in elementary school learn how to multiply by 10, by 100, and by 1000 by simply adding the appropriate number of zeros. Help students expand this idea by examining powers of 10 on a calculator that handles exponents.

Activity 23.4
Exploring Powers of 10

Have students use any calculator that permits entering exponents to explore some of the following:

- Explore 10^N for various values of *N*. What patterns do you notice. What does 1E15 mean? (1E15 is the typical calculator form of 1×10^{15}.)
- Find different expressions for one thousand, one million, one billion, one trillion. What patterns are there in expressions you found?
- Enter 45 followed by a string of zeros. How many will your calculator permit? What happens when you press Enter? What does 4.5E10 mean?
- What does 5.689E6 mean? Can you enter this another way?
- Try sums like $(4.5 \times 10^N) + (27 \times 10^K)$ for different values of *N* and *K*. What can you find out?
- What happens with products of numbers like those in the previous item?

It is useful to become comfortable with the power-of-10 expressions in Activity 23.4. Students should eventually discover that when scientific or graphing calculators display numbers with more digits than the display will hold, they use scientific notation. For example, on a TI-73, the product of $45,000,000 \times 8,000,000$ is displayed as 3.6E14, meaning 3.6×10^{14}, or 360,000,000,000,000 (360 trillion).

Ask students why there are only 13 zeros. What happens when the numbers in the computation do not involve a lot of zeros?

❚❚ ———————— *Pause and Reflect*

With each factor in the product expressed in scientific notation: $(4.5 \times 10^7) \times (8 \times 10^6)$, or 4.5E7 × 8.0E6, can you compute the result mentally?

Notice the advantages of scientific notation, especially for multiplication and division. Here the significant digits can be multiplied mentally ($4.5 \times 8 = 36$) and the exponents added to produce almost instantly 36×10^{13} or 3.6×10^{14}.

Integers

Almost every day students have some interaction with negative numbers or experience phenomena that negative numbers can model, as shown in the following list:

Temperature	Money
Altitude (above and below sea level)	Time lines (including BC)
Golf	Football yardage (gains/losses)

In fact, almost any concept that is quantified and has direction probably has both positive and negative values.

Generally, negative values are introduced with *integers*—the whole numbers and their negatives or opposites—instead of with fractions or decimals.

However, it is a mistake to stop with integer values, because students must understand where numbers like ⁻4.5 and $-1\frac{3}{4}$ belong in relation to the integers. In fact, research has shown that students often place $-1\frac{3}{4}$ between ⁻1 and 0 instead of between ⁻2 and ⁻1.

Contexts for Exploring Integers

As with any new topic or type of number, it is important to start with familiar contexts so that students can use this prior knowledge to build meaning. With integers, students often get confused as to which number is bigger or which direction they are moving when they do operations, so having a context is particularly important. As students learn to compare and compute, they can use the contexts

to ground their thinking and justify their answers. For example, some contexts for integers involve quantities and some contexts are linear.

❚❚ ———————— *Pause and Reflect*

Review the list of contexts in the introduction to this section. Which do you think are quantity contexts and which are linear contexts? In the following sections, both quantity and linear contexts are discussed, followed by models for illustrating integers for both types.

Quantity Contexts

Golf Scores. In golf, scores are often written in relationship to a number considered par for the course. So, if par is 70 for the course, a golfer who ends the day at 67 has a score of ⁻3. Consider a player in a tournament with day-end scores of ⁺5, ⁻2, ⁻3, ⁺1. What would be his or her final result for the tournament? How did you think about it? You could match up the positive and the negatives (in this case, ⁺5 with ⁻2 and ⁻3 to get a net result of 0), and then see what is left (in this case, ⁺1). The notion that opposites (5 and ⁻5) equal zero is a big idea in the teaching of integers. You can post a mixed-up leader board of golf scores and ask students to order them from first through tenth place. Emphasize that first place is the *lowest* score—and therefore the *smallest* number. As you can see, golf scores provide a great context for comparing and computing with integers.

Money: Debits and Credits. Suppose that you are the bookkeeper for a small business. At any time, your records show how many dollars the company has in its account. There are always so many dollars in cash (credits or receipts) and so many dollars in accounts payable (debits). The difference between the debit and credit totals tells the value of the account. If there are more credits than debits, the account is positive, or "in the black." If there are more debits than credits, the account is in debt, showing a negative cash value, or "in the red." With the bookkeeping context, it is possible to explore addition and subtraction of integers, as in the example illustrated in Figure 23.4. An advantage of money is that it can be used for negative values that are not integers, specifically decimals. As noted earlier, it is important to engage students in thinking about negative numbers that are decimals and fractions once they have explored integer values.

Linear Contexts. Many of the real contexts for negative numbers are linear. In addition, the number line provides a good tool for learning the operations that relates well to what the students have done with whole number and fraction operations.

Credits		Debits		Balance
In	Out	In	Out	Begin 0
50				+50
		30		+20
	10			+10
			50	−40
25				−15
			20	+5

Debit $20

Figure 23.4 A ledger sheet context for integers.

Temperature. The "number line" measuring temperature is vertical. This context demonstrating negative integers may be the most familiar to students, as they have either experienced temperatures below zero or know about temperatures on the North or South Pole. A good starting activity for students is finding where various temperatures belong on a thermometer. For example, Figure 23.5 displays a thermometer marked in increments of five degrees, and students are asked to place on the number line the following temperatures from a week in North Dakota: 8,

Figure 23.5 Thermometers provide an excellent tool for exploring positive and negative numbers.

⁻2, ⁻12, 4, ⁻8. Ask students to order them from the coldest to the warmest (least to greatest). Temperatures as a context have the advantage that you can also use fractional and decimal values.

Altitude. Another vertical number-line model, altitude, is also a good context for integers. The altitudes of sites below sea level are negative, such as the town of Dead Sea, Israel, with an altitude of ⁻1371 feet and in the United States, Badwater, California, in Death Valley has an altitude of ⁻282 feet. Positive values for altitude include Mount McKinley (tallest mountain in North America) at 20,322 feet. Students can order the altitudes of various places around the United States or around the world (data easily found through a Google search on the Web) or find the difference between the altitudes of two different places—a good context for subtraction of integers. Beyond exploring real altitudes, using a model of a hill and a valley over which a toy car moves up and down can be a graphic way to explore integer operations.

Time Lines. Asking students to place historical events on a time line is an excellent interdisciplinary opportunity. The time line is useful for examples with larger values (e.g., 1950) as well as negative values (e.g., ⁻3000). Or students can explore their own personal time line (Weidemann, Mikovch, & Hunt, 2001), in which students find out key events that happened before they were born (e.g., birth of an older sibling) and since they have been alive (e.g., move to a new house). They then place these events on a number line. By partitioning a year into months, students can gain experience with rational numbers (twelfths) on the number line. Continue to reinforce the connection to the size of numbers, asking students, "Which number (year) is the smallest (earliest)?

Football. A statistic reported on every play in a football game is yards gained and yards lost, which provides a good context for exploring integers, especially when it comes to comparing and adding integers. Students can be asked questions like "If the Steelers started their drive on the 20 yard line and the first three plays were recorded as ⁻4, ⁺9, ⁺3, did they get a first down?" or "On the Broncos first play, the yardage is ⁻4. Where are they in relation to the line of scrimmage (using negatives, if behind the line of scrimmage, in this case ⁻4) and where are they in relation to the first down marker (⁻14)?"

Activity **23.5**
Football Statistics

Look up the average yards gained for some of the best running backs in the NFL or from college teams popular with your students. Ask students to use average yards gained per down to create a possible list of

yardage gains and losses for that player. **For example, if a player had an average of 4 yards per carry in a game, the following could have been his data:**

10, ⁻3, ⁻2, 21, ⁻5, 3, ⁻1, 5, ⁻1, 13

You may want to do one like this together and then have students create their own. The football context provides an excellent way to *use* integers meaningfully, integrated with the important concept of averages.

 The calculator is a tool that might be explored early in the discussion of integers. It gives correct and immediate results that students can justify on a number line or with one of the contexts described.

Have students explore subtraction problems such as 5 − 8 = ?, and discuss the results. (Be aware that the negative sign appears in different places on different calculators.)

Students can benefit by using the calculator along with the intuitive models and questions mentioned earlier. For example, how can you get from ⁻5 to ⁻17 by addition? 13 minus *what* is 15?

Meaning of Negative Numbers

Negative numbers are defined in terms of whole numbers. Therefore, the definition of negative 3 is the solution to the equation 3 + ? = 0. In general, the *opposite of n* is the solution to $n + ? = 0$. If n is a positive number, the *opposite of n* is a negative number. The set of integers, therefore, consists of the positive whole numbers, the opposites of the whole numbers, or negative numbers, and 0, which is neither positive nor negative. This is the definition found in student textbooks. Like many aspects of mathematics, abstract or symbolic definitions are best understood when conceptual connections link to the formal mathematics.

Absolute Value. The distance between two points, either on the number line or in the plane, is often an important concern, especially in applications of mathematics. We need to be able, for example, to tell a computer how far a train is from a station regardless of whether it is to the north or the south on the track. "Distance" can also refer to a mathematical distance as in the amount of possible error between a measurement and the true value, and the measures could be weight, time, voltage, and so on.

The *absolute value of a number* is defined as the distance between that number and zero. The notation for absolute value consists of two vertical bars on either side of the number. Thus, the absolute value of a number n is $|n|$. Opposites, such as ⁻12 and 12, are the same distance from zero, and therefore have the same absolute value.

In most middle school books, students are asked only to evaluate numeric expressions such as $|^-8|$ or $|6 − 10|$. The unfortunate consequence of these exercises is that stu-

dents quickly learn to simply do the computation and then ignore or "remove" the negative sign if there is one.

Notations. Because students have only seen the negative sign when doing subtraction, the symbolic notation for integers may be confusing. It is important to help students understand and use the appropriate symbols. Students may find it confusing that sometimes the negative sign appears at different heights (e.g., −7 and ⁻7). Also, sometimes parentheses are placed around the number so that it is separate from the operation—for example, 8 − (−5). Students have not seen parentheses used in this way and may think there is multiplication involved. It is important to connect to their prior knowledge and add to it. In this case, therefore, you might ask students, "When do we use parentheses in mathematics?" Students might say they are used for grouping a series of computations to show what to do first and that it can also mean multiplication. Point out that parentheses are also used to make a number sentence more readable—separating the negative number from the operation.

Tech NOTES On graphing calculators, these expressions are entered using the "negative" key and the "subtraction" key. The difference between those two symbols is evident in the display. The redundant superscript plus signs are not shown. Students can see that 3 + ⁻5 and 3 − 5 each results in ⁻2 and that 3 − ⁻5 and 3 + 5 are equal. ◆

Two Models for Teaching Integers

Two models, one denoted by quantity and the other by linear operations, are popular for helping students understand comparisons and the four operations (+, −, ×, and ÷) with integers.

Counters. One model consists of counters in two different colors, one for positive counts and one for negative counts. Two counters of each type result in zero (⁺1 + ⁻1 = 0). Consider money: If yellows are credits and reds are debits, 5 yellows and 7 reds is the same as 2 reds or 2 debits and is represented as ⁻2 (see Figure 23.6). It is important in using this model for students to understand that it is always possible to add to or remove from a pile any number of pairs consisting of one positive and one negative counter

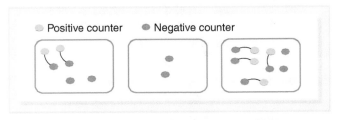

Figure 23.6 Each collection is a model of negative 2.

without changing the value of the pile. (Intuitively, this is like adding equal quantities of debits and credits.)

Number Lines. The number line is the second model. For instance, a thermometer would be considered a number line. A number line has several advantages. First, it shows the distance from 0 (or the absolute value of the number). In addition, it is an excellent tool for modeling the operations. Jumps can be shown in the same way as with whole numbers and fractions. Students can see that integer moves to the left go to smaller numbers and moves to the right go to larger numbers. Also, the number line allows students to explore noninteger negative and positives values (e.g., $^-4\frac{1}{2} + 3\frac{1}{4}$) that cannot be modeled very well with counters.

In modeling operations, arrows can be used to show distance and direction. For example, 4 can be modeled with an arrow four units long pointing to the right, and $^-3$ can be modeled with an arrow three units long pointing to the left (see Figure 23.7). The arrows help students think of integer quantities as directed distances. A positive arrow never points left, and a negative arrow never points right. Furthermore, each arrow is a quantity with both length (magnitude or absolute value) and direction (sign). These properties are constant for each arrow regardless of its position on the number line.

Which Model to Use. Although the two models appear quite different, they are alike mathematically. Integers involve two concepts—*quantity* and *opposite*. Quantity is modeled by the number of counters or the length of the arrows. Opposite is represented as different colors or different directions.

Many teachers decide to use only the model that students like or understand better. This is a mistake! Remember that the concepts are not in the models but rather must be constructed by the students and imposed on the models. Seeing integers across two models can help students extract the intended concepts. Students should experience both models and, perhaps even more important, discuss how the two are alike.

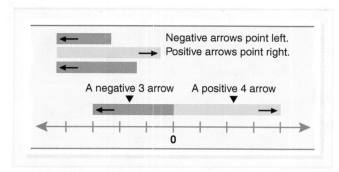

Figure 23.7 Number-line model for integers.

Operations with Integers

Once your students understand how integers are represented by each of the models, you can present the operations for the integers in the form of problems. In other words, rather than explaining how addition of integers works and showing students how to solve exercises with the models, you pose an integer computation and let students use their models to find a solution. When solutions have been reached, the groups can compare and justify their results using one of the contexts or models described earlier in this chapter.

Addition and Subtraction

Since middle school students may not have used counters or number lines for some time, it would be good to begin work with either of these models using positive whole numbers. After a few examples to help students become familiar with the model for addition or subtraction with whole numbers, have them work through an example with integers using exactly the same reasoning. Remember, the emphasis should be on the rationale and not on how quickly students can get correct answers.

Introduce negative values using one of the contexts discussed earlier in this chapter. For example, golf scores can be used as a context. Personalize the story by telling students that each weekend you golf a round on Saturday and on Sunday. The first weekend your results were $^+3$ and $^+5$, the next weekend you scored $^+3$ and $^-5$, and on the last weekend you scored $^-6$ and $^+2$. How did you do overall each weekend? Because this is a quantity model, counters are a good choice for modeling (though number lines can also be used). A linear context could be football yards gained and lost on two plays. See Figure 23.8 for illustrations of how to use both models for addition.

Several examples of addition are modeled in Figure 23.8, each in two ways: with positive and negative counters and with the number-line-and-arrow model. First examine the counter model. After the two quantities are joined, any pairs of positive and negative counters combine to equal zero, and students can remove these, making it easier to see the result.

To add using the arrow model, note that each added arrow begins at the arrowhead end of the previous arrow. Recall that subtraction can be used for take-away situations (e.g., start with 7 and take away 10) or in comparisons (What is the difference between 7 and $^-3$?). The quantity model is appropriate for take away and the number line can be used for either take away or comparisons.

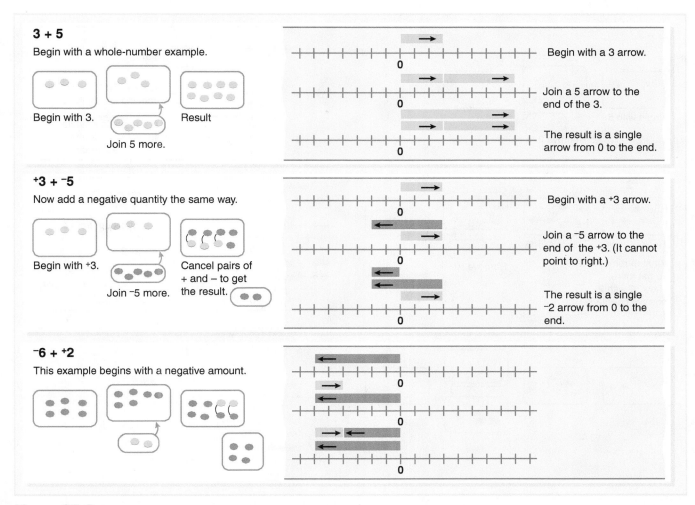

3 + 5

Begin with a whole-number example.

Begin with 3.

Join 5 more.

Result

Begin with a 3 arrow.

Join a 5 arrow to the end of the 3.

The result is a single arrow from 0 to the end.

+3 + ⁻5

Now add a negative quantity the same way.

Begin with +3.

Join ⁻5 more.

Cancel pairs of + and − to get the result.

Begin with a +3 arrow.

Join a ⁻5 arrow to the end of the +3. (It cannot point to right.)

The result is a single ⁻2 arrow from 0 to the end.

⁻6 + +2

This example begins with a negative amount.

Figure 23.8 Relate integer addition to whole-number addition with counters and number lines.

Consider the problem ⁻5 − +2, the second example modeled in Figure 23.9 (the first being a whole number example for the sake of making the connection). If using a quantity model, the context could be money, such as, "I start with a debt of $5 and then charge (take out) $2 more to my account. What balance will my bank account show (if no fees have been charged yet for my overdrawn account)? To model it, you start with the five red counters. To remove two positive counters from a set that has none, a different representation of ⁻5 must first be made. Since any number of neutral pairs (one positive, one negative) can be added without changing the value of the set, two pairs are added so that two positive counters can be removed. The net effect is to have more negative counters.

In a number model, subtraction can be modeled using arrows. When subtracting positive values, as in the second example in Figure 23.9, this works just as with whole numbers, moving to the left. Using temperature as a context, the explanation could be: "The day begins at 5 below zero. Then the temperature drops +2°, which means it just got colder and is now ⁻7°. The difficulty

comes when trying to provide an authentic explanation of subtracting a negative value. For example, ⁻4 − ⁻7 (see Figure 23.9, third example). In this case you start with thinking about taking away, but because it is negative temperature (or coldness) that is being taken away, you are in fact doing the opposite—warming up by 7 degrees. Modeling on the number line, you start at ⁻4, then reverse the arrow going left to one going right 7 moves. Number lines can also be used for comparison or distance. What is the difference between ⁻7 and ⁻4? In other words, how do you get from ⁻7 to ⁻4? You count up 3.

Pause and Reflect

Before reading further, go through each example in Figures 23.8 and 23.9. Explain each problem using both a quantity and a linear context. You should become comfortable with both models.

Have your students draw pictures to accompany integer computations. Set pictures are easy enough; they may consist of Xs and Os, for example. For the number line,

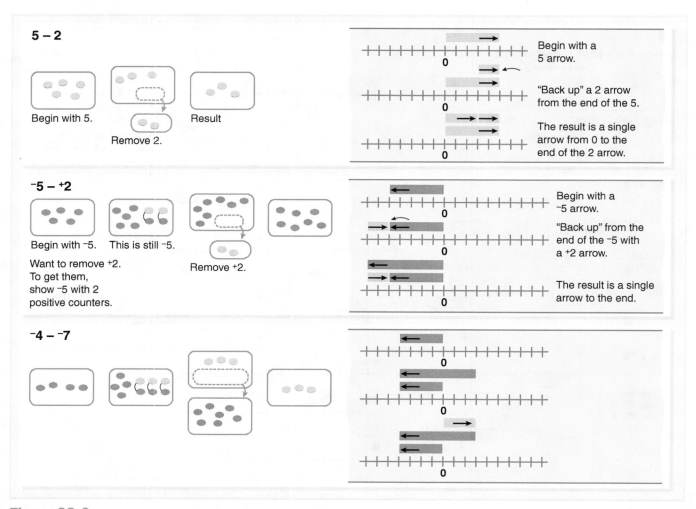

5 − 2

Begin with 5.

Remove 2.

Result

Begin with a 5 arrow.

"Back up" a 2 arrow from the end of the 5.

The result is a single arrow from 0 to the end of the 2 arrow.

⁻5 − ⁺2

Begin with ⁻5.

Want to remove ⁺2. To get them, show ⁻5 with 2 positive counters.

This is still ⁻5.

Remove ⁺2.

Begin with a ⁻5 arrow.

"Back up" from the end of the ⁻5 with a ⁺2 arrow.

The result is a single arrow to the end.

⁻4 − ⁻7

Figure 23.9 Integer subtraction is also related to whole numbers.

arrows can be used. Figure 23.10 illustrates how a student might draw arrows for simple addition and subtraction exercises without even sketching the number line.

It is important for students to see that ⁺3 + ⁻5 is the same as ⁺3 − ⁺5 and that ⁺2 − ⁻6 is the same as ⁺2 + ⁺6. With modeling addition and subtraction problems in both ways, students will see the connection and recognize that while these expressions are quite distinguishable, they have the same result.

Multiplication and Division

Multiplication of integers should be a direct extension of multiplication for whole numbers, just as addition and subtraction were connected to whole-number concepts. We frequently refer to whole-number multiplication as repeated addition. The first factor tells how many sets there are or how many are added in all, beginning with 0. This translates to integer multiplication quite readily when the

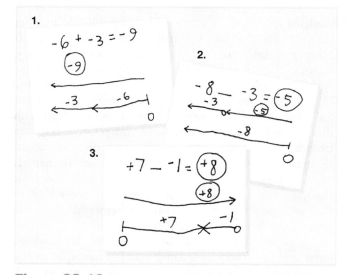

Figure 23.10 Students can use simple arrow sketches to represent addition and subtraction with integers.

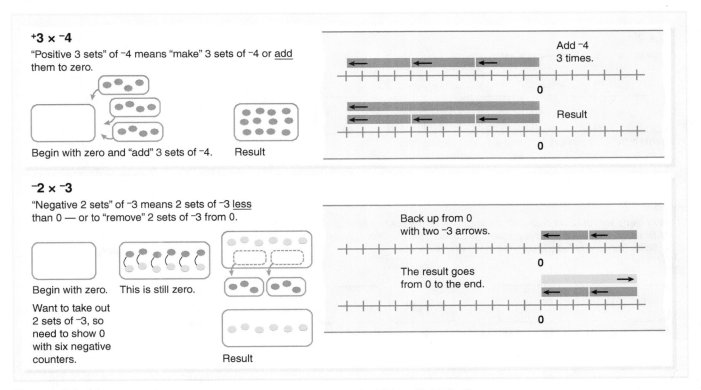

Figure 23.11 Multiplication by a positive first factor is repeated addition. Multiplication by a negative first factor is repeated subtraction.

first factor is positive, regardless of the sign of the second factor. The first example in Figure 23.11 illustrates a positive first factor and a negative second factor.

What could the meaning be when the first factor is negative, as in ⁻2 × ⁻3? If a positive first factor means repeated addition (how many times added to 0), a negative first factor should mean repeated subtraction (how many times subtracted from 0). The second example in Figure 23.11 illustrates how multiplication with the first factor negative can be modeled.

The deceptively simple rules of "like signs yield positive products" and "unlike signs yield negative products" are quickly established. These models allow students to understand why those rules work.

With division of integers, again explore the whole-number case first. Recall that 8 ÷ 4 with whole numbers has two possible meanings corresponding to two missing-factor expressions: 4 × ? = 8 asks, "Four sets of *what* make eight?" whereas ? × 4 = 8 asks, "How many fours make eight?" Generally, the measurement approach (? × 4) is the one used with integers, although both concepts can be exhibited with either model. It is helpful to think of building the dividend with the divisor from 0, or repeated addition—to find the missing factor.

The first example in Figure 23.12 illustrates how the two models work for whole numbers. Following that is an example where the divisor is positive but the dividend is negative.

Pause and Reflect

Try using both models to compute ⁻8 ÷ ⁺2. Draw pictures using Xs and Os and also arrows. Check your understanding with the examples in Figure 23.12. Once you understand that example, try ⁺9 ÷ ⁻3 and also ⁻12 ÷ ⁻4.

Understanding of integer division rests on a good concept of a negative first factor for multiplication and a knowledge of the relationship between multiplication and division.

Do not rush your students into difficult problems. It is much better that they first think about how to model the whole-number situation and then figure out, with some guidance from you, how to deal with integers.

NCTM Standards "Positive and negative integers should be seen as useful for noting relative changes or values. Students can also appreciate the utility of negative integers when they work with equations whose solution requires them, such as 2x + 7 = 1" (p. 218). ◆

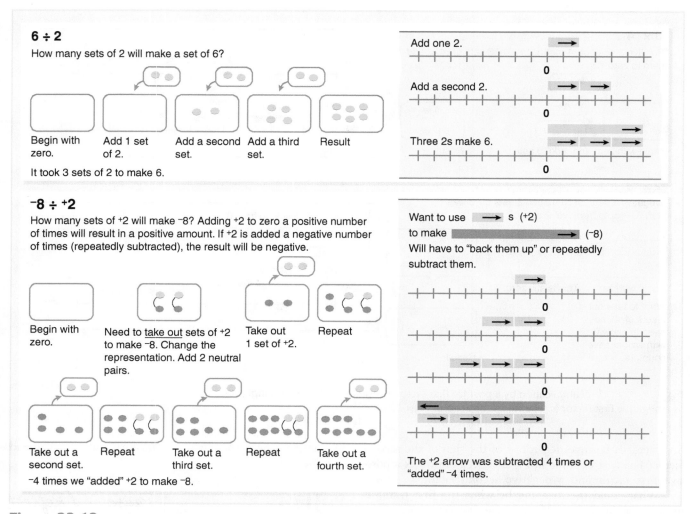

6 ÷ 2

How many sets of 2 will make a set of 6?

Begin with zero. Add 1 set of 2. Add a second set. Add a third set. Result

It took 3 sets of 2 to make 6.

Add one 2.

Add a second 2.

Three 2s make 6.

⁻8 ÷ ⁺2

How many sets of ⁺2 will make ⁻8? Adding ⁺2 to zero a positive number of times will result in a positive amount. If ⁺2 is added a negative number of times (repeatedly subtracted), the result will be negative.

Begin with zero. Need to take out sets of ⁺2 to make ⁻8. Change the representation. Add 2 neutral pairs. Take out 1 set of ⁺2. Repeat

Take out a second set. Repeat Take out a third set. Repeat Take out a fourth set.

⁻4 times we "added" ⁺2 to make ⁻8.

Want to use ⟶ s (⁺2) to make ⟶ (⁻8) Will have to "back them up" or repeatedly subtract them.

The ⁺2 arrow was subtracted 4 times or "added" ⁻4 times.

Figure 23.12 Division of integers following a measurement approach.

Real Numbers

We began with whole numbers, then moved to rational numbers, and now, in this chapter, has explored integers. All of these are rational numbers. Irrational numbers are numbers such as $\sqrt{2}$—numbers whose value cannot be written as a fraction and whose value can only be estimated. All these numbers are part of the *real numbers*, which are the only types of numbers students explore until high school where they consider the square roots of negative numbers, called *imaginary numbers*. Each of these sets of numbers are interrelated, and some are subsets of other sets. Figure 23.13 provides an illustration of the types of numbers and how they are interrelated.

Rational Numbers

Rational numbers comprise the set of all numbers that can be represented as a fraction—or a ratio of an integer to an inte-

ger. Even when numbers are written as whole numbers or as terminating decimals, they can also be written as fractions and thus are rational numbers. In fact, in most textbooks and state curriculum guides the term *rational numbers* is often used to refer to fractions, decimals (terminating and

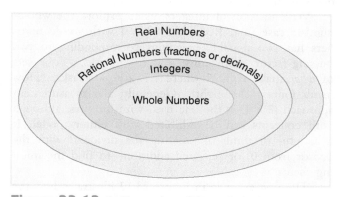

Figure 23.13 An illustration of the real numbers.

repeating), and percents. These are rational numbers, but so are integers, including whole numbers. To help build this notion of rational numbers, it is important to be able to move between fractions and decimals and between fractions and whole numbers.

Moving among Representations. Because children tend to think of fractions as parts of sets or objects, they remain, in the minds of children, more physical object than number. This is one reason that students can have such a difficult time placing fractions on a number line. A significant leap toward thinking about fractions as numbers is made when students begin to understand that a decimal is a representation of a fraction. Earlier, we explored the idea of the "friendly" fractions (halves, thirds, fourths, fifths, eighths) in terms of their decimal equivalents.

In the middle grades, it is time to combine all of these ideas:

- $4\frac{3}{5}$ is 4.6 because $\frac{3}{5}$ is six-tenths of a whole, so 4 wholes and six-tenths is 4.6.
- $4\frac{3}{5}$ is $\frac{23}{5}$, and that is the same as $23 \div 5$, or 4.6 if I use decimals.
- 4.6 is read "four and six-tenths," so I can write that as $4\frac{6}{10} = 4\frac{3}{5}$.

Similarly, compare these three expressions:

$$\tfrac{1}{4} \text{ of } 24 \qquad \tfrac{24}{4} \qquad 24 \div 4$$

This discussion can lead to a general development of the idea that a fraction can be thought of as division of the numerator by the denominator or that $\frac{a}{b}$ is the same as $a \div b$.

What becomes clear in a discussion building on students' existing ideas is that any number, positive or negative, that can be written as a fraction can also be written as a decimal number. You can also reverse this idea and convert decimal numbers to fractions. Keep in mind that the purpose is to see that there are different symbolic notations for the same quantities—not to become skilled at conversions.

When a fraction is converted to a decimal, it is interesting to note that the decimal either terminates (e.g., 3.415) or repeats (e.g., 2.5141414 . . .).

Is there a way to tell if a given fraction is a terminating decimal or a repeating decimal? The answer lies in the denominator. The following activity can be used to discover why.

Activity 23.6

Repeater or Terminator

Have students generate a table listing in one column the first 20 unit fractions ($\frac{1}{2}$, $\frac{1}{3}$, $\frac{1}{4}$, . . . $\frac{1}{21}$). In the second column they list the prime factorization of
the denominators and in the third column the decimal equivalent for the fraction. Have students use calculators to get the decimal form.

After completing the table, the task is to see if they can discover a rule that will tell in advance if the decimal will repeat or terminate. They can test the rule with fractions with denominators beyond 21. They may also wish to confirm that it makes no difference what the numerator is.

If you try the last activity yourself, you will quickly discover that the only fractions with terminating decimals have denominators that factor with all 2s and/or 5s. The explanation for why this is so is also within the reach of students. As students work on this task, they will notice various patterns, as can be seen in the student work provided in Figure 23.14.

Irrational Numbers

Students have encountered *irrational numbers* as early as fifth grade when they learn about π. However, the discussion of what an irrational number is occurs later in middle school, probably seventh or eighth grade. As noted, *irrational* numbers are not rational, meaning they cannot

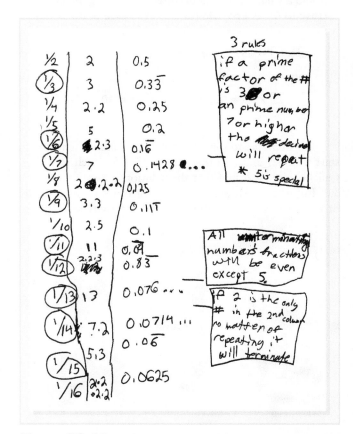

Figure 23.14 A student notes patterns as he explores the "Repeater or Terminator" activity.

be put in fraction form. The irrationals together with the rational numbers make up the *real* numbers. The real numbers fill in all the holes on the number line even when the holes are infinitesimally small. Students' first experience with irrational numbers typically occurs when exploring roots of whole numbers.

Introducing the Concept of Roots. The following activity provides a good introduction to square roots and cube roots. From this beginning, the notion of roots of any degree is easily developed.

Activity 23.7

Edges of Squares and Cubes

Show students pictures of three squares (or three cubes) as in Figure 23.15. The edges of the first and last figure are consecutive whole numbers. The areas (volumes) of all three figures are provided. The students' task is to use a calculator to find the edge of the figure in the center. Explain to students that they are not to use the square root key, but to estimate what they think the side would be and test it by squaring it. Ask students to continue to estimate until they have found a value to the hundredths place that gets as close to 45 as possible (or 30 in the case of the cube). Solutions will satisfy these equations:

$$\square \times \square = 45, \quad \text{or} \quad \square^2 = 45$$

and

$$\square \times \square \times \square = 30, \quad \text{or} \quad \square^3 = 30$$

For example, to solve the cube problem, students might start with 3.5 and find that 3.5^3 is 42.875, much too large. Quickly, they will find that the solution is between 3.1 and 3.2. But where? Although a calculator can find these square or cube roots quickly, the estimation activity strengthens

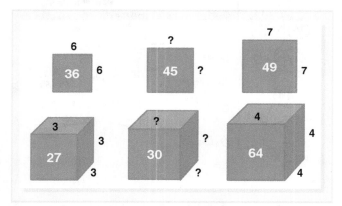

Figure 23.15 A geometric interpretation of square roots and cube roots.

students' understanding of squares and square roots and the relative sizes of numbers.

⏸ ——————————— *Pause and Reflect*

Use a calculator to continue getting a better approximation of the cube root of 30 to the hundredths place.

From this simple introduction, students can be challenged to find solutions to equations such as $\square^2 = 8$. These students are now prepared to understand the general definition of the *nth root* of a number N as the number that when raised to the *n*th power equals N. The *square* and *cube roots* are simply other names for the second and third roots. The notational convention of the radical sign comes last. It should then be clear that $\sqrt{6}$ is a number rather than a computation. The cube root of eight is the same as $\sqrt[3]{8}$, which is just another way of writing 2.

In middle school, students encounter irrational numbers primarily when working with the Pythagorean theorem ($a^2 + b^2 = c^2$), which is used to find the distance between two points (the distance being the diagonal or c). If $a = 3$ and $b = 4$, then $c = 5$. All sides are rational numbers. But this case is the exception to the rule. More often sides will be something like 4 and 7 units, in which case $c = \sqrt{16 + 49} = \sqrt{65}$. Although sometimes there is a perfect square that can be simplified, in this case there is not one and the distance is $\sqrt{65}$, an irrational number.

An engaging middle school project applies the Pythagorean theorem and irrational numbers to create a Wheel of Theodorus, as described in Activity 23.8. Theodorus was one of the early believers that irrational numbers existed (quite a contentious issue for the Pythagoreans, who were against the idea of irrationals!).

Activity 23.8

Wheel of Theodorus

Ask students to construct a right triangle that measures 1 centimeter on each side adjacent to the right angle and then draw the hypotenuse and record its measure. They then use the hypotenuse as a side and draw a new right triangle with this as side *a* along with a side *b* that is 1 cm. Draw and record the new hyptonuse ($\sqrt{3}$). Create the next triangle, which will have sides of $\sqrt{3}$ and 1 and a hypotenuse of $\sqrt{4}$ or 2, and so on. Doing this about 30 times will form a wheel. (See Bay-Williams & Martinie, 2009, for a complete lesson or search online for instructions and diagrams.)

NCTM Standards "In grades 6–8, students frequently encounter squares and square roots when they use the Pythagorean relationship. They can use the inverse relationship to determine the approximate location of square roots between whole numbers on a number line"

(p. 220). As examples, the authors note that $\sqrt{27}$ is a little more than 5 because $5^2 = 25$ and $\sqrt{99}$ is a little less than 10 since $10^2 = 100$. ◆

Density of the Real Numbers

One important aspect of real numbers that is not well understood by students is that they are infinite. This means that for two values, such as $\frac{7}{9}$ and $\frac{8}{9}$, you can find infinitely many rational numbers between them. This is a concept that warrants exploration and discussion, which is the intent of Activity 23.9.

If the density of the rationals is impressive, even more astounding is that the irrationals are also dense. And the irrationals and the rationals are all mixed up together. The density of the irrationals is not as easy to demonstrate and is not within the scope of the middle school.

The following activity can help students develop a better understanding of the structure of the rational number system.

Activity 23.9

How Close Is Close?

Have students select any two fractions or any two decimals that they think are "really close." It makes no difference what numbers students pick or even how close together they really are. Now challenge them to find at least ten more numbers (fractions or decimals) that are between these two numbers.

"How Close Is Close?" is an opportunity to find out how your students understand fractions and decimals. (The activity should be done in both forms eventually.) The activity offers a great opportunity for discussion, assessment of individual students' fraction and decimal concepts, and the introduction of perhaps the most interesting feature of the rational number system: density. The rational numbers are said to be *dense* because between any two rational numbers there exists an *infinite* number of other rational numbers.

 Ask students "How many numbers are between these two numbers?" for each of the following:

$$\frac{3}{5} \text{ and } \frac{4}{5}$$

$$0.6 \text{ and } 0.7$$

$$^-2 \text{ and } ^-3$$

As part of this "interview" assessment, ask students to provide examples and to explain how they are finding the numbers in between. Students should be able to manipulate the numbers to find values in between and should know there are infinitely many.

If they are stuck and say there are none, ask if they can write an equivalent form of the numbers to help them find a number in between. ◆

Reflections

Writing to Learn

1. What strategies can you use to help students understand and appropriately use the order of operations?
2. How can a calculator be used to explore the order of operations?
3. Explain how powers of 10 are used to write very small and very large numbers. What is the particular form of the power-of-10 symbolism used in scientific notation and on calculators?
4. Use a context and a model to solve the following:
   $^-10 + {}^+13 = {}^+3$ $^-4 - {}^-9 = {}^+5$ $^+6 - {}^-7 = {}^+13$
   $^-4 \times {}^-3 = {}^+12$ $^+15 \div {}^-5 = {}^-3$ $^-12 \div {}^-3 = {}^+4$
5. For each of the following numbers, tell all the kinds of numbers it is (real, rational, integer, whole). For example, $^-8\frac{1}{2}$ is real and rational.
   $^-3$ 120 $\frac{4}{5}$ $\sqrt{5}$ $.323232 \ldots$ $^-1.4$
6. How would you explain the difference between a rational and an irrational number to a middle school student?

7. What does $\sqrt{6}$ mean? How is $\sqrt{6}$ different from $\sqrt{4}$? How are they the same?
8. What does it mean to say that the rational numbers are dense?

For Discussion and Exploration

1. How might teachers help students become fluent in moving between equivalent representations of numbers, for example, changing fractions to decimals flexibly to fit the situation?
2. Some exponent values are easily confused by students. Two of the most common cases are listed below. For each example,
   • Explain how the values are different in meaning.
   • Draw a representation to show how they are different.
   • Describe what investigation you would plan to help students see the differences in these values.
   Case 1: 2^3 and 2×3 and 3^2
   Case 2: $2n$ and n^2 and 2^n

Resources

Literature Connections

Some topics in this chapter present opportunities for "playing around" with ideas and numbers. In the middle grades using literature is a great springboard for doing mathematics. The following ideas offer a change of pace in the upper grades.

The Number Devil *Enzensberger, 1997*

Full of humor and wit, *The Number Devil* lays out a collection of interesting ideas about numbers in 12 easily read chapters. Robert, a boy who hates mathematics, meets up with a crafty number devil in each of 12 dreams. On the fourth night's dream, Robert learns about infinitely repeating decimals and the "Rutabaga of two" (the square root of two), providing a connection to rational and irrational numbers.

Oh, Yikes! History's Grossest, Wackiest Moments *Masoff, 2006*

In this picture-rich reference book, the author describes important historical events and people with facts that are interesting to middle schoolers. Her topics include, "Aztec Antics," "Cruel Constructions," "Humongous Hoaxes," "Pirates," and so on. In several cases, she takes a topic, such as brushing teeth and briefly describes how this was handled across all of history, which provides the opportunity to do time lines that include dates such as 2500 BC. Students can create a time line that is proportionally accurate to tell the events related to the topic they have selected. In addition to integers, this lesson includes measuring, proportional reasoning, and fractions.

Recommended Readings

Articles

Graeber, A. O., & Baker, K. M. (1992). Little into big is the way it always is. *Arithmetic Teacher, 39*(8), 18–21.
This is one of the few articles that discusses the issue of a fraction as an indicated division. The authors look at practices in the elementary school that suggest why the difficulty exists and make practical suggestions for working with middle school students.

Reeves, C. A., & Webb, D. (2004). Balloons on the rise: A problem-solving approach to integers. *Mathematics Teaching in the Middle School, 9*(9), 476–482.
Expanding on a discussion of the possibility of helium party balloons making you weigh less if held while on a scale, the fifth-grade students in this article generalize the concepts of integers and use their ideas for addition and subtraction. The authors point clearly to the value of a context to help students develop a new concept.

Online Resources

The Evolution of the Real Numbers
www.themathpage.com/areal/real-numbers.htm
> This is an interesting description of many topics related to the real number system. Although mostly text, the pages are filled with interactive questions.

National Library of Virtual Manipulatives (NLVM)
http://nlvm.usu.edu
> Among the many applets on this site are "Color Chips—Addition," "Color Chips—Subtraction," "Rectangle Multiplication of Integers," and "Integer Arithmetic." These applets focus on using models for integer computation.

Tic-Tac-Go Negative Numbers (Freudenthal Institute)
www.fi.uu.nl/toepassingen/03088/toepassing_wisweb.en.html
> In this game, students pick addition, subtraction, or multiplication and find the equation to match an answer, trying to get three in a row.

Volt Meter (Illuminations)
http://illuminations.nctm.org/ActivityDetail.aspx?ID=152
> Click and drag batteries with negative and positive voltage to explore integer addition and subtraction.

Exponential Growth (Otherwise)
www.otherwise.com/population/exponent.html
> This site offers an applet to experiment with population (exponential) growth.

The Next Billion (Illuminations)
http://illuminations.nctm.org/LessonDetail.aspx?id=L715
> In 1999 the world population passed 6 billion. In this lesson, students predict when it will reach 7 billion. Students discuss their predictions, past trends in population growth, and social factors—a good interdisciplinary opportunity.

Field Experience Guide Connections

This chapter covers a range of topics, so there are a number of excellent lessons and resources in the *Field Experience Guide*. FEG 3.5 ("Web of Ideas") can be an excellent task for teachers and students to explore the relationships among rational numbers (integers, fractions, whole numbers, etc.). FEG Expanded Lesson 9.2 ("Close, Far, and In Between") focuses on the relative magnitude of numbers and FEG Expanded Lesson 9.10 ("How Close Is Close?") focuses on the density of rational numbers. The order of operations is the focus of FEG Activity 10.5 ("Target Number") and Balanced Assessment Task 11.1 ("Magic Age Rings").

ndex